RELIVING THE DREAM

RELIVING THE DREAM

The Triumph and Tears of Manchester United's 1968 European Cup Heroes

Introduction by GEORGE BEST

DERICK ALLSOP

MAINSTREAM
PUBLISHING

EDINBURGH AND LONDON

First published in Great Britain in 1998 by
MAINSTREAM PUBLISHING COMPANY (EDINBURGH) LTD
7 Albany Street
Edinburgh EH1 3UG

ISBN 1 84018 056 0

A catalogue record for this book is available from the British Library

Typeset in 11 on 13pt Garamond
Printed and bound in Great Britain by Butler and Tanner Ltd, Frome

For Matt, Jimmy and the boys

ACKNOWLEDGEMENTS

This book has been made possible thanks to the help and forbearance of many people. Not every member of the '68 team was able – or willing – to give unlimited co-operation. Some are less enthusiastic about their manager and club than others, and their candour is appreciated. But all the players have contributed years of inspirational input, for which I am grateful. The players are Alex Stepney, Shay Brennan, Tony Dunne, Pat Crerand, Bill Foulkes, Nobby Stiles, George Best, Brian Kidd, Bobby Charlton, David Sadler, John Aston, Jimmy Rimmer and Denis Law.

I also wish to thank Wilf McGuinness, Tommy Docherty, Martin Edwards, Ron Atkinson, Alex Ferguson, Eusebio, David Coleman, Frank McGhee, John Baumann and the staff at Great Fosters, the staff at Manchester United, Mick Docherty, Peter Slater, the BBC for giving me access to their archive material, Keith Hilton, The Speaking Book Company for permission to quote from their cassette tapes entitled 'Manchester United – The Busby Years', narrated by Pat Crerand and Denis Law, *The Independent*, *The Sunday Telegraph*, David Meek, especially for wading through the proofs, Luis Vasconcelos, Ray Matts, Stan Piecha, Jane Nottage, Jim Hutchison, Jim Mossop, Sue, Natalie and Kate Allsop, and, not least, Bill Campbell and Cathy Mineards of Mainstream for their enthusiasm and support.

PROLOGUE

A middle-aged man coaxes his bicycle to a halt at the top of the forecourt, dismounts and walks slowly, quietly down the slope towards the great brick bowl that is the stadium. His eyes are fixed on a large bronze figure, and the closer he gets, the slower his stride becomes. It is a respectful, almost awestruck approach. He might be walking down the aisle of a church. At last he stops, as he might before an altar. He has tousled hair, a beard and a rucksack on his back. He stands motionless, his gaze intense, for two or three minutes and then, still slowly, still quietly, turns and wheels his bicycle away.

The bronze figure, standing on a simple bronze plinth, seems to watch the cyclist go back across the forecourt. The statue is of a man in perhaps later middle years. His countenance is benign, the smile gentle, the stance relaxed. He is wearing a blazer which carries the club crest. Under his left arm he holds a football. It captures the image and aura of Sir Matt Busby perfectly.

Above him is a plaque laid out like a football pitch. The words on it read: 'In memory of the officials and players who lost their lives in the Munich air disaster on the 6th February, 1958.' The names of those who perished are spread out on the pitch – Walter Crickmer, Tom Curry, Bert Whalley, Roger Byrne, Geoff Bent, Mark Jones, Eddie Colman, David Pegg, Duncan Edwards, Tommy Taylor, Billy Whelan.

The first three named were officials, the others players, members of the fabled 'Busby Babes', a Manchester United team acknowledged as one of the best ever produced by British football. Busby, their manager, almost died at Munich too. The club were returning from a European Cup tie against Red Star Belgrade, where they had secured a place in the semi-finals. Deprived of so many players, they were unable to progress further that season. But the team, like Busby, recovered, and ten years on accomplished the mission on which their lamented forebears had set out.

For Busby it was the realisation of a dream, and redemption. He had defied the strictures of the Football League to take his players into the European Cup competition, and the loss of so many lives, in particular the young lives, left him carrying a cross of contrition. Winning the European Cup could never bring them back or exorcise the ghosts. But it was the most appropriate and poignant tribute any human could have hoped for. Fittingly, too, Busby's United became the first English club to win European club football's highest honour.

Busby's new team claimed that prize on the balmy evening of 29 May 1968 at Wembley Stadium. They beat Benfica of Portugal 4–1 in a final that went into extra-time. Three goals in a devastating period of seven minutes fulfilled what many of the players considered their destiny. Perhaps even their duty. And now they were legends. Busby, recognised for his achievement with a knighthood, was not merely a football manager but the patriarch of a dynasty and institution unparalleled in the English game.

The emotional forces generated in the wake of the Munich tragedy conveyed the club to an unprecedented position in the consciousness of the nation, and the '60s' team sustained the momentum. They, however, failed to retain the European Cup and it was not until the final months of Busby's life that United won another Championship – and with it the right to compete again for the champions' trophy. Under the stewardship of Alex Ferguson – like Busby, a Scot – United took the English title four times in five seasons between 1993 and 1997, and in the process became the first club in the country to complete the double of Championship and FA Cup twice.

The club's expansion in the '90s has been commensurate with that success. Their Old Trafford stadium holds more than 55,000, all seated – making it the biggest football ground in Britain outside Wembley – and is full for virtually every match. The club, now a plc, is worth more than £400m. Television revenues, sponsorship, merchandising and spin-off ventures of almost every conceivable nature keep the money rolling in daily, not solely on match days.

You wonder what the 'Old Man', as he was affectionately known, makes of it all, peering down from his plinth, for here is the dichotomy. At the far end of the forecourt, beyond the bearded man with the bicycle, a party of children are making their way back to their coach. They are armed with bags full of souvenirs trawled from the megastore. Not one of them turns to look at the statue, or the plaque. If anyone checks the time on the clock hung further along the outside wall of the stadium, the chances are they will not notice that, also, commemorates the Munich air crash. He may be forgiven for feeling he has created a monster rather than a glorious, heroic empire.

But then he will understand. The world keeps turning and he, more than anyone, looked forward. He was the visionary. He gave young men their head and sought new frontiers. Why should youngsters be expected to look over their shoulders, especially when they have bags of David Beckham T-shirts and Ryan Giggs pillowcases? They have their dreams, just as he had.

And therein lies the abiding bond, the common cause. Younger generations of United supporters and players dream of winning the European Cup. They embarked upon the 1997–98 season, the 30th anniversary of that triumphant campaign, still seeking to emulate their illustrious predecessors. Those who have aspired to that and failed will testify that the '68 victory is a monument to the greatness of a manager and his team. It should also be an inspiration to those who now pursue the dream.

The diehard fans glory in their heritage and crave more of the same. They still sing the praises of the patriarch, of 'walking down the Warwick Road to see Matt Busby's aces'. Today Warwick Road is called Sir Matt Busby Way, but they march to the same tune, to the same crusade.

INTRODUCTION

by

GEORGE BEST

When Manchester United won the European Cup in 1968 they not only became the first English club to reach the pinnacle, but also penned the final chapter of perhaps the greatest story in the history of football. If it had been fiction, people would have scoffed and dismissed it as too far-fetched. And yet it happened. It was true, it was real, and no script could have come up with anything like it; no one could have written a human drama to compare with it.

Matt Busby had to rebuild his team after Munich, and just ten years later there he was, holding aloft that massive trophy at Wembley. This was the Holy Grail. To Sir Matt (as he became) it meant everything – and I mean everything. It was his whole life and the pursuit of it almost cost him his life. So many of his great players had lost their lives in the crash. And now the mission had been accomplished. We'd beaten Benfica in seven glorious and unbelievable minutes of extra-time. It was just amazing.

When United crashed at Munich, in 1958, I was a kid in Belfast, and it obviously stunned everybody, football fans in every part of Britain and beyond. And if you hadn't supported Manchester United before, well, they became your second favourites from then on. Everyone took them to their hearts because of the tragedy. And to think that just three years later I'd be at the club! It still seems hard to take in.

It wasn't exactly taboo to talk about Munich at the club, but people just didn't. They didn't have to. It was there in the atmosphere. And soon I found myself part of this great crusade to make United the best in England again, and then the best in Europe. Just getting the club back on its feet again was a huge job in itself, and at the time I don't think anyone involved realised what an enormous task – and what a great achievement – it was. But Sir Matt had his dream and he was determined to turn that dream into reality.

He was one of the greatest managers – if not *the* greatest – of all time. He took his first team to FA Cup success in 1948 and the Championship in 1952, then brought in a totally new team, the magnificent Babes, who won the Championship in '56 and '57. He had to build a third team after Munich and he went about it in such a decisive way. He knew he had to bring in quality players to complement those he had, so he said, 'Hey, I want Denis Law and Paddy Crerand,' and he went and got them. Later he decided he needed a goalkeeper to complete his side, and so he got Alex Stepney. He set his sights, made up his mind that he wanted to get a great side together again and did it.

I came into the side in September 1963, and by then the team had started to turn the corner by winning the FA Cup. We won the League in '65 and again in '67 and were there or thereabouts in everything else, but the 'biggie' was the European Cup. We had a great chance in '66 after a fantastic performance away to Benfica, a match that holds particularly fond memories for me. We demolished them 5–1, I scored a couple of goals and everything really took off for me. Unfortunately, I then got injured and we went out in the semi-final against Partizan Belgrade.

When we got another crack at it, in the '67–'68 season, we were better prepared for it and had the perfect blend of experience and youth. People say the team was over the hill, but it wasn't really. Sure, Bill Foulkes was in his mid-thirties, and Bobby Charlton and Shay Brennan had turned 30, but Brian Kidd was 19 on the day of the final and the rest were in their twenties. John Aston was only 20, I was just 22 and David Sadler was only a few months older. The balance was spot-on.

But then we come back to this incredible script. Both sides had battled for 90 minutes without deciding it. We were locked at 1–1. And then, all of a sudden, it's over. In seven minutes of the first half of extra-time, a spell of sheer magic, the whole competition, the whole season, a whole decade, Sir Matt's whole life, were complete and fulfilled. We scored three goals and Benfica were finished. The European Cup was ours.

The strange thing is I can remember nothing of the build-up to the final or what happened afterwards. A total blank. But the match itself is as vivid as if it were yesterday, every fabulous detail crystal clear: Bobby's header for our first, their equaliser, thumped in by Graca, Alex's fantastic save from Eusebio, my little side-step round the keeper for our second, Kiddo's header, and Bobby's terrific goal to round it off.

We had class and character right through that side, and when it mattered we produced. We made history for the club and the country, and we did it in style. Allow me to introduce you to the heroes of '68.

1. Alex Stepney

There were so many great goalkeepers around at that time, particularly English goalkeepers, and as a consequence Alex suffered at international level.

Had there not been people like Gordon Banks and Peter Bonetti to compete against, he would have won a lot more than the one cap he got. But for the club he was a gem. He made it look easy – the mark of a great keeper. He was never flash or flamboyant. He didn't need to be. He had the knack of being in the right place at the right time.

2. Shay Brennan

Here's Mr Cool, off the pitch and on it. He was always such a calm, cultured player, who made his debut as a left-winger but found his best position at right-back. No matter how depressed or down you might be, Shay would be sure to pick you up with that great smile on his face. He was so easy-going he was the last person you'd expect to have a heart attack, but typically he bounced back. He's one of my biggest pals and we're even closer now than when we were playing.

3. Tony Dunne

People talk about quick players today, but Tony wasn't just quick, he was lightning. The winger would think he was past him and suddenly Tony would be back at him, taking the ball away. He covered so decisively. He was always there. And he had such a terrific temperament. He never got flustered, always remained composed. He was a quiet lad. Others would go off for a game of snooker after training, but Tony would be away to his family. That's the sort of guy he was.

4. Pat Crerand

We had a lot of great players at the time and you didn't want any of them to be out of the side, but I always said that if there was one player I didn't like to be injured it was Paddy. He made us play. Long passes, short passes – he delivered them on the spot. We used to take the mick about his lack of pace, but he didn't need it. He made the ball do the work. He was temperamental, but you had to accept that. He was my minder. He's still United-daft, a great bloke and a great pal.

5. Bill Foulkes

He was very different from Tony in stature and wouldn't claim to have been as quick, but like Tony he was such a reliable figure in our defence. He was a real stopper and not much got past him, especially in the air. He'd get it and give it. He knew what he could do and didn't try to complicate things. He was a survivor of Munich, so Europe meant such a lot to him. When he finished training he liked to head for the golf course. He was good at that, too.

6. Nobby Stiles

Every team needed a Nobby-type player, but there was only one Nobby. He did his job brilliantly wherever he did it – and he could play anywhere. For us he settled into a defensive role alongside Bill, and, of course, he marked Eusebio. I knew what it was like being marked by Nobby, because he did it on me in internationals. He'd apologise at the end but I told him it was okay, he was doing his job. Off the pitch he was different again: a lovely man, and so accident-prone. We called him Clouseau – a walking nightmare!

7. George Best

I'd like to think I can look back, all these years on, and feel pretty proud about my contribution to the team. I was top scorer for the club for five consecutive seasons and joint top scorer in the First Division (before there was a Premier League, of course) one year. And I played on the wing! I think I also played my part in the European Cup win, along the way as well as in the final, and that I played the game the way the United fans wanted to see it played.

8. Brian Kidd

I remember when he first came into the team, as an 18-year-old, and found himself against Mike England, one of the best centre-halves in the business. Kiddo turned Mike inside out and you knew he was something special. He had great skills for a big lad, and a terrific shot. And can you imagine scoring on your 19th birthday – in a European Cup final? Off the field he was always quieter, but Alex Ferguson realised what an asset he could be as his assistant manager. Alex is full of praise for him.

9. Bobby Charlton

'Amazing' and 'incredible' are words that spring to mind. Bobby did it all for club and country, and loved United. Still does. I've never seen a player go past defenders as easily as Bobby did. He'd just glide past them. Then, from 30 yards or more, left foot or right, he'd just hammer it. Such an exciting player. Like Bill, he was a survivor of the crash and went through it all. Big pal of Nobby and Shay, and another family man who liked to get back to his wife and daughters.

10. David Sadler

Almost every club in the country wanted Dave when he was playing amateur football in the South, but he opted for United and became a good pal. We were in digs together and roomed together at away matches. He was originally a centre-forward but proved versatile, operating in midfield or central defence, where I felt he was at his best. He had a number of games for England at centre-half. He was a studious, intelligent lad and that showed in his play. Great guy and now runs our old boys' association.

11. John Aston

Everybody agrees he was the man of the match in the European Cup final. He absolutely murdered their poor right-back. But unfortunately people just seem to remember his performance that night, when in fact he played a lot of terrific games for us. He was often underestimated because there were so many big-name players in our team, but he never gave less than 100 per cent. His strength was his running and he would be up and down that left flank all day. He grafted non-stop.

Substitute: Jimmy Rimmer

We were allowed a substitute goalkeeper in those days but poor Jimmy didn't actually get the chance to come on in the final. He was also unlucky that we had Alex at the time because he was another international-class keeper and, like Alex, he played for England. He was still a young lad in '68 and went on to prove his quality with two other big clubs, Arsenal and Aston Villa. He also got a European Cup-winners' medal with Villa, so he did pretty well for himself in the end.

Denis Law

It would be impossible to talk about all the players we had in those days, but equally I couldn't possibly ignore this fella. He couldn't play in the final because he was in hospital, but he was with us in spirit. He had some mates round for a bevvy or six and I don't think he remembers too much about the match. As a player he was up there with the all-time greats. Electric. He'd snap up any half-chance. As a bloke and as a pal, he's different class. Nobody has a bad word for Denis.

I think it's a measure of the standard we set that three of us won the European Footballer of the Year award: Denis in 1964, Bobby in 1966 and myself in 1968. When you've got three players like that you've got a chance. But we had quality right through the team and we had to have, because to win the European Cup in those days you had to be a bit special. And it was the way we played, with flair and imagination. If the other team got three, we knew we were going to get four or five. We were good and we knew we were good.

This was the way Sir Matt believed the game should be played, and he brought together the players he knew could do it. And he knew how to get the best out of them, how to build their confidence and encourage them to express themselves. He was a great manager and a great man. He was like a second father to me and I was really touched at his funeral when his family told me he regarded me as a son. I like to think his football family did him proud.

PART I

ONE MAN AND HIS DREAM

It is inevitable the poorer and harsher environments of the world should spawn hungry fighters and footballers, but the Scottish coalfields exceeded their quota by yielding three of the beautiful game's greatest men and managers. Jock Stein would make Celtic the first British champions of Europe, Bill Shankly would convey Liverpool from the Second Division of the English Football League to the threshold of European supremacy. And yet most observers concur with the view that they and their achievements were probably eclipsed by Matt Busby and his management of Manchester United.

These three extraordinary individuals shared not only their roots but also a contact with football's soul. Their teams were the manifestation of the purist's ethos, their triumph the deliverance of the faithful. Detractors would argue spiritual virtues and principles would not have survived the constraints of more pragmatic later generations. In which case, let us give thanks they lived when they did.

The case for proclaiming Busby's pre-eminence, even in this noble company, is founded on his record over a quarter of a century and a legacy that cannot be measured adequately in titles and trophies. It was convenient to depict him as the manager who inherited a great team that won the FA Cup in 1948, the team that died at Munich in 1958 and the team that won the European Cup in 1968. Life and reality, however, rarely conform to such symmetry.

He did not merely 'inherit' and 'buy' teams, just as he did not have merely three teams. He constantly moulded, developed, revised and refined his teams. The most dramatic and significant unforced changes were made to accommodate the introduction of the 'Busby Babes' in the '50s, but even that fabled side was shuffled and added to before the crash. Busby did spend in order to hasten the club's recovery, yet his line-up against Benfica at Wembley included only two players who had cost transfer fees of any consequence. And Alex Stepney and Pat Crerand had arrived at a combined expense of little more than £100,000.

19

Busby's teams won also the League Championship in 1952, 1956, 1957, 1965 and 1967, and the FA Cup in 1963. The ground he moved into when it was a bombed-out shell became the finest in English League football and has been improved still further in recent years. In the 1967–68 season the average home attendance was a record 57,549. The club is simply the biggest in the land and one of the biggest in the world. Everywhere the game is played – and you suspect some places where it is not – they know of Manchester United. Matt Busby was the perpetrator of this phenomenon.

Busby was born into a Catholic family in Orbiston, near the town of Bellshill, Lanarkshire, on 26 May 1909. The menfolk of the area worked at the coalface and played football, and young Matt was no different. One activity provided essential income, the other equally necessary escape. He did not, however, seek to shirk his responsibilities. He was six when his father was killed in the First World War and he grew up quickly as a consequence. His maturity became evident in his playing days, when he was a natural captain, and in the way he both settled into and redefined football management.

He played, ironically, for Manchester City, and then Liverpool. He was what was commonly referred to as a 'cultured' wing-half and was much vaunted for his 'reading and understanding' of the game. He won only one full Scotland cap but led his country in a number of wartime internationals. Like many of his contemporaries, he lost much of his playing career to the Second World War, although he might have continued when peace was restored to Europe in 1945.

Instead he accepted an invitation to become manager of Manchester United. It was a career move that appealed to him, and he and his wife Jean liked Manchester. At that time, however, the job did not have the cachet it has now. United had modest status, having spent the inter-war years shuffling between the First and Second Divisions. The club had begun life in 1878 as Newton Heath, founded by employees of the Lancashire and Yorkshire Railway Company as a cricket and football club. They were admitted to the Football League in 1892, losing their first match, against Blackburn Rovers, 4–3. They became Manchester United in 1902, were champions in 1908 and 1911, and FA Cup winners in 1909. By the time Busby took over they were in the shadow of Manchester City, who had Championship and FA Cup success in the '30s. They also had a ground United were to use in the immediate aftermath of the Second World War because enemy bombers had destroyed much of Old Trafford.

The role of the manager, also, was very different from the one with which we are now familiar. Club secretaries and directors assumed it was their right and duty to run affairs, even to the extent of influencing team selection. Working parameters demanded by Busby in 1945 were instrumental in changing the nature and power of management. He insisted on absolute control. He would do it his way or not at all. The club complied and on 19 February 1945 appointed him for five years, at an annual salary of £750.

Busby admitted he had no training for the job, but believed he knew the game and knew players. He felt that losing his father at such a tender age made him sensitive to the vulnerability of young footballers, many of whom lived away from home. The 'Father' of Manchester United was already embracing his new family. The paternal instincts were apparent in his firm but compassionate handling of players. He took the view that if they were made to feel comfortable, wanted and respected, they would respond positively on the field. He encouraged them to be expressive, creative and assertive.

The wider scope of Busby's managerial function necessitated another innovation: the proactive No. 2. He wanted someone closer to ground level. Someone who would work with the players constantly and fire some of his bullets for him. Someone who would growl and cajole, yet teach and nurture with no less care. Someone who would complement yet never seek to undermine him or aspire to his position. If appointing Matt Busby was the single most important decision in the history of Manchester United, sanctioning the recruitment of Jimmy Murphy as his right-hand man might be the second most important.

Murphy, too, had been a wing-half and played for West Bromwich Albion. He was Welsh, played for his country and later managed them on a part-time basis. He was more at ease, however, as a No. 2. Especially Busby's No. 2. A stint as his stand-in after Munich confirmed as much. He turned down many invitations to manage club sides, including one from Juventus. He was content with a low profile, working with his players, honing their raw talent for professional careers. They grew to appreciate his dedication and warmed to him, even those who felt the sharp edge of his tongue. They believed his contribution was not always sufficiently acknowledged. Murphy was 'promoted' to assistant manager in 1955 and in his later years scouted for the club.

The Busby–Murphy partnership established a mode of management aped by some of the sport's most successful figures. Shankly had Bob Paisley; Brian Clough had Peter Taylor. The format worked, and United garnered the benefits after doubtless holding their breath. Busby and Murphy saw no logic in the old maxim that you 'starve a player of the ball in the week and he will be hungry for it on the Saturday'. They trained with the ball, they 'practised' their trade. And eventually they were made almost perfect.

United, redirected and fashioned by Busby, were runners-up in the Championship for three consecutive seasons from 1947, and in 1948, captained by the revered Johnny Carey and playing in blue shirts because of a colour clash with Blackpool, won a classic FA Cup final 4–2. United trailed 2–1 with little more than 20 minutes remaining and Stanley Matthews was reaching out for his winner's medal. But Busby's players, exhorted to keep faith in their practised game, turned the match with three goals.

The Cup was welcomed home to Manchester with a public show of jubilation, yet Busby knew the Championship was the only genuine gauge of the best. Finishing runners-up again in 1951 heightened the frustration – and made the success of the following year all the more precious. It was the club's first title for 41 years.

Equally important were the foundations being laid for the future. United had moved back to Old Trafford in 1949 and Busby believed his players should be bred at home, raised to play the game of his dreams. The first wave of young footballers were already being groomed by the time United won the Championship, and the intake that summer included a boy from Dudley, near Birmingham, called Duncan Edwards. Barely a year later he played, along with Eddie Colman, Billy Whelan, David Pegg and Albert Scanlon, in the first leg of the FA Youth Cup final against Wolverhampton Wanderers at Old Trafford. United won 7–1, and the senior English game was about to succumb to a new, exciting, irresistible force.

Edwards was a real-life comic hero: gifted, strong, modest. He was recognised as a left-half but could play anywhere. In times of need, he would venture forward and plunder match-winning goals. He had a ferocious shot and a presence that intimidated seasoned players. He made his debut for United at 16 and became England's youngest player of the century when he was awarded the first of his 18 caps against Scotland in April 1955 at the age of 18 years and 183 days. Those who knew him and saw him said he towered above all others, the greatest player the club ever produced.

And around him Busby and Murphy assembled a pack of bright cubs. They not only dominated youth football in this country through the '50s but also took over the man's game. The Busby Babes were set free from their pen. The manager may have been mildly embarrassed by the tag, but the alliteration was too good to miss. So was their football. It flowed with the fearless, unrestrained exuberance of youth.

In goal was Ray Wood; at right-back, Bill Foulkes, summoned from the pits of South Lancashire. The left-back and captain was Roger Byrne, a conscientious leader who suffered fools not at all. At right-half was Eddie Colman, a local lad, small and full of mischief and tricks. Mark Jones and Jackie Blanchflower vied for the centre-half's shirt. No one competed for Edwards's place. Busby had to look afield for the centre-forward to lead his attack and paid Barnsley a fee disclosed as £29,999 for Tommy Taylor. Busby felt the burden of a £30,000 transfer might be too much for the lad. His other forwards were Johnny Berry, Whelan, Dennis Viollet, Pegg and Scanlon, the competition further intensified by the likes of Kenny Morgans and the emergence of a youngster from the North-East. The word was he had an even harder shot than Edwards. His name was Bobby Charlton.

The Busby Babes, or the Red Devils, as they were alternatively known, swept to the Championship in the 1955–56 season, beating their closest rivals, Blackpool, by 11 points. This when only two points were awarded for a win. They retained the League trophy and were expected to complete the domestic double in the FA Cup final against Aston Villa, but Peter McParland's infamous challenge on Wood – which reduced United to ten men, one of them an emergency goalkeeper in Blanchflower, for much of the match – proved decisive. United lost 2–1.

In December 1957, Busby paid a world-record fee for a goalkeeper, £23,500, to sign Harry Gregg, an irascible but brave and talented Ulsterman, from Doncaster Rovers. Gregg was recruited to reinforce United's prospects not only at home but also abroad. By then Busby had made his boldest and most momentous move of all.

Chelsea, England's Championship winners in 1955, had been firmly steered away from any fancies of entering a newfangled foreign competition drummed up by the French. The idea was to determine the best team in Europe. Champions of national leagues would compete on a knock-out basis, all the ties up to the final to consist of two legs, home and away. The English Football League, however, dismissed the initiative as an irrelevant fad. The nation that gave the game to the world had no need for such gimmicks. Their clubs had plenty to occupy them in this country. The European Cup was out of bounds.

Busby disagreed and challenged that ruling. He recognised the blossoming of a new game on the Continent, played by artists who caressed the ball and were able to do wondrous things with it. Hungary's humiliation of England at Wembley and in Budapest ought to have been proof enough. Now it was evident in the European Cup, won in 1955–56, its inaugural season, by the Spanish champions Real Madrid. In the final, played in Paris, they beat the host nation's representatives, Reims, 4–3.

The enlightened United manager saw a stage to inspire his team and the country. Here was a competition to fire the imagination and stretch his tyros. Here was a world of romance, mystery, magic, fantasy. New names, new places. A new kind of football. Manchester United would defy the English authorities and enter the European Cup for the 1956–57 season. Busby would pursue a dream to emulate Real Madrid and see his team saluted as the best in Europe.

It is a testament to Busby's managerial acumen that he not only led a later team to European Cup triumph but that he was also coveted and courted by the Spaniards, who offered him 'heaven' at the Bernabeu. He politely but unreservedly declined, explaining he had his heaven at Old Trafford. He had young footballers who played like angels, their wings extended by the demands of a celestial Continental game.

United's impact on the European Cup was instant and spectacular. According to the *Manchester Guardian's* report, datelined Brussels, 12 September 1956, 'By an Old International', 'Manchester United bore themselves nobly' to beat Anderlecht of Belgium 2–0, with goals by Viollet and Taylor, in the first leg of their preliminary-round tie. The correspondent declared that the resumption of the contest, at Moss Side, should not be missed. It was sound advice. United won that second leg, played at Maine Road because Old Trafford was not equipped with floodlights, 10–0. At a stroke, they had etched their name on the European football map.

Borussia Dortmund – who would feature prominently in United campaigns to come – threatened to erase it in the first round proper. The Germans were defeated 3–2 in Manchester but squandered chances in the return leg, which ended goalless. United were to have another close encounter in their quarter-final with Athletic Bilbao. Their naivety was exposed as they lost the away match 5–3, leaving them with a formidable task at Maine Road. That night of 6 February 1957 remains one of the landmarks in United's European odyssey. They won the leg 3–0 to go through 6–5 on aggregate, and a 65,000 crowd produced an atmosphere probably unprecedented in an English ground. The *Daily Express* reporter Henry Rose, as much a legend at that time as any United player, revealed 'My hands are still trembling as I write' and proclaimed it 'the greatest soccer victory in history'.

Journalists could not only get away with stuff like that in those days, they built reputations on it. United, however, could not get away with another two-goal deficit in the semi-finals. Their opponents were the holders, Real Madrid. The Spaniards won 3–1 in Madrid and two first-half goals in the return leg put the tie beyond recall for United. They did at least salvage self-respect and parity in the second half at Old Trafford, Charlton scoring the equaliser. But Madrid were through to the final again, and beat Fiorentina of Italy 2–0 to retain the Cup.

United regrouped for the following season's competition in bullish mood. They were a year older, more experienced, wiser. More specifically, they were smarter to the ways and wiles of the team that set the standard for the rest of Europe. They would be better prepared for all-comers. Even Real Madrid. United brushed aside Shamrock Rovers 6–0 in Ireland, then found them a more persistent irritant in the second leg and progressed with a 9–2 aggregate win. Three goals at home gave them a comfortable cushion against Dukla Prague, the 1–0 away defeat causing no obstruction to their passage.

Red Star Belgrade were United's quarter-final opponents this time and a 2–1 home win, after conceding the opening goal and inspired by Charlton, sent them to Yugoslavia on a difficult mission. United's planning for the trip involved more than match strategy. They chartered a plane to avoid changing aircraft in London. They took provisions such as eggs and chocolate in case sustenance behind the Iron Curtain proved inadequate, and they sharpened their appetites with a rousing 5–4 League victory at Arsenal. Murphy could not be with United in Belgrade because of commitments with Wales. Injury cost Wilf McGuinness, another promising player, his place in the party and Geoff Bent, a reserve full-back, was preferred to Ronnie Cope.

Their concerns, on and off the pitch, seemed unfounded as they reached half-time leading 3–0. Charlton again galvanised the side. He scored two of the goals, Viollet the other. Sloppiness crept into United's game in the second half and Red Star scrambled an improbable draw, but Busby's players had done just enough to make it to a second semi-final of the European Cup. They enjoyed the evening, Yorkshiremen Jones and Taylor leading a rendition of 'Ilkla Moor Baht 'At'. Later still Colman was up to typical mischief, swapping shoes put outside the hotel rooms to be polished. He was stopped in his tracks when a team-mate warned him he was tampering with the boss's shoes! Here was a group of young men with the world at their feet and not a care to burden them.

The United team that serenaded Belgrade on the afternoon of 5 February 1958 was: Gregg, Foulkes, Byrne, Colman, Jones, Edwards, Morgans, Charlton, Taylor, Viollet, Scanlon.

The following morning the United party headed for home, via a snowy Munich, where the BEA Elizabethan aircraft had to stop for refuelling. Soon the plane was rumbling down the slushy runway in Bavaria, only for take-off to be aborted. The engine sound was not normal but, in the view of Captain James Thain, who was in command although not at the controls of Flight 609, gave no cause for alarm. Such a hiccup was nothing new to these now-regular travellers. Little more than a year earlier they had swept snow from the wings of their plane before returning from Bilbao. A smiling David Pegg was pictured with a brush over his right shoulder after doing his bit.

United's Elizabethan began take-off procedures again, and again came to a halt. This time the passengers were returned to the terminal building and an engineer was called. He suggested the engines could be retuned and the flight resumed the next day, but he affirmed Thain's contention that 'boost surging' was not unusual at high-altitude airports. Staying overnight was not a popular option, so a third take-off attempt was made. This time it was not aborted, but the plane failed to leave the ground. At 3.04 p.m. the Elizabethan and Manchester United FC were decimated.

Two of the survivors were Bill Foulkes and Harry Gregg. Thain was another. He shouted at them to run because there could be an explosion. Foulkes remembers running through the snow with no shoes. Gregg heard the cries of a baby, turned back and re-emerged from the wreckage clutching the infant. In near frenzy, he helped rescue several others before being driven to hospital in a van along with team-mates and their manager. Busby was one of the more seriously injured. Edwards was another. Blanchflower and Berry were badly hurt and never played again. Charlton, Viollet, Scanlon, Morgans and Wood recovered to resume their careers. The full horror hit Foulkes as he checked on the survivors and asked about the rest of his friends, to be told they were dead.

Back in Manchester the first reports were sparse and confusing. Gradually names of survivors filtered through. By the Friday morning the families of those killed were confronting the awful reality. So was the entire city. Children went to school in silent procession, wearing their United scarves. Adults lined the streets to Old Trafford as the coffins were brought home and laid in the gym. All night people arrived to watch, pray, lay their flowers and weep.

The crash had left 21 people dead. (The toll would rise to 23.) They included the coach Bert Whalley, the trainer Tom Curry, the secretary Walter Crickmer, and seven players: Byrne, Colman, Jones, Whelan, Taylor, Pegg and Bent. Also dead were journalists Alf Clarke (*Manchester Evening Chronicle*), Don Davis ('Old International' of the *Manchester Guardian*), Tom Jackson (*Manchester Evening News*), George Follows (*Daily Herald*), Archie Ledbrooke (*Daily Mirror*), Eric Thompson (*Daily Mail*), Frank Swift (*News of the World* and former Manchester City goalkeeper) and Henry Rose.

Fears remained that Busby would not pull through. Twice he was given the last rites at the Rechts der Isar Hospital. Edwards, too, was gravely ill, but he hung on into a second week and surely could not die. Not big, strong, indestructible Duncan. On 21 February, 15 days after the crash, Edwards lost his fight for life. He was 21.

Many years later, another United player celebrated as the most complete footballer in the country, Bryan Robson, asked his manager Ron Atkinson, 'How good was Duncan Edwards?' Atkinson pondered for barely a second and replied, 'About twice as good as you.'

Every year, on 6 February, the *Manchester Evening News* carries in its remembrance column loving messages to the victims of Munich, and especially to Colman, the boy from Salford who proved you did not have to be built like Duncan Edwards to be a great player, or a Busby Babe.

Busby's was a psychological as well as a physical struggle. While the doctors worked on his body, he grappled with his conscience. A sense of guilt was inevitable and almost overbearing. He had taken his boys into Europe despite the opposition of the League. None of this would have happened had he obeyed them. As Chelsea had. He felt he could have nothing more to do with football. Friends and colleagues gradually and gently urged him to reconsider. In his own time. Life had to go on and the club had to go on. They would need him. He would need them. Busby became reconciled by the realisation that his lost boys would want him to go on. They had relished the great European venture as much as he had. They had risen to the challenge of competing against and beating the best. It would still be their crusade. And one day they would win the European Cup.

In Busby's absence Murphy took charge of the team. What team? Just 13 days after the crash United were to play again, in a fifth-round FA Cup tie against Sheffield Wednesday at Old Trafford. Every position on the United team-sheet, laid out in the match programme, was blank. Murphy had to beg, borrow and steal to make up a side that included Gregg, Foulkes, 17-year-olds Alex Dawson and Mark Pearson, and, at outside-left, Shay Brennan.

Almost 60,000 were in the ground, many more thousands locked outside. The great swell of emotion throughout the land closed in on Wednesday's players that night. It was a match they could not win. They must have known that as they stepped out on to the pitch. United were led by their new captain, Foulkes, who won the toss. Was even that in doubt? Brennan, who would complete the journey to Wembley in 1968 with Foulkes, scored the first two goals, one directly from a corner kick, the other drilled in from close range. Dawson completed the 3–0 victory.

United earned a home replay against West Bromwich Albion in the sixth round and, with the considerable help of another survivor of the crash, Charlton, who set up the only goal for Colin Webster, went through to the semi-finals. They had to negotiate a further replay, against Fulham, Charlton scoring three times in the two matches, and incredibly they were in the final.

Alas, the fairytale ended there. Even with Busby back to look on and inspire, Charlton could not weave his spell over Bolton Wanderers. As in the previous year, United were undone by a challenge on their goalkeeper that would not be tolerated in the modern game. Nat Lofthouse barged the ball in, leaving Gregg prostrate and groggy for some time. The Lion of Vienna scored both goals in Bolton's 2–0 win.

The sympathy that had ushered United through their domestic programme was conspicuously absent when they took up the European Cup torch. They recovered splendidly after going behind in the first leg of their semi-final against Milan at Old Trafford. Viollet, another survivor, equalised and Ernie Taylor converted a penalty. In Italy, however, the reception from their opponents and supporters was overtly hostile. Missiles were thrown at the team coach. Unnerved or not, United, deprived of Charlton's services because he was on England duty, were outclassed and lost 4–0. The return journey overland was long and sobering. Real Madrid, who went on to win the final again, were more gracious, offering United the trophy in tribute to those who had died. United, appreciative as they were, felt they had to decline.

Now the real task of rebuilding began. Busby could not wait for another generation of Babes to come through *en bloc* and could not, in any case, guarantee to produce the likes of the Babes ever again. A club renowned for its tight purse strings would have to spend, and Busby had an ally in a new director, Louis Edwards, a rotund, affable businessman who would succeed Harold Hardman as chairman in 1965. Albert Quixall, who had captained Sheffield Wednesday in United's first match after Munich, went to Old Trafford early in the 1958–59 season for a British record fee of £45,000. United were runners-up in the Championship, but this was a false dawn. More strengthening was required. Maurice Setters, Noel Cantwell and David Herd were recruited. Cantwell became captain.

In the summer of 1962 Busby pulled off his most ambitious, delicate and expensive transfer, signing Denis Law from the Italian club Torino for £116,000. The Scot became an idol overnight and was soon to be acknowledged by the fans as their King. Now United had two great players, even if Charlton had been switched from inside-forward to outside-left. On 6 February 1963, Pat Crerand, the Celtic wing-half, came on board. United completed the season narrowly avoiding relegation and winning the FA

Cup. The anxieties of the preceding months were cast aside by a performance at last evoking memories of the great days. Law turned on to Crerand's pass to beat Gordon Banks and give United the lead against Leicester. The two Scots were magnificent. Scottish-born Herd scored the other two in United's 3–1 win.

Busby had his first trophy since before the crash and a passport back into Europe, albeit for the Cup-Winners' Cup. United flexed their muscles and skills with a 7–2 aggregate win against the Dutch team Willem II, Law scoring a hat-trick in the home leg. In the second round they met the holders, Tottenham Hotspur. They lost 2–0 away but retaliated 4–1 at home, Herd and Charlton each scoring twice.

When United won 4–1, with a hat-trick from Law, in the home leg against Sporting Lisbon, the semi-finals beckoned. Instead came humiliation. To Busby's unbridled fury, they capitulated 5–0 in the Portuguese capital. There was no sign of the benign expression or gentle smile this night. Factions within the camp blamed the manager for his 'play your usual game' creed. The team left themselves exposed and were consequently punished. There had been a discernible undercurrent of discontent. Cliques were threatening to split the family. The 'home' players blamed the 'outsiders'.

Busby and his aides were conscious that this was a matter they had to address, and their course was eased by the graduation of a new class at their academy. Among them was a wisp of a lad from Belfast who, at the age of 17, had his first experience of European football in the ill-starred tie against Sporting Lisbon. George Best, more than any other player, would avenge that 5–0 embarrassment. Busby now had three great players, a pyramid on which to build his dreams. The rest would have their qualities and be essential to the structure, and all would be loyal to the cause.

United were runners-up in the Championship that season to a new power in the English game, Bill Shankly's Liverpool. Early the following season Quixall departed, to be followed by Setters. Cantwell, the club captain, played only two League games. Brennan settled at right-back, Tony Dunne at left-back. Foulkes was established at centre-half. Pat Dunne was in goal. Nobby Stiles, local boy and United fan, found a regular place. John Connelly arrived from Burnley to play on the right wing. Charlton, Herd and Law formed the awesome inside trio.

This time United's rivals for the title were yet another emerging force, Don Revie's Leeds United. Busby's team had the edge going into the last week of the campaign and, with two goals from a patched-up Denis Law, beat Arsenal 3–1 at Old Trafford in their penultimate match. Leeds had to win at Birmingham in their final fixture that Monday evening to send United to Aston Villa, 48 hours later, on tenterhooks. Developments at St

Andrews were relayed north and Birmingham's 3–0 lead prompted premature celebrations. By the time Leeds drew level tension had gripped the United crowd. To an eruption of relief and joyous invasion of the Old Trafford pitch, Birmingham held on for a 3–3 draw. Busby had another champion team.

He also had an Inter-Cities Fairs Cup (forerunner of the UEFA Cup) semi-final against Ferencvaros of Hungary to encounter. United had overcome Djurgarden (Sweden), Borussia Dortmund (that club again), Everton and Racing Club Strasbourg (France) to reach the last four. The tie went to a play-off after a 3–3 aggregate draw; United lost the toss for the right to stage it and were defeated 2–1.

A return to the European Cup provided more than ample consolation. United eased into their stride, beating the Finns Helsinki JK 9–2 on aggregate in the preliminary round and ASK Vorwaerts of East Germany 5–1 in the first round to earn a meeting with one of the most feared clubs on the Continent, Benfica. The Portuguese had made four appearances in the final, winning the trophy twice. They were a side of gifted, exciting individuals, none more gifted or exciting than the 'Black Panther' from Mozambique, Eusebio. His lithe body and languid style belied explosive pace and ferocious power in his shot. He demonstrated his potential at Old Trafford, and although United scraped a 3–2 win, the portents for the second leg in Lisbon were not good.

As United were driven from their hotel in Estoril to the Stadium of Light that warm March evening in 1966, they were taunted by the natives brandishing open hands, the five digits reminding their visitors of the score the last time they had been in town and presumably what they should expect this time. The previous visit, after all, had been to Sporting. Now they were at the mercy of mighty Benfica, a team unbeaten in 19 home games in European competition. United's nerves were further tested by a delay to the kick-off as Eusebio was presented with his European Footballer of the Year award. Denis Law, recipient the year before, dutifully posed for pictures, shaking hands with his successor.

Chants of 'Ben-fi-ca, Ben-fi-ca' boomed from the steep gallery as the Italian referee, Concetto Lo Bello, at last summoned the teams to action. The lesson of '64 heeded, Busby ordered a strategy of containment for the first 20 minutes, hoping to frustrate the opposition and silence the 80,000 crowd. That objective was accomplished, although not in the manner the boss had instructed. United were three up in 14 minutes. The Eagles had been grounded; the contest was over. The mocking hands proved prophetic, United eventually winning 5–1.

It was one of the most astonishing performances and results in the history of the European Cup, and the pivotal figure was 19-year-old Best. He headed the first goal after six minutes, darted through Benfica's bewitched defence to despatch the second after 12, and tormented them throughout. Connelly scored the third, and after Brennan's miscue presented the Portuguese with a goal early in the second half, Crerand and Charlton completed the magnificent atonement.

In the mayhem that followed, Charlton had his shirt ripped from his back and United's trainer, Jack Crompton, goalkeeper in the 1948 FA Cup-winning team, was struck to the ground by an irate fan. But nothing could leave a blemish on this perfect night. It was almost midnight as the wires hummed across Europe news of this vibrant, imaginative display by United, given its extra dimension by the effervescent Best. He was called 'O Beatle' by the Portuguese, which became 'El Beatle' in the English press. In Portuguese or Spanish, he was the symbol of an age as well as a team.

United were through to the semi-finals, as they had been in 1957 and 1958. The draw, pairing them with the unexceptional Partizan Belgrade, reinforced their belief they would go on to win the Cup. That confidence may have turned to carelessness come the first leg in Belgrade, yet they were probably too dependent on Best. Busby played the winger despite a troublesome knee and the gamble failed. The Irishman created a chance which Law, a player also hindered by knee problems, should have converted, but contributed little else. Busby, flanked by Murphy and Crompton, watched from the bench in dismay as his wonder boy went down clutching his knee. It was his last match of the campaign and United had to try to overturn a two-goal deficit in the home leg without him.

An own goal, palmed in by Partizan's goalkeeper Soskic, was all United could dredge from the game, and Crerand's dismissal, along with his Yugoslav sparring partner, compounded Old Trafford's despair. *The Sun* newspaper declared, 'End of a Busby Dream.' Even within the camp they feared as much. The manager was down and although the players offered words of encouragement, that they would win the Championship the following season and then the European Cup, it was mere rhetoric. All conviction had been drained.

United had failed to qualify for Europe in 1966–67 but that, along with their summary elimination from the League Cup and rare early demise in the FA Cup, enabled them to focus on the Championship. Busby solved a lingering goalkeeping problem by signing Alex Stepney from Chelsea and his stars lit the road to the title. They completed the triumphal march with a characteristically flamboyant victory, 6–1 away to West Ham United, a side that included three of England's World Cup-winners, Bobby Moore, Geoff Hurst and Martin Peters.

Busby and his players were back on the trail of the dream after all and, but for that priority, might not have yielded their domestic dominion to neighbours City. Much was made of the 'ageing' side, but youngsters David Sadler and John Aston now featured regularly, and there was a new Kidd on the block. Brian Kidd, an 18-year-old local boy, was a forward with skill, strength and thunder in his left boot.

United's European programme began with a regulation loosener, Law and Sadler scoring two apiece in the 4–0 home win against Hibernians Valletta of Malta, although the goalless return leg caused unscheduled discomfiture. A 0–0 draw away to Sarajevo was distinctly more satisfying, even if they had to ride their luck. United were, it seemed, getting the hang of this two-legged European game. Goals by Aston and Best gave them a 2–1 entry to the quarter-finals, after an ill-tempered encounter. Kidd followed up an own goal with a late strike to provide United with a 2–0 advantage for the trip to Katowice in Poland and the return against Gornik Zabrze. There they defied the icy bite of winter as well as a sustained onslaught and came in from the cold with a 2–1 aggregate success. They had reached the semi-finals of the European Cup for the fourth time.

Whatever role fate or destiny might have played at this stage, it was appropriate they should now face Real Madrid, the first club to eliminate them from the competition back in 1957, their inspiration and their friends, Busby having secured diplomatic relations by organising a series of friendly games between the clubs in the interim. The Spaniards had claimed the European Cup for a sixth time two years earlier and, although they had descended some way from their zenith of 1960, they remained a valid challenge for aspiring champions.

For all United's endeavour, and the exhortation of their most vociferous followers on the Stretford End, they had only a 1–0 lead, courtesy of Best's left-foot whiplash following Aston's cut-back, from the first leg at Old Trafford. The Bernabeu loomed: large, awesome, intimidating. The auguries before the game were not encouraging. Law failed a fitness test on his knee and was resigned to surgery. United appeared in need of a miracle rather than an operation as Madrid swaggered into a 3–1 half-time lead, Zoco's own goal proffering an apparent morsel of consolation.

From somewhere (the lap of the gods?) they found the resolve to make a match of it and Best's header presented Sadler with the chance to bundle in a second. Best then appeared in more familiar guise, taking the ball to the line and pulling it back for a supporting forward. Except that the support arrived in the least familiar guise: Bill Foulkes. The 36-year-old centre-half, survivor of Munich, dogged of late by injury, was driven by some unfathomable urge to execute the decisive flourish. United had drawn 3–3 and won 4–3 on aggregate.

As the players made their way to the team coach after the match, Stiles, having left the dangerous Amancio his calling card, was hit on the head with a beer bottle. He dabbed the trickle of blood with his fingers but was quietly shepherded on board by Busby. Now was not the time to make a fuss or do anything to spoil this. Now was the time for glorious reflection. Just ten years on from Munich, Busby was leading his team into the final of the European Cup, against Benfica, at Wembley. The dream was there to be lived. Who said it was not destiny?

PART II

DAY OF DESTINY

Great Fosters is the sort of place you would have in mind for that special occasion: a historic, dignified haven, all polished oak and ornate ceilings, peaceful gardens and water. The publicity material says the Grade 1 listed building 'was once a royal hunting lodge in the heart of Windsor Forest and for nearly four centuries the stately Elizabethan home of many notable families'. Since 1930, when it became a hotel, it has provided food and shelter for such distinguished travellers as Charlie Chaplin, Orson Wells, Vivien Leigh, Nijinsky – the dancer, that is – and the Emperor Haile Selassie of Ethiopia. Anyone who happened to be here in this corner of Surrey towards the end of May 1968 may have recognised the guests as the management and players of Manchester United.

This is where Matt Busby chose to prepare his charges for their special occasion. Here he would fine-tune them, mentally perhaps more than physically, for the European Cup final. Wembley was a relatively short journey away yet might have been in another world. The players relaxed, cocooned as they were from pressure and much of the hype. They recall the soothing atmosphere of the old brick building, even if there is no sign of the suits of armour one of them talks about. The long walk down the field that Bill Foulkes recollects would now be brought to an abrupt end by the M25.

Thirty years on there are inevitable changes. Facilities have been updated, converted and modified to cater for conferences and weddings. But the antiques, log fires, Jacobean chimney pieces and mullions are sacrosanct. The players would doubtless recognise the topiary garden, the moat, the Japanese bridge and the rose garden. On the wall of a corridor hangs a montage of press cuttings. At the top is a picture of Bing Crosby, the hotel behind him. A smaller picture shows the Manchester United team, with the European Cup, and an understated caption which explains they stayed here.

The local paper, the *Surrey Herald*, made rather more of the visit in their edition of Friday 31 May. Under the headline 'United stars stay at Egham hotel', the story revealed that half a dozen members of the party began match day by celebrating Mass in the chapel of the Salesian College, Chertsey. The paper identified the worshippers as the assistant manager Jimmy Murphy, physiotherapist Ted Dalton, an old boy of the college, and players Pat Crerand, Nobby Stiles, Brian Kidd and Francis Burns.

Crerand is pictured with excited pupils on the school lawn and Stiles apparently told a *Staines and Egham News* reporter, 'We find praying helps to ease our minds before a big game.' The headmaster, Fr Edward O'Shea, said, 'It is a great privilege to have you here on the greatest day in the club's history.' Crerand took away a ball to be autographed by the United and Benfica players.

The article went on to disclose that on the Tuesday morning, the day before the match, the party had 'split up into twos and threes. Some strolled in the bright sunshine, and others caught taxis into Egham, where they visited some of the shops. Some visited Eric Williams's menswear shop in the High Street. On the day of the match Bobby Charlton was having a cup of morning tea in the hotel when our reporter asked him how he felt. "Great," he replied, "and the hotel's just right – very pleasant."' Charlton was pictured taking the air, and signing autographs. The intrepid reporter also caught up with the manager. 'Matt Busby said, "We're in pleasant surroundings which are just right for relaxing before the match." After watching the Derby on television the players boarded a coach for Wembley, where they later realised their manager's lifetime ambition by winning the European Cup.'

The manager of the hotel at the time, John Baumann, is still here, as general manager and director. Coincidentally, he retires just before the 30th anniversary of United's European Cup win. He is dapper, his hair and beard grey. He is softly spoken and apologises he does not remember more than he does of those few days, 30 years ago.

> I remember young girls gathering at the front entrance to see George Best. We were asked to keep it away from the press but these things get out. I can remember a birthday party. [Brian Kidd was 19 on the day of the final.] I don't think they'd been before and I don't know why they chose here. I believe they were here two nights but we do not have the register from that time.
>
> I was very proud because I met Sir Matt Busby in the corridor on the evening before the occasion and he said, 'Are you going to watch the final?' I said, 'No, I'm afraid we haven't got any tickets.' He said, 'Don't worry about that, I'll get you a couple of tickets,' and he produced two tickets. I

went with my brother and there we were, sitting in the most marvellous seats, in the middle of the stands at Wembley. I remember Bobby Moore and all sorts of England players at the time were watching. It was quite fantastic.

At the time we were using different accommodation. We were using what we now use for staff quarters, over on the other side. I remember Alex Stepney being there. But Sir Matt was in one of the suites upstairs in the main hotel here. I believe most of them liked their breakfast in bed. My wife says she can recall they were allowed only tomato juice and steak for dinner. She says they had tea and papers in their rooms. She took the papers to them herself and collected their signatures for her brother. When she came to reception she asked this person if he was connected with Manchester United. He said, 'Not really, I'm just the one who looks pretty and doesn't do very much.' She later found out he was the trainer [Jack Crompton].

The grounds went back much further then, about a third as far again, and the avenue of the lime trees extended back there where the M25 now runs. And, of course, in those days it was much more peaceful. We also had a bit of extra space at the front, which the council foreshortened some years ago. But they would certainly recognise the place. It's not really changed externally. We would have had a swimming pool and tennis court. We've added a games room in the conference centre, and a sauna.

David Coleman was here doing interviews for his television programme. He interviewed the players, and me, in the Anne Boleyn Room. I asked him if he could just make mention of the fact they were staying at Great Fosters. He said, 'We're not supposed to do that, but I'll see what I can manage.' He did manage it. Just a very short mention, that they were staying at the hotel in Egham. It was after that a lot of local people came to the front entrance. George Best was the one all the girls came to see. There was a lot of screaming. There were also a lot of police here, and they had a job to make clearance for the coach to depart to the match. Manchester United didn't stay here the night of the match, and to my knowledge they didn't stay here again.

David Coleman, a former Stockport County youth player and athlete of some repute, has 'majored' in the two sports during a distinguished career as BBC commentator and presenter. Many viewers suspected he had leanings towards United and he tracked them all the way to Wembley that season. The club patently regarded him as a talisman. He explains,

Louis Edwards and the directors had a superstition about me because they'd never lost when I commentated. I did all the rounds up to the final but Ken Wolstenholme was contracted to do the final, so Louis rang up the BBC's head of sport, Bryan Cowgill, and asked him to put me on the match. Bryan didn't believe it was Louis Edwards, asked him for his number and rang him back. That satisfied him it was Louis, but he had to explain there was nothing he could do about the commentary.

I did have a special affection for United and they helped me as much as they could that season. I had difficulty getting to Katowice for the Gornik game because I'd been asked to speak at an Olympic fund-raising dinner on the Monday and couldn't travel with the team. When I finally got there at six o'clock on the Wednesday morning I bumped into Louis, getting out of a taxi. He said I should have told him and they could have helped in some way. Then, as he went to his bed, he said, 'Don't tell Matt.' It was as if he was a player and didn't want the boss to know he'd been out late. It was snowing and bitterly cold there. I did the match wearing a balaclava. There was no policing of industrial emissions there in those days and I remember the snow turning black.

I travelled with United to Madrid, went on the team coach and had the special privilege of access to the dressing room. I remember, when Bill Foulkes scored and I said on the commentary 'Foulkes, 3–3', suddenly thinking, 'Oh my God, I've got the wrong player,' because he never crossed the halfway line! I was sitting in the team bus next to Paddy Crerand after the match when we heard this crash of glass. Somebody had dropped a bottle from one of the tiers at the Bernabeu on to Nobby Stiles's head. Paddy said coolly, 'It's a good job it's only his head. It might have done some serious damage.'

On the day of the final I was linking our programme from the lawn of the team's hotel. It was Derby day and the players were put to bed in the afternoon, but they were leaning out of their windows asking what was happening. I'd interviewed the players the day before for the programme. Each did a piece about the match. They were in good spirits. Kiddo, who grew up not far from Nobby, was regaling us with stories about the Stiles family business. They were funeral directors.

The mood of the party heading for Wembley was anything but funereal. The accompanying cheers and waves rekindled the sense of national pride England had generated two years earlier when they won the World Cup at the same venue. Outside the stadium supporters sauntered, mingled and sat in the warm sunshine that early evening of 29 May. A group of Benfica fans were engaged in good-humoured banter with their English counterparts. The Portuguese had arrived in a van of some vintage, decorated for the occasion with the names of the players, daubed in white. Charlton, whose goals had defeated Portugal in the semi-final of the World Cup, was spelt out in capital letters. Stiles, too, was singled out for special recognition. He was billed as 'The Bad One'. The little man had terrorised Eusebio during their international encounter here and was planning more of the same. United would be content to play, effectively, ten against ten.

As the players strolled on to the turf at Wembley for the ritual 'feel of the pitch', Kidd was greeted with a chorus of 'Happy birthday to you'. When they came out again, both teams in change strips because of a colour clash, United all in blue, Benfica all in white, the great bowl reverberated to the thunderous reception. Scarcely a face in the 100,000 crowd was visible through the giant mosaic of flags and banners. This was now the people's dream, as well as Busby's, and Benfica must have felt the pitch becoming heavier even as they filed towards the halfway line for the pre-match formalities.

The teams were:

Benfica: Henrique, Adolfo, Humberto, Jacinto, Cruz, Graca, Coluna, Augusto, Torres, Eusebio, Simoes.

Manchester United: Stepney, Brennan, Dunne, Crerand, Foulkes, Stiles, Best, Kidd, Charlton, Sadler, Aston.

The referee, Concetto Lo Bello of Italy, was as familiar to the players as they were to each other. He had officiated at the Stadium of Light when United won 5–1.

Charlton had taken over the captaincy from Law, who was recovering in hospital after a cartilage operation, and much as the Scot might have been missed, it was perhaps appropriate the privilege should have been the

Englishman's on this night. Having lost the toss to Coluna, the Benfica skipper, appearing in his 50th European game, it was Charlton who kicked off and directed the opening move which established a pattern for the match. Aston accelerated and Benfica had to resort to foul means to stop him. Often the butt of United fans' scorn, the winger was almost irresistible. It was the performance of his life.

Sadler, too, gave a glimpse of what was to come, his stretch proving insufficient to turn in Crerand's free-kick. Eusebio skipped past Stiles with rather more conviction and thumped the bar with his right-foot shot. Best had a half-chance and Sadler again stretched in vain for Kidd's header after Aston had surged away from the hapless Adolfo. Kidd had a shot blocked before Sadler squandered another opportunity. He scuffed his left-foot shot wide with Henrique at his mercy following a return pass from Kidd. Sadler slammed the turf with the palms of his hands in frustration. Busby, sitting on the bench, Murphy and Crompton to his right, lit a cigarette. So did McGuinness, now also a member of his coaching staff, sitting behind with Burns and the substitute goalkeeper, Jimmy Rimmer.

The award of a free-kick to Benfica just outside the area earned Lo Bello a close-up of Stiles's notorious fangs. Eusebio's low shot defied the wall but not Stepney's safe hands. Eusebio incurred the boos of the crowd and the wrath of Stiles after tumbling under his challenge. In truth, he was chopped, and in today's game Stiles would have been booked. Thirty years ago he protested Eusebio had conned the referee and bizarrely mocked the great man's fall to the ground. The free-kick was awarded but Stiles's theatrical antics evidently amused Lo Bello and Coluna. It was not enough, however, to assuage the United fans, their drone at half-time reflecting a dismay their side had not capitalised on that early superiority.

Best was similarly unimpressed at being fouled soon after the resumption of play, indicating his marker had a mental problem. An unlikely head was to present Benfica with more serious trouble after 53 minutes. Sadler, out on the left, checked on to his right foot and atoned for his first-half profligacy with a chip towards the near post, which Charlton headed on and beyond the reach of Henrique.

While Wolstenholme, assisted spasmodically by the meticulous enunciation of the former United player and England manager Walter Winterbottom, provided the words to the BBC's pictures, Alan Clarke and a promising broadcaster called Peter Jones were entrusted with the corporation's radio commentary:

> It's there, a great goal by Bobby Charlton, from the head as well, and the cross, a beautifully placed one, by David Sadler.

> And so Manchester United in the lead by one goal to nil,
> eight minutes into the second half.

Best popped the ball into Benfica's net, but the officials had signalled for offside. The Irishman burst clear again, this time to have his path blocked by Henrique outside the area. Best responded with something from his mesmerising repertoire, twisting past three defenders and bringing Henrique to an excellent save. Sadler seized on the rebound, only for his shot to hit the goalkeeper's legs and balloon over.

United's dominance appeared to lull them into a false sense of security and Eusebio, with Coluna's support, nearly punished them. Stiles berated his collegues in the usual way. Whether or not they took heed, their lead was cancelled out after 79 minutes. Augusto, Torres and Graca were involved in the move which melted away the left side of United's defence. Augusto eventually flighted the ball, Torres beat Foulkes in the air and headed down in the direction of Eusebio, who was covered by Stiles. The ball evaded both and was met by Graca, arriving unhindered, to score with a first-time right-foot shot.

Suddenly Benfica were the team moving forward with confidence, United anxiously seeking to regroup. Eusebio played a one-two with Torres but could not unsettle Stepney. Then, with normal time almost up, he was released to confront the goalkeeper again. Charlton was muscled off the ball on the edge of Benfica's area and Graca's swift counter exposed United. Stiles was instinctively lured to Graca, who played the ball forward into the path of Eusebio. He had a clear passage between Foulkes and Dunne, and although both defenders converged on him, United's fate was in Stepney's hands. Eusebio, at speed, took one touch with his right foot and, from just inside the area, thrashed at the ball with his left. Stepney, all in green, stationed seven yards off his line, was thrown back three yards and on to the ground by the force of the shot, yet climbed back to his feet still clutching the ball. Eusebio, following through, pawed Stepney, then applauded him in a lavish gesture of appreciation. Stepney merely kept his eye on the target for his throw-out, barely acknowledging Eusebio.

> Anxious eyes on the watch now. Three minutes of full time
> to play. Benfica 1, Manchester United 1. Nodded away by
> Benfica to Charlton. Can Charlton get a shot in? No he can't.
> And so Benfica come racing away, and it's up to Eusebio, up
> through the middle. He's clear now, can he shoot? He does,
> and Stepney saves it, a great save by Stepney, and Eusebio
> goes right up to him and pats him on the back there. A great

save by Stepney because Eusebio was clear, and he's applauding goalkeeper Alex Stepney for that save.

The European Cup final required extra-time for only the second time and United were the team more relieved still to be in the contest. Busby and his bench men came on to administer massage and faith. Charlton had his socks rolled down in extra-time. Best and Stiles followed suit. They also rolled up their sleeves, literally and metaphorically, as darkness at last descended. It now seems strange they wore long sleeves on such a warm evening.

Barely three minutes into the first extra period, Stepney gathered a throw-in from Dunne and rolled the ball to Brennan, only for it to be knocked back to him. Now he opted for the direct approach, hoofing it upfield. Kidd won the header, flicking it on for Best to dispute with the last defender, Jacinto. Best got to the ball a vital split second ahead of Jacinto, who was reduced to a forlorn fly kick as Best slipped the ball through his flimsy resistance. Henrique advanced towards the edge of his area but this time Best was in command of the situation. His right foot dragged the ball to the left, away from the stranded keeper, and his left foot guided it gently towards the beckoning goal. For a tantalising moment it seemed that Humberto might track back in time, or even that Henrique might recover his ground and salvage his cause. But their combined efforts were to no avail, Henrique's despairing lunge carrying him into the back of the net, close to the nestling ball.

> Stepney comes out this time, kicks it right-footed, high inside the Benfica half, a chance here for George Best. George Best is through, he goes round Henrique, he must score, George Best must score. George Best has scored. George Best has put Manchester United into the lead. Bobby Charlton sinks to his knees, Nobby Stiles does a cartwheel. United are in the lead again, two goals to one, two and a half minutes into the first period of extra-time . . . and the red and white banners really are reeling now away to our right.

A minute later Aston's pace won a corner on the left. Charlton arced in the kick and Sadler won the ball in the air. Kidd headed it towards goal, and although Henrique saved, the birthday boy nodded the rebound back over him. Aston, having expended so much energy destroying Benfica, could not face another gallop to join the celebrations wheeling around Kidd on the other wing.

It's Charlton, the man who does everything, to take the
corner . . . Here it comes, right footed, swirling in the lights,
inside the penalty area, a chance there for United . . . and it's
there . . . and Brian Kidd celebrates his 19th birthday in the
grand manner, by scoring the third goal for Manchester
United in the fourth minute of extra-time.

United were rampant, Benfica in disarray. Best's deflected cross bounced
off the top of the bar, and from the terraces and stands they sang, 'We'll be
running round Wembley with the Cup.' Wolstenholme told his television
audience, 'Undoubtedly the Manchester United fans are outshouting and
outsinging the England fans in the World Cup final.' By way of underlining
the fact that this was no ordinary spectacle, Charlton was penalised for a foul
on Eusebio and suggested his old adversary was diving. His case was backed
up by Stiles, of course. Eusebio restored himself to a vertical position and
struck the long-range kick into United's defensive wall.

United had no such difficulty breaching Benfica's defences. Brennan played
the ball up to Kidd, who laid it off to Charlton and, in the blink of an eye,
spun out to the right to receive the return. The youngster sucked in Cruz,
hurdled his desperate tackle, hared down the wing and, with his weaker right
foot, stroked the ball into the stride of the advancing Charlton. The captain
unhesitatingly, and unerringly, looped his shot into the far corner.

Bobby Charlton makes it four for Manchester United and
does that characteristic little throw salute of the arm, a little
jump in the air, and a battery of photographers come on.
Bobby Charlton, for my money, certainly in my time, the
greatest of them all, scores with ease and confidence. But
some splendid running by Brian Kidd, who went round
Cruz, no trouble at all, gave it to Charlton, and Charlton
hammered it home for number four, and his own second
here tonight. United 4–1 up, nine and a half minutes into
the first period of extra-time.

Kidd almost added to his account but Eusebio mustered a semblance of
retaliation, his header exercising Stepney. Dunne was hurt in the challenge
and Eusebio's sporting gesture, staying with the full-back until play was
stopped and help summoned, won him warm applause. But then it is easy
to be gracious when you are 4–1 up and the job is done.

Aston, too, might have pondered on the fickle nature of football fans as
he received treatment on the touchline after being assaulted by Henrique in

a position where he might have anticipated a tackle from the right-back. 'John-ny Aston, John-ny Aston,' cried those who had barracked him on not-so-good days. On this night of nights, however, he had been a revelation, and his father, John Aston senior, a member of the 1948 FA Cup and 1952 Championship-winning sides, then a member of Busby's staff, watched with pride and satisfaction.

Eusebio remained dangerously defiant to the end, and Stepney remained his Nemesis, holding on to a scorching shot, unleashed with virtually no backlift. Charlton, still working, fetching and carrying, was back in his area to head clear. Best decided it was party time, audaciously flicking up the ball before lobbing it into the area. Now the songsters gave us, 'Goodbye Benfica, goodbye.' A couple of fans ran on to the pitch in premature celebration and Wolstenholme resisted any temptation to recycle his 'they think it's all over' classic. But then, just two years on, it was not yet a classic.

By the last throes Stiles had become sportsmanlike, acknowledging Eusebio had outwitted him to create another shooting opportunity. Even he found it easy to be gracious when the shot soared off target. His job was done.

The referee's final blow of the whistle confirmed that Manchester United, the first English club to enter the European Cup and the first to reach the final, were now the first to win it. Busby was not chasing rainbows after all. His was a dream to be lived. Now he strode out on to the pitch to share the joy with his players. He was followed by his entourage, including a wildly grinning McGuinness, who unashamedly directed his excited applause at the manager. McGuinness was not alone in absorbing the personal meaning of this crusade.

Busby's eyes searched out Charlton from the growing confusion of bodies at the centre of the pitch and they embraced in a moment that required no caption. One by one, the rest hugged their boss. Tony Dunne gave him a playful tap on the back of the head. Torres, hovering for his chance, then moved in and asked Charlton to exchange shirts. The Englishman apologetically explained he couldn't, or not yet, anyway. There was something he had to go and get first. He found a fresh spring as he negotiated the steps and combed his wispy hair with his hand.

> Bobby Charlton, coming up to the royal box, below us now, to receive the Cup on a night of nights here at Wembley. There's a big roar of the crowd as he shakes hands. Bobby Charlton, lifting the Cup high above his head. A wonderful scene here at Wembley, the banners away to our left here, the red and white, waving. And to our right, too, because this is certainly a great night.

In fact, it was as much as Charlton could do to raise that gigantic piece of silverware chest-high. His colleagues wore exhausted expressions. Viewed now, they seemed surprisingly subdued. Perhaps they felt an obligation to observe some perceived, dignified protocol. Many things have changed in 30 years. More likely, a psychological burden, intensified over the years, had taken its toll. Kidd, the 19-year-old, was less inhibited. He smiled happily, naturally, and kissed his medal. They put on a celebratory show for their delirious, besotted fans, but for some this was an ordeal too far. The fun for them would begin the day after, when they took the European Cup back to Manchester. The satisfaction, private or public, would be with them for the rest of their days.

Eusebio received more appreciation as he again retreated, the vanquished hero. During the 1966 World Cup finals he had seduced the nation with his majestic football, his fabulous goals – he was the tournament's top scorer – and his angelic demeanour, only to be eliminated by Charlton's two goals. And then this. *Déjà vu*. Like Charlton, he is now an ambassador for his club, country and game. He was given a rapturous reception as a guest at Old Trafford in 1997. Looking back, however, he is not fawning or patronising. Portugal's greatest player says, 'I have a good relationship with United, as I do with football people in many, many parts of the world. We all know the great players United had in 1968 and for them it was a home match. Stepney made a good save from me but I was not really fit. I had a fractured knee. We played with injuries like that. It was nice for Matt Busby to win the European Cup, but I was not happy that night.'

David Coleman was back in the United camp after the match and recalls,

> I remember the boys taking the mick out of Bobby for scoring with his head. They were a very together club and team, from Matt all the way through, although the person who looked after Bobby and a lot of those players was Jimmy Murphy. We were going to link up to the hospital where Denis Law was and speak to him, but we got a message back from a nun, who said, 'He's too emotional to talk to you.' Denis had had some pals round and he told me later he was actually sloshed. They'd fed him with McEwan's.
>
> The teams and guests went to a central London hotel [The Russell, in Bloomsbury] afterwards and my wife and I were invited to the private party. I remember travelling along the M4 at eight o'clock in the morning to get back and get the kids to school, but I don't remember too much about the night before. For Matt's 80th birthday he was given a party

by the ex-players' association and he invited me as one of his own guests, along with the likes of Denis Compton, Tom Finney and Cliff Morgan. We were all made honorary members of the association.

The newspapers devoured the story of the dream that came true. 'WHAT A GREAT DAY FOR BUSBY,' the broadsheet *Daily Express* of 30 May splashed across its front page. In a ghosted piece he said, 'At last, at last! We have done it. It is Manchester United's European Cup, my dearest longing for the club. It is the greatest moment of my life.' Accompanying the words was a cartoon by Roy Ullyett, capturing the 'end of an 11-year dream'. Busby, in striped pyjamas, is sitting up in bed, smiling, his left hand clasping the European Cup, which is sitting on his bedside cabinet. He is saying, 'I woke up and it was REALLY THERE!' General de Gaulle's possible resignation as president of France was reduced to a short single-column story. United's betting fraternity may have noticed, at the foot of the page, the report of Sir Ivor's win in the Derby.

But this was a day to acclaim another win. *The Guardian* took up on the common theme. 'Busby dream comes true at long last,' the front page heralded. *The Sun* proclaimed, 'Busby's marvels win like a dream.' A picture of Busby holding the Cup aloft with apparently greater ease than his captain had dominated page one of *The Mirror*. The paper declared, 'MATT'S MADE IT!' and carried his quote: 'It's bloody marvellous . . . I'm the proudest man in England.' Frank McGhee introduced his match report in *The Mirror* with 'Manchester United are the new kings of Europe'. Elsewhere there was a picture of the 'emotional' Law, entering into the spirit of the occasion as he watched on television, and the first snaps of revellers in Trafalgar Square. There would be more party pictures from the homecoming, said to have been witnessed by 250,000 in Manchester's streets and Albert Square. Ten days later Busby, already a freeman of his adoptive city, was knighted.

McGhee, like Coleman, had covered the long and steep ascent to the summit. Not only that season but for many seasons. Also like Coleman, he was comfortable in Busby's company. The Old Man, as we shall hear, perfected the art of making every media man feel good, but McGhee belonged to a generation of media men that was trusted by managers and players, in an age before the uncaging of Fleet Street's 'Beastie boys'.

Retired from full-time work but still penning match reports for *The Observer*, McGhee remembers how it used to be:

> I don't think anyone in the press today is as close to Alex Ferguson as I was to Matt. Or, for that matter, to Don Revie and Bill Shankly. Managers and players just don't trust the press

these days, and you can understand why. I remember talking to Tom Finney in the 1958 World Cup and he was moaning about Derek Kevan. He said he felt he should expect to pass to an England colleague who could stop the ball. He knew I wouldn't turn him over, but if an England international criticised another player now he'd wake up sweating it might be in *The Mirror* as 'Player slams England team-mate'.

A lot of the problem is caused by the disparity in earnings now. At the end of an England tour in my day the press would have a collection, a tenner a head, to give the players a party. You just couldn't imagine that now. Players and press generally had a much better relationship. I got on well with the United lads. I'm still pals with Denis and Paddy. I still get a Christmas card from Bobby and his wife, Norma. The present players may have as good a relationship with each other, but I can't imagine them having the sort of relationship with the press that the '60s side had.

I had a soft spot for Matt but guarded against showing too much sympathy for the team. I was as critical of them as anyone, but it was impossible not to have an affection for them after Munich. A tide of emotion carried almost everyone along. But there was also an anti-United contingent and a backlash against them.

I think psychologically they'd got the final won going into it. They were, after all, effectively at home at Wembley. They had to do it that year. Matt had had enough. He didn't want the responsibility any more. He was hanging on for it. The team could have been shored up, but the question was, 'Who was going to do it?' Giving the job to Wilf McGuinness was the wrong route. Revie might have done it. It needed someone prepared to emerge from Matt's shadows.

That was the challenge for those who followed Busby, and the thorny problem for the club. Despite McGhee's view, shared by a number of the players, that the Old Man, now in his 60th year, had had enough, Busby concluded that ghosted article in *The Express* of 30 May 1968 with the pledge: 'It must not be the end. It must only be part of the beginning.' He did indeed go on, for another year, and then came back for still more. But in reality this was the end. The end of an epoch as well as a dream and a crusade.

PART III

THE PLAYERS

1. ALEX STEPNEY

Born: Mitcham, Surrey, 18-9-42
Debut: v Manchester City (h), 17-9-66
United career: Football League – 433 appearances, 2 goals;
FA Cup – 44, 0; Football League Cup – 35, 0; Europe – 23, 0.
Total – 535, 2.

At the start of the 1966–67 season the team fashioned to realise Matt Busby's European dream remained incomplete. He had his great artists, all in their pomp: sublime, beguiling, awesome. The rest of the cast, not merely supporting players but skilled and essential performers, were in place also. All, that is, except the goalkeeper. The decline of Harry Gregg, survivor and hero of Munich, had left a void still inadequately filled. David Gaskell, potentially outstanding, in reality undependable, had been tried and discarded. Pat Dunne, potentially dependable, was never likely to be outstanding. Busby recognised it was time to address the weakness in his line-up.

He looked to Chelsea, managed by Tommy Docherty and bizarrely, though conveniently, blessed with two of England's best goalkeepers. Peter Bonetti, already recognised as perhaps second only to Gordon Banks, had been joined at Stamford Bridge by an emerging talent in Alex Stepney, signed from Millwall. Busby sensed Chelsea could not indulge themselves in an embarrassment of riches indefinitely and offered a solution. He would have taken Bonetti; he was content to take Stepney.

Stepney arrived in the mainstream English game through the non-league side door. He distinguished himself sufficiently with his famous local team, Tooting and Mitcham, to attract the attention of Millwall. He graduated with distinction and became a member of the Chelsea academy in the summer of 1966. He stayed with the club less than five months. He would stay with United for 13 years.

47

Stepney gave United the missing ingredient. He would not, perhaps, rank among the all-time greats, but without him Busby's dream might have remained precisely that. Such was the significance of his contribution. He went about his job with a calm self-belief that had not been apparent for some disconcerting time behind United's defence. He had what the game refers to as 'good hands'. He was capable of breathtaking saves, yet never prone to displays of gratuitous flamboyance, even if he converted two penalties in the 1973–74 season. He had his lapses of concentration and, in his later years, his vulnerability inevitably became more costly. In his prime, however, he was an excellent goalkeeper, a principal character of United's halcyon period.

* * *

He was known to his team-mates as 'Big Al' but now seems a figure of modest stature, almost dwarfed by the young giants who represent the modern breed of goalkeeper. As the outfield players are put through their training paces by the club's new manager, Stepney exercises the goalkeepers. This is his role, a specialised job for a man equipped to provide the special requirements. But this hero of United's European Cup success had long since ceased to ply his trade at Old Trafford. He had even drifted out of the game after shuttling between America and Altrincham. He had a pub, worked as a transport manager at Trafford Park and then helped run a van-hire company in Rochdale before an opportunity to scout for Southampton in the North-West presented him with a way back.

Alan Ball, the then Southampton manager, decided Stepney had a more specific role to play, coaching his goalkeepers, but that would have meant moving home. No sooner had the dilemma arisen than Ball was on his way to Manchester City, and Stepney was invited to join him. Work on the doorstep. Now he needed not a second thought. To his relief, Frank Clark, put in charge at City after the departure of Ball, asked him to continue at the club. So here he is, this bright, crisp, winter's morning, stretching his charges left and right, high and low, with catching practice at Platt Lane, Manchester City's training ground.

Upstairs in the restaurant at the club's modern complex, he sits down to a late lunch and shares his memories of a playing career that found fulfilment across the city, memories that flow the moment he turns on the tap.

I'll never forget anything of it from the time I joined United, because I'd signed for Chelsea in the May and the

48

arrangement was, I was assured, that Peter Bonetti was leaving. That was the opinion of not only Tommy Docherty but also Joe Mears, the chairman, and I wanted that made quite clear before I signed. I wanted first-team football. I'd just won three England Under-23 caps in the Third Division, with Millwall.

Unfortunately, Joe Mears died that summer and the new chairman wanted Peter Bonetti to stay, which obviously caused a problem. Then Peter got injured after about six games of the new season and I played in the game against Southampton. We won, I think, 3–0, and on the Monday morning Tommy Doc called Peter and me in and said, 'I'm in a ridiculous situation. I'm going to have to play you in alternate games.' We both looked at each other and looked at him, and he said, 'Right, Peter, you're fit now so you play on Wednesday, and Alex, you'll play here on Saturday.' So that was it, and off we went training.

After training (ironically at Mitcham) it was, I think, Frank Blunstone who told me the boss wanted me back at the ground. So I went back to Stamford Bridge, not knowing what was happening, and Tommy Doc says, 'I've got a surprise for you. Get in the car.' He took me to the White House Hotel, near Euston Station. I asked him what was happening and he just said, 'Wait and see.'

And then the revolving doors started moving and in walked Sir Matt, with his trilby and his pipe, with Jimmy Murphy trailing behind, carrying a case. Within half an hour I was a Manchester United player. It was a wonderful time to come to the club. The team was at its peak. But it was also the way the whole thing was done that impressed me. Matt introduced himself and said, 'Look, Alex, I'm going to go with Tom in my room; Jimmy, you take Alex in your room.' Just for ten minutes. And, of course, Jimmy just reeled off all the names at the club, your Laws, your Bests, your Charltons, and then in came Matt and they changed over. He said, 'I want you. You'll play in my first team.' It just didn't sink in, but I was a United player straightaway. Unbelievable.

There was something about the atmosphere at the club and it came from Sir Matt. He was one of those guys . . . directly you met him, he was your grandfather. It was as if

you'd known him all your life. When I was house-hunting he
showed us round. Wonderful. He had class and the respect
was there straightaway.

Stepney had the self-assurance to assume a familiarity not all of his team-
mates shared with Busby. For others the great man remained a distant if
unusually benign figure, a man to be in awe of. He was, after all, the
manager. But Stepney, like Paddy Crerand and, later, Willie Morgan, was
more at ease with Busby, able to socialise and play golf with him. The other
two were Busby's countrymen. He was a Londoner and Londoners were
perceived as pushy. Perhaps that was it. Or perhaps, arriving from outside
at this stage, he carried none of the emotional and psychological baggage
that burdened some of the longer-serving players. Stepney confirms, 'I
never felt out of it or in any way that I didn't belong.'

His new colleagues welcomed that self-confidence and fed off it. They
won their second League Championship in three seasons with greater
conviction and Busby paid public tribute to the decisive role played by his
goalkeeper. That declaration served also as a reminder that he considered his
own judgement as sound as ever. There was universal accord on the point.
Stepney was acknowledged as a wise investment, and now United had
another chance to deliver that elusive trophy. Stepney recalls,

> I think there was a feeling in 1967–68 that this was the last
> chance of the European Cup. We had won the
> Championship and won it well, and we were still up there.
> But how many more chances do you get? I felt our hardest
> game was Sarajevo. Gornik was hard, but not as hard as in
> Sarajevo. And then, of course, came the semi-final, against
> Real Madrid, although I thought that was the final, really. It
> was as well we won it, because we were sort of left in the
> lurch as far as the League was concerned and Manchester
> City won that.
>
> It was Matt again who did it in Madrid. When we were
> 3–1 down at half-time we just sat in the dressing room in
> silence. Everybody was down and Matt really didn't say
> anything – until the whistle went to go out for the second
> half. He just said, 'Hold on, it's only 3–2, you know? You're
> only a goal behind. Go out and play.' Everyone had forgotten
> about the great goal George had scored at Old Trafford. And
> then we got a goal and were back. They probably went the
> other way.

I don't think we were in any danger of being too confident for the final, because after we won the League in '67 we went on a world tour and we played Benfica in Los Angeles. They beat us 3–1 and caused us a lot of trouble in the game, and that put us in good stead for the final. There was something to prove. We wanted revenge.

This day of judgement began in an environment just a few miles from Stepney's home, yet it might as well have been on a different planet. The splendour of the team hotel, Great Fosters, at Egham, Surrey, provided a measure of how far the boy from Mitcham had come.

It was a really olde worlde hotel. Wonderful grounds. And every room was different. There were four-posters and there were suits of armour and it was a place where you could just stroll around and occupy yourself. Very historic. I watched the Derby on television but otherwise just walked around and it helped me take my mind off the final. I came from Surrey but I didn't even know the place existed.

It was a very hot summer's day. It was so humid. I've got a picture of me holding the Cup and my shirt and shorts are absolutely drenched. I'd been given a taste of the Wembley atmosphere the week before by Sir Alf Ramsey. He gave me my only England game against Sweden, although I was sub 20 times. He didn't say it was to help me in the final, but knowing Alf he might well have thought, 'Why not?'

Before the final it was much the same as a normal game. The same rituals, the same people making most of the noise. I never got changed until half an hour before the game. Bestie would come in ten minutes before the game. We all had our ways. We never went out and warmed up in those days. Paddy had plenty to say and Bobby, being the captain, would go round talking to the players. Nobby was another talker. We also had Wilf McGuinness, a good talker, geeing everybody up. Basically, though, we were left to do our own thing. We had that feeling we were part of Matt's jigsaw. We played the way he wanted us to play. We were in that team because there was something about us that he liked. That night we had that feeling we were definitely going to win. There was never any doubt.

I thought the first half of the game was boring. It seemed

so, anyway. Yet we had lots of chances, which you realise when you see it again. And Eusebio hit the bar, and he got one through the wall. I got that and it settled me. The goal they got was always going to be a danger: Torres in the air, knocking it down. We knew all about Eusebio, of course, but we had a belief in Nobby. I don't think Nobby would get away today with a lot of what he did, but there were a lot of things then, like barging keepers, you can't do now.

The only time he got away from Nobby was just before the end of normal time and it was 1–1. Wembley's pitch at that time was notorious for slowing up the ball. It was before the Horse of the Year Show ruined the pitch. When Simoes, I think it was, hit that through ball I thought it was mine, so I came off my line. And the bloody thing slowed up, and now I'm in no-man's land. I then went back because I thought Eusebio was going to chip me. If he had done, I was beaten. So I went back just a couple of yards. Then he just set to hit it and that gave me the moment to come forward, and fortunately he hit it straight at me. But he did hit it. I've still got an inverted Mitre stamped on my chest! I was able to stand there, holding the ball, thinking 'Thank you'. I think that save stands out in people's minds because of the time in the game. If it had been three minutes after the start instead of three minutes before the end nobody would have remembered it.

If it does not challenge Banks's save from Pele in the 1970 World Cup finals as 'the greatest', it was undeniably more important. And almost as vivid in the memory as the ball clasped in Stepney's midriff is his apparent cold indifference to Eusebio's gracious acknowledgement. Stepney now explains,

It goes back to Millwall, and I was very fortunate to play for them. I was taught, when I got the ball, to concentrate on what I had to do, my next move. I didn't come into the pro game until I was 20 and had a good three-year apprenticeship as an amateur with Tooting and Mitcham. I was told not to worry about anyone around me, to get on with my game, because they can cheat you. I'm not saying he was trying to cheat me, knock it out of my hand or whatever, but my concern was 'come on, let's get away'. I knew there

52

was very little time left and we had to hold out. I don't think they ever pushed us after that.

After the 90 minutes we all sat down and had Johnny Aston and Jack Crompton coming round, rubbing our legs, and then it was just 'keep playing, keep playing'. Funny part about the second goal is that I threw the ball to Tony Dunne, he played it back to me. I threw it to Shay Brennan, he played it back to me. So then I kicked it, Brian Kidd flicked it on and George went round the keeper. Shay Brennan reckons he started that move! On the day, Johnny Aston had an unbelievable game. That was incredible for him. If you are going to have a game like that, then that was the one to have it in.

Bobby, Nobby, David and I were in the England party leaving the following morning for a friendly in Germany and then going on to Italy for the Nations Cup, and Alf had said we weren't allowed to go out after the final. In fact, Nobby, David and I, with our wives, finished up in Danny La Rue's after the official function at the Russell Hotel. Bobby was sick and didn't even go to the banquet, and Paddy Crerand was the same.

Of course I was aware of what it meant to Matt and Bobby and Billy. It's one of those where you will always be asked, 'Where were you when United's plane crashed at Munich?' I was still at school, and after school I walked home and heard the news. I used to work for the local corner shop and go round with the greengrocery on a bike. I remember riding round and at every house I came to, I'd ask what was the latest news.

It's amazing when you look back over your career how things turn out and what coincidences crop up. When I signed for Millwall in 1963, the manager gave me two tickets for the Cup final. I'd never been to a Cup final in my life, but I went to Wembley that year. And, of course, I saw Manchester United beat Leicester City. Who would have believed I'd end up playing for Manchester United in a European Cup final there?

I can only say I've been very fortunate in the sense that I played in a team that had three European Footballers of the Year, all forwards, all in the same team. Think about that. Unbelievable. But we all fitted Busby's jigsaw. Defensively we were tight, strong. We had Nobby, a good reader. We had Pat and Bobby, breaking out from midfield. But then Matt always used to say, when you win the ball, just make sure you give it to them, and those three great players always ran into space.

The others were underrated, though, definitely. Tony Dunne, for instance, was the best left-back I ever played with. Denis Irwin reminds me so much of him. Quick, dependable, gets on with it. Very quiet. Arthur Albiston, who came into the team in the 1977 FA Cup final, was similar as well. United have always had someone steady there, someone who's never really in the limelight but done it. The club have basically had three left-backs over a 30-year span.

Matt won lots of recognition for his achievements, and rightly so. He was given the freedom of Manchester, he was knighted and he had all sorts of other tributes. But he wasn't a young man any more and I think he was understandably feeling the pressures, so the next year he let it go to Wilf McGuinness, and Wilf changed it to his way of thinking, which he was completely entitled to do. But Wilf was unfortunate. He got to semi-finals and with a bit of luck would have won something. But it just didn't happen for him.

The early years of Stepney's career with United catapulted him to the pinnacle of the game. For the most part, his middle and later years at Old Trafford conveyed him on an emotional roller-coaster of a ride that was never boring, if, alas, never as successful. The euphemistic 'transitional period' seemed unending, Busby briefly returning to the helm before Frank O'Farrell came and went. Tommy Docherty took the club down to the Second Division, instantly returned them to the First, and although Stepney and United were surprisingly defeated by Second Division Southampton in the 1976 FA Cup final, they beat Liverpool the following year. Within months, however, Docherty was sacked, and Dave Sexton was Stepney's last manager at United. Stepney recalls,

We started well under Frank O'Farrell and went to the top, but after Christmas it all went wrong and we never did anything. That was really the end of the team. Tommy Doc came, Denis left, Bobby retired, Nobby left for Middlesbrough, David Sadler left. I was still around, but the European Cup team was no more.

But we'd done it. It's a completely different game today. The game has obviously improved. Everything does, records get broken. I just feel when I watch the games now that the team spirit isn't the same. They are very much more individualistic today. They do it their own way, they do their own thing. It just doesn't seem the same. Forget the hugging and kissing. We had great individuals, but we worked and played as a team. We had the experience of playing at the highest level. This team hasn't done it. They've got a fourth go at the Champions League and they should have a chance.

I don't go up to Old Trafford now. If I wanted tickets I could get them, but I don't think there's the same feeling there now. I still mix with the lads. David Sadler has his get-togethers and works really hard at it. He's a diamond, David. Always been the same. It's unbelievable most of the lads are still in the area. I think that says a lot about the bond and the team spirit.

The area has held Stepney as it has held most of the '68 team, but his children have pursued their own sporting interests. His two sons went to a rugby-playing school and found contentment in the oval-ball game. One of them became head greenkeeper at Ashton-on-Mersey Golf Club. His daughter, from his second marriage, cares more for horses than football or any other game.

Stepney, however, remains a football man and his enforced exile from the game hurt and frustrated him.

I tried to get back into the game when I came back from America but couldn't. The game didn't really want goalkeeping coaches or anything like that, and I think they paid the price for that and realised it. When I played you could say we had 12 or 13 English goalkeepers who could play for any country in the world. Where are they now? Then you could reel off the likes of Bonetti, Banks, Montgomery, Corrigan, myself, Rimmer. All class keepers.

The difference in the make-up of the lads now is that they haven't been given the structure to be top class, but I think we are changing that and doing something about it. I'm enjoying doing my bit and enjoying being with City. I've no problems working here. I'm not the first to have crossed the city. It's a very friendly club and I've been well received by everyone. It doesn't bother me or anyone that I'm an ex-United player now with City. My interest now is City and doing the best I can for them. There's so much potential here and I'd like to help them get back to the top – and if that's at United's expense, so be it.

2. SHAY BRENNAN

Born: Manchester, 6-5-37
Debut: v Sheffield Wednesday (h), FA Cup Fifth Round, 19-2-58
United career: Football League – 291 (1) appearances, 3 goals;
FA Cup – 36, 3; Football League Cup – 4, 0; Europe – 24, 0.
Total – 355 (1), 6.

The lean, dark Mancunian of Irish stock was not one of those in the
Munich air crash, yet emotionally, perhaps even spiritually, he was
subjected to that brutal ordeal and came through the other side as much as
if he had found himself in the snow and debris that bleak afternoon of
1958. He had been back at home, but there was no sanctuary for Seamus
Brennan or any of the players and members of staff not aboard that ill-fated
flight. Those killed and injured were his work-mates, friends and more. He
was in awe of Duncan Edwards and did not compare himself with many of
the others.

In the days, weeks and years that followed, however, he would become
an important and much-loved figure in the rebirth of Manchester United,
this modest though mischievous full-back cum wing-half cum inside-
forward cum unlikely outside-left stepping from the shadows to score the
club's first two goals post-Munich and later sharing the ultimate fulfilment
of Wembley. He discovered his niche at right-back and developed into one
of the most stylish practitioners of that unglamorous craft. He represented
the Republic of Ireland on 19 occasions.

But as important to club and country as his intelligent defending was his
contribution to team spirit. Almost to a man, the United team of the '60s
would vote Brennan their most popular colleague. He masked his humility
and vulnerability, if not an inferiority complex, behind his *joie de vivre*. He
might have been the original loveable rogue. Like Best he enjoyed drinking,

and if that meant breaking a curfew, then so be it. Unlike Best, his comrade in arms, he was not a superstar and it never became such a drama, never headline material. His appetite for betting was just as voracious. And yet everything he did he smeared with his infectious smile and unfading charm, and the others adored him for it.

There were tears, too, not least when he learnt he was no longer wanted by United. The boss steered him towards a coaching/managerial career in Ireland, but Brennan was smart enough to realise he was not cut out for the job. He involved himself in a courier service in Waterford, and when the Big Ref in the sky showed him the yellow card of a heart attack, he moved over and allowed his second wife, Liz, to run the business. United responded with a benefit in Dublin. Now he contentedly occupies himself on the golf course and relishes his trips back to the bosom of his football family.

* * *

He ambles through the foyer of the Midland Hotel, or whatever the modern name for it is. To Shay Brennan it is still the Midland, United's hotel in the heart of Manchester, a place to soothe the soul and rekindle the memories. He is here this time for United's European Cup semi-final, second leg, against Borussia Dortmund in 1997. He had arrived the previous day and spent a long evening exploring old haunts and reviving old acquaintanceships.

Now, this mid-morning of match day, he has the air and appearance of an affiliated member of the Rat Pack: slightly haggard in a distinguished kind of way, good looks fighting a spirited battle with the good life. The hairstyle is still circa 1968, though greying, the shirt open-necked. Outside a typical Mancunian reception sends a group of Dortmund fans, eager to accept civic hospitality and party in Albert Square, scurrying beyond reach of a pernicious shower. Inside the refurbished hotel, Shay Brennan is unhurried. It was, he explains, an extremely convivial evening. 'Went to the Circus, on Portland Street. Get all sorts of people in there. We had a good time. Too good.' Make his tea.

The Wythenshawe accent has withstood the Irish influences, although he takes the opportunity to stress he comes from genuine Republic stock and was entitled to represent the country. 'Now it's enough if your father drinks Guinness. No, honestly, tea will be fine.'

The bond with United was equally strong. Brennan recalls,

> I loved Manchester United when I was a boy. Johnny Carey,
> Johnny Berry . . . I idolised them. When they came back with

the Cup, in '48, I ran after the bus along Princess Parkway. There were thousands of people lining the road. But the great team was the one that died at Munich, the Babes, and when I went on the groundstaff, at 15, I trained with those great players – Roger Byrne, Eddie Colman, Duncan Edwards. We'd have to do the chores, clean the dressing room, clean the boots. I signed professional at 17 but, I have to be honest, I would never have got into the Manchester United first team but for the accident.

Duncan was the best player United ever had. Jimmy Murphy was in charge of our Youth Cup side and brought Duncan in from the first team and told the rest of us to play our normal game. Of course, when we were 1–0 down at half-time he told us to look for Duncan – and, sure enough, Duncan scored twice and we won the game. As Jimmy used to say, he was like a man playing with boys, even though he was only a boy himself.

A couple of weeks after the accident we had our first match, an FA Cup tie against Sheffield Wednesday at Old Trafford. Jimmy had taken us to the Norbreck Hotel in Blackpool, and a lot was being bandied about as to who would be in the team. A few, like Harry Gregg, Bill Foulkes and Ian Greaves, were certainties. But my name was never mentioned, so the night before the game I went out with a friend and we had a few drinks. Next morning, Jimmy told me I was in the team. At outside-left. I'd been playing inside-forward in the reserves. I didn't have time to think about it. I phoned my father at work, and my brothers, but I can't remember much more about that day.

I remember the match. I scored two goals and I was the worst player on the park. The first goal was lucky, a corner. All I wanted to do was make it look decent and reach. But the wind caught it and it went into the back of the net. And all of a sudden you're a hero, because you've scored a goal. I've played 100 times better games for United at full-back or wing-half and never got a mention.

We finished up winning 3–0 and Wednesday could never have won that match. United could have fielded a team of women, because nobody would have beaten us that night. The ground was packed and the crowd that was locked out didn't go away. They just listened to the cheers. The world wanted

Manchester United to win. The sympathy we had was incredible.

The FA Cup eluded United that season, as did the European Cup, but a new team and new friendships would flourish, as Brennan remembers.

Wilf McGuinness and I were very close. He and I were best men for each other at our weddings. He was very unlucky, getting injured and having to retire from playing. Nobby and Bobby were the ones I'd play cards with. We had crib challenges. I roomed with Bobby around the time of the European Cup final. There were one or two cliques over the years, but I could get on and mix with all the lads.

Bestie I first remember on the groundstaff, and he was always pleasant, always smiling. You'd tell some of the apprentices to go and get a tracksuit or something and they'd kind of sneer, 'Who does he think he is?' But Bestie always had a smile and was likeable. I liked to drink, but I didn't lead him astray. George was a nice fella then and he is now. Every time he comes to Ireland I go and meet him. Even now, when maybe they wouldn't recognise me any more, they'd recognise George all right. I've seen him at airports, being late for his flight because he's been stuck signing autographs and having his photograph taken. He's always been good to his father. He used to fly him over for home matches. He always had a word, a little joke for people. But the papers didn't write that sort of thing.

I used to be thankful every match I wasn't the full-back marking him. You would have to foul him to stop him. You'd have to pull him or kick him. You couldn't play him fairly and expect to get the better of him. He'd be through you. He was good on both sides and had so much confidence. He knew he was going to beat you. Sometimes the boss would switch it round in training, the reserves' forwards for ours, and I'd do a marking job on Bestie. You'd get the ball and think you'd got plenty of time, and he'd be after you. He was such a good tackler. He could have played midfield after the wing and strolled it. He could create so much space for himself, from nothing.

Bobby was serious about his game and when the boss made him captain he took it very seriously. He always gave

101 per cent. He'd be up and down when you didn't really need him to do that. But that's how he was. He wanted to play and he was such an honest player. His asset was on the ball. He would come two yards off you to get the ball. You'd think, 'I want it, let me have a go.' But Bobby, and Bestie and Paddy, they were the ones who could use it. That's why it was easy for us at the back. We always had three or four players who wanted the ball off us. We were always spoilt for choice.

Bobby, of course, had come through it all and what a great player he was for the club. I remember, after the maximum wage was abolished, that Bobby was paid five pounds more than me. Five pounds? He should have been on three times as much as me. He was recognised all round the world. I remember he stopped the traffic once in Italy. The crowd were all chanting, 'Charlton, Charlton' when they saw him on our coach. United were never known as the best payers, but everyone wanted to play for them. Even Jimmy Greaves and Bobby Moore asked Bobby if there was any chance of joining us when they were on England trips together. Mind you, we had crowd bonuses, for over 25,000. We got gates of 60,000-plus.

Even when Paddy was having a bad time he would still want the ball. He was a great passer of the ball, but some days he'd be off and give it away. Denis would shout to him, 'Don't forget, Paddy, we're playing in red.' Denis was a great mickey-taker, and, of course, he was another great player and, like Paddy, a great character. It was never boring with those two.

Nothing and no one frightened Paddy. I remember a trip behind the Iron Curtain when it was all very strict and we had all sorts of forms to fill in. Paddy filled in his: 'Name: Bond. Occupation: Spy.' He didn't care. And he was always getting up late. The coach would have to go and pick him up at his home. I'd have to get his cornflakes and boiled eggs for breakfast to get him going. What a character.

So was Nobby, but in a different way. We used to call him Inspector Clouseau. He was accident-prone. He'd lean over for the toast and get butter on his sleeve. He'd regularly walk into glass doors. He'd have blood on his collar after shaving and he'd spill beer down his tie. He once got to his car and thought he'd lost his keys, so he got a taxi home for the spare ones, came back again and discovered the original keys in the ignition and the car unlocked. We used to play cards for forfeits, and on the way back from a trip Nobby had to carry Bobby's duty free. He dropped it, the bottle of whisky broke and it went all over Bobby's cinecamera. He could also get nasty and angry, especially when David Herd used to wind him up. But what a player. He was brilliant for us, and England. He and Billy were great together. One little, one big and both so hard. If you brushed alongside them it would hurt you. They wouldn't do it deliberately, it was just the way they were. Hard.

It makes me laugh when I hear all the talk about how much quicker the game is now and how much quicker the players are. Well, if there's any full-back today as quick as Tony Dunne they should put him in the Olympics. There's nobody faster than Tony. I don't think I was slow, either. And Denis, over 20 yards, was electric. And all this about time on the ball. Try playing against Leeds, Norman Hunter and all, and expect time on the ball!

Before Johnny Giles left us for Leeds he and Nobby [brothers-in-law] were always taking the mickey and I was on the end of their fun. I was a bad header of the ball. I admit it. We were being beaten somewhere and they shouted at me to go up for a corner: 'Go on, Bomber, go up.' After that I was 'Bomber'. It just stuck.

But I like to think I played my part. I wasn't a great tackler or passer but I suppose I could read the game and I kept it simple. At a place like Manchester United you're always in fear of losing your place and sometimes I did. When I was dropped I felt it more for my father, who'd get ribbed by his work-mates. The best footballing full-back we had at United was Frank Kopel. In the reserves, he could do anything. I'd watch him in games and think, 'Once he gets in the first team he'll keep me out.' But he just went. Whether it was the atmosphere, I don't know. There are lots of kids who look great players at 15 and then just go.

The task of nurturing that raw talent lay with Busby and Murphy.

Jimmy would frighten you in practice matches. He'd play with you and shout at you. He'd say, 'You want to start worrying when I don't shout at you.' But a great man and a great coach.

The boss did it in a quieter way. If you were having a bad time he would never come in and slate you. Every player knows when he's having a bad time. He'd say, 'Defensively we're not doing this.' He wouldn't upset you personally by saying 'You're not doing this'. But you knew. And you'd play for him. Some managers go effing and blinding at players, and I don't think I could have handled that. He knew how to handle players. Professionally, he knew what he was doing. I was lucky to play not only with great players but for the best manager in the game.

The boss knew everything. He knew his players. I broke the curfew a few times at the Norbreck – down the fire escape and off to Brian London's club. There were a lot of nasty people around who used to phone in and I was reported a couple of times. Jimmy Murphy once took a call from somebody who said I was drunk in Wythenshawe. I'd missed the bus but I'd only had one drink. That was the sort of thing that used to happen.

The boss would tell us we had to behave like professionals. We used to drink at a pub called the Brown Bull, but although the boss knew everything he'd get names mixed up and he said, 'I've been hearing reports about you drinking at this Black Cow.' He knew we'd been there till two or three o'clock in the morning sometimes, and he made sure it didn't get out of control. He knew how to handle it.

He knew I liked a bet and if I was going through a bit of a bad spell the boss would say to me, 'Are you gambling again?' I'd say, 'No . . . well, a little bit.' He'd know. I couldn't kid him. Sandy, his son, was a mate, a good lad. It was a great family. Jimmy's family were lovely, as well. The players became, in a way, part of the family.

The father may have been all-knowing, but there was a feeling that Busby's commitment to a cavalier game unsullied by tactics and pragmatism rendered him incapable of handling the changing trends. Brennan concedes there is evidence to that effect. He recollects,

The worst day of his life after Munich was in the Cup-Winners' Cup in 1964, when we were beaten 5–0 away to

Sporting Lisbon after winning 4–1 at Old Trafford. We felt we were through after that first leg and that's how we played. Dave Gaskell reckoned they looked dangerous every time their keeper got the ball. We had a three-goal lead but the boss wanted us to win the game. He always wanted to show off Manchester United, whereas most teams would have shut up shop, as Fergie did with United away to Porto in 1997. If we got one goal he'd never say, 'We'll keep that.' He'd always go for another and want us to win in style.

Ironically, it was United's unnatural instinct to try and protect a one-goal advantage that almost proved their undoing in the European Cup final. Brennan enjoyed the first part of a win double in the afternoon.

I watched the Derby with Nobby. I backed the winner, Sir Ivor, and ended the day with a nice double. I watched the game on television in full for the first time only four or five years ago and didn't realise it was such a good game. I didn't realise how many chances they had. I thought they only had one apart from the goal. We missed lots. It was a great game of football.

I'd always thought Eusebio hit that late shot with his right foot. He actually hit it with his left foot. Simoes never really got a mention, so I take that as a compliment. Johnny Aston should have retired after that game. He had a magnificent game. They knew all about Bestie and watched him closely, but nothing about Johnny, and he revelled in the space. I wouldn't have liked to have played against him that night. Nobody could have topped that.

I remember sitting with Bobby in the stand at Wembley after the game. He wasn't well. It was all very emotional for him, I think. He had to get away from all the fuss. They were already taking the seats out for something else. Maybe it was the Horse of the Year Show. We had the official reception at the Russell and then I remember going to Danny La Rue's club with Nobby and his wife. I had breakfast before I went to bed.

There is a school of thought, to which a number of the '68 side subscribe, that they were unfortunate not to retain the trophy. The contention is they were cheated out of a crucial goal in the second leg of the semi-final, against Milan, at Old Trafford. Brennan issues an unequivocal challenge to the theory: 'That talk is wrong. I don't think we were unlucky at all, not over the two legs. We lost 2–0 over there but we were murdered. They missed two or three sitters.'

Brennan's career at Old Trafford ended a year after United relinquished the European Cup. Busby had handed over team affairs to Wilf McGuinness, Brennan's friend. His best man. He hoped and had begun to believe they would work another season together. He felt as if his life had shattered with the illusion.

> I thought I was going to be kept on. We were going on tour in the summer and I'd been measured for my suit. I took that as meaning I was going to get another year's contract. I was late for training that morning and sneaked into the gym, pretending I'd been doing weights. Jimmy Murphy came out – and I'd got friendly with Jimmy over the years – and he told me they were letting Denis go. I was shocked but at the same time relieved, because I thought if he was telling me about Denis he would have told me if I was going. Then Jimmy Ryan and Don Givens were sent for. Next thing, I was sent for.
>
> It was the boss who told me, not Wilf. And he was a bit emotional, a bit upset. And then I just filled up. I told the lads and I think they were upset. Then I went back to the ground to tell the women there. Jimmy was there and he had just heard. He didn't know. We were both upset. I think he felt he'd been squeezed out a bit by then, even though he was still assistant manager. Jimmy wouldn't have taken over as manager. He was a great coach, great working with players, but I don't think he wanted to be manager. I was never bitter towards Wilf, and we're still pals. Now we have a chuckle about it. I tell people he's the man who sacked me.
>
> The boss advised me to take a pension [twenty pounds a week] rather than a testimonial. I think Nobby got a pension, as well. I was gambling and it was good advice. He thought if I got a testimonial I'd blow it, so I should have a pension for the rest of my life. I suppose he was right; I would have blown it. He was trying to help me.
>
> After United I didn't want to go anywhere out of the First Division. I'd seen players leave, go lower down the League and never be the same. The boss advised me again. He

thought I could be a manager and Waterford, a good team in Ireland – we beat them the previous year in the European Cup – came for me as a player-manager. He advised me to take it and learn the trade. So I went over, but I didn't really enjoy it.

I wasn't a manager-type person. I was caught between the players and the directors. The chairman was a friend of mine and he listened to me, but mostly the directors talked a load of rubbish. I didn't like dealing with the press, either. When the press rang I'd tell one of the lads to say I was in the shower. At a sportswriters' dinner one of the reporters said, 'You might not be the best manager in the country, but you must be the cleanest.' I packed up before I was sacked. My good friend told me they were going to.

I met Liz, my second wife, at that time and we had the idea to set up a courier business, shifting parcels. It's gone all right. I had a heart attack and a big by-pass so Liz runs it. I'm settled in Ireland and it's only an hour away. We have two daughters and I also have two daughters from my first marriage. I enjoy my golf now. I'll never be a good golfer, but the exercise is good. And I still enjoy a drink – too much, I think. I'll have a Caffrey's now. Will you have one?

His friend Best has admitted to a similar liking, but Brennan can at least satisfy himself he played out his peak years.

George never gave himself a chance to prove he was *the* best. He went in his prime, and that's the tragic part. He talked to me about his lifestyle. He'd agree it had to stop – then carry on. That was George.

It's good to see him and all the other lads when I can. I can't get to all the association dos but come over when I can. It's not only the likes of Bobby and Denis I like to see again, it's also the reserves who were there, all great lads. When we have our get-togethers and remember the old days, we don't talk about the football as much as the nights out. What I miss is not the actual game but the training, the five-a-sides, the fun, the banter. The lads.

We have this daft thing going. When I walk into a room and the lads are there, Paddy starts off the applause. If the others don't join in I walk out. I'll go to a function where

Denis or Bobby is the chief guest and the MC will say, 'We've got one of the greatest players of all time . . . did this . . . did that . . .' And I stand up. I can get a laugh and get away with that. It's the way I am.

When I go back to Old Trafford I go to see Mrs Burgess, the lady in the players' lounge. She used to look after the kitchen and after training we'd go to the kitchen and have a cup of tea. I like to see the people from way back and I'm cheeky enough to go back, whereas someone like Tony Dunne, who was always a bit quieter, doesn't find it so easy. I think Alex got refused one time.

From what I see of the present team, mainly on TV, I don't know whether they are good enough to win the European Cup. We were a great team. Defensively they are about the same, but we had three great players. There aren't three like Charlton, Law and Best in the present United team. England, Scotland and Ireland don't have three great players like those between them. Those three are the main difference. Beckham is certainly no Bobby and I don't take seriously Schmeichel's comments that this team would thrash the '68 team.

Bear in mind that England had won the World Cup two years earlier. Today England, Scotland, Ireland and Wales together wouldn't win the World Cup. There's a big difference now. United have definitely been the best team in England over a number of years, but whether they are good enough to win the European Cup is another matter. I feel terrible going on about our 'three great players' when we also had Johnny Aston, Brian Kidd and David Sadler, all tremendous forwards. But because they were playing alongside three world-class players, they have tended to be overlooked.

United's 1997 European campaign ended a few hours later, but you suspect Shay Brennan made the most of the evening nonetheless.

3. TONY DUNNE

Born: Dublin, 24-7-41
Debut: v Burnley (a), 15-10-60
United career: Football League – 414 appearances, 2 goals;
FA Cup – 54 (1), 0; Football League Cup – 21, 0; Europe – 40, 0.
Total – 529 (1), 2.

United's other Republic of Ireland full-back hailed from Dublin and followed a well-charted course across the water to Old Trafford. Although he was already an established player in Irish football, he is remembered as a shy, self-effacing young man, nothing like that rascal Brennan, from Manchester. Also unlike Brennan, he established himself in the team in the early '60s and remained a fixture for more than a decade. Busby paid Shelbourne United £3,000, plus an appearance-related bonus, for his services. It was one of the great yet understated deals of his stewardship.

Busby, the other United players and scores of frustrated opponents over the years gave Dunne rave reviews. Some called him a model pro. That was almost demeaning. Some reckoned he was the best left-back in the world. That was more like it. A small figure with Beatles-style dark hair, he was as quick as a whippet and had the sharp but fair bite of a tackle to match. Busby, as we shall hear, relied heavily on his pace in defence. Later, as overlapping full-backs became *de rigueur*, Dunne was able to deploy a natural resource as an offensive weapon also. He played at right-back in United's 1963 FA-Cup-winning side but eventually became the regular left-back.

He left the club still the unassuming little Irishman, but harbouring a sense of injustice and betrayal over his testimonial match. He found sanctuary and a new lease of life at Bolton Wanderers, where the management and atmosphere evidently facilitated such discovery on a regular basis. He retained his fitness, his appetite and, crucially, his speed to play on for another five seasons in the Football League before running down the clock in America.

His coaching/management ambitions proved less enduring. He hoped to find a niche at Bolton but things did not go to plan. He went to Norway and enjoyed some success, although he did not enjoy part-time football. He tried scouting but the role did not fit – or perhaps he did not fit the role. Either way, it was the end of the football dream. Reality dawned in golf, albeit in a humble form. He now runs a driving range in Altrincham.

* * *

Follow the signs to Altrincham Municipal Golf Club and Old Hall, sweep up the drive . . . and start looking again. Even now, he is apparently cast as the quiet, self-effacing little Irishman. Not for Tony Dunne the grand stage, the limelight or the ready acclaim. He is tucked away in the wings, down a muddy track across the cobbles and in a crevice of an old barn. A handsome, converted barn, mind. But there is nothing elegant about his workshop. He leans through a hatch to hand over a basket of yellow golf balls and a customer heads out into the bright winter sunshine as it grapples with overnight frost.

Dunne's face is round, beaming like the morning sun; familiar, welcoming. A silver tinge is recolouring its frame but the hair is still Beatles-style. That, too, is somehow welcoming. He leads the way into his office, a tiny room behind the 'shop front'. Pictures of cars offer a defiant gesture to the starkness. On a typewriter sits a black and white photograph of the 1968 European Cup-winning team. Dunne, wearing a Manchester United anorak, nestles in an old garden chair – and begins to confound the typecasting of a quiet, self-effacing little Irishman. He talks, willingly, candidly, often passionately, sometimes sadly, about his life with United and beyond.

> I was not really a United fan as a boy. Just a football fan. Like most of the lads in Ireland, I got all my football information from the radio, on a Saturday. But I did happen to go and see United play Shamrock Rovers in the European Cup. Shamrock Rovers were a very good team at the time. And, of course, Manchester United had Billy Whelan playing for them, who was marvellous – and Irish. But, unfortunate as it is to say it, the crash was the thing that made Manchester

United such a worldwide name and has so much to do with the aura of the club. History is so often wrapped up around sad occasions.

I had no real hesitation in going to United but it was like going into a blind alley for us from Ireland. We all wondered whether we were good enough. That's what frightened us. We didn't see ourselves with players like they had. They were just names, heroes. Back home you played in the street and said, 'I'm Billy Whelan today'. But you couldn't imagine this happening. My mother calmly put it in perspective. She said, 'Well, you can always come back home.'

You were conscious they were something you weren't part of. You were in awe of people there because they were there when the crash happened, and they came out of the crash and performed again. So you tended to think they were always that much better than you, more knowledgeable, more respected. It was intimidating at times. I always felt the European Cup was in honour of the people who had died in the crash, because you felt they would possibly have achieved it. They were a great team and I think that was the feeling in the town and country. I think that was the feeling of the people who followed, including those who were dismissed, because it's a very ruthless game. The European Cup had to be won for those who had died.

Matt Busby really thought only of two things: the League and the European Cup. The European Cup was an obsession for him. No doubt about it. He always said he felt duty-bound or honour-bound to do it for the people who had died in the crash. He must have had nightmares about it, as must Bobby Charlton and Billy Foulkes. I don't think he felt guilty, but I think there was a feeling in him that he wanted to finish the thing he had set out to do, to fulfil the mission. He was a fairly religious man and, on the night the European Cup was won, he would have felt there were a lot of happy faces up there, looking down.

When he had succeeded I don't think he could jump out of his seat quick enough. I don't think he felt such an obligation to the people who'd done it. Billy Foulkes had carried on and done it, and Bobby Charlton obviously had. Wonderful player, and played a great part in winning it. But there were a lot of people who had disappeared and gone their separate ways, some through injuries, and probably felt like outsiders because they were never really accepted. The people who'd done it weren't really the most important people for him.

I never talked to Bill or Bobby about the crash. I was too much in awe of people like that to ask questions. I looked at them as professionals, ready-made professionals, and I was always trying to be a professional. I never had this wonderful touch that Bobby Charlton had, this wonderful movement. In Ireland we practised playing and kicking the ball in the road, and a lot of kids had skill. But when you come to Manchester United and see the likes of Bobby Charlton . . .

Dunne arrived at Old Trafford during an uneasy time for the club and management. The sympathy that cradled United through the immediate post-Munich period had gone. Players came and went. Some clashed with other players, some with the management. Dunne kept quiet, stayed and played his way into the team.

Matt Busby actually came for me earlier in the 1959–60 season but left me to play for Shelbourne because they had a chance of winning the Cup, and we did win it. I headed straight over and went with the youth team to a tournament in Switzerland. We won the Cup and I made my senior debut that year. It was a difficult time for United. People were still supporting them and they'd had so much success over the years, but I think they were only coming because they felt obliged to. Matt Busby and Jimmy Murphy and all the backroom staff were trying to get it going again, trying to bring through young players and trying to bring in the right players from outside.

Maurice Setters was one of those who came and went. Great character. Used to stand there with those big shoulders and give anybody a piece of his mind. I remember he gave another lad from Ireland, Eamon Dunphy, a rollicking. Eamon was a cocky little devil. For a little Irish fella it was strange, because normally they were very quiet and got on with it, but he was always that way. Once you knew Maurice he was a really wonderful character. I think he must now look back and rue certain things he did. He was a brilliant defender but suffered through trying to do things he wasn't so good at. He could tackle, jump, head. He was a really strong, aggressive player. A winner. But he tried to do clever things in tight situations that the best players wouldn't try to do, and once his mind was made up, that was it with Maurice. And as a defender that can create problems. But he should never really have left United because his ability as a defender was top class.

Matt Busby's players had to play a certain way. He didn't ask a good forward to defend. He asked a good defender to defend and keep the good forward supplied. Matt wasn't a great tactician, but he was a psychologist. Everything was a jigsaw to him. He believed in his people. He believed he could have his people out there and they would perform. If they couldn't perform he would get somebody that would perform.

As a jigsaw, every piece was a complementary factor. If Bobby Charlton was behind me and got into trouble, I would get a rollicking. If I went ahead of Bobby and was trying to cross it, Bobby would get the rollicking. He'd say if he wanted somebody crossing the ball he wanted Bobby doing it, and if he wanted somebody to defend he wanted Tony doing it.

He knew your ability. He knew I was very quick so he tried to make me the last man. He knew I was not so sure of myself. I did extra training to make myself better and he knew it. He knew his people. He knew how to talk to people. He knew how to give you a rise – half of what you were going to ask for and you'd come away thinking he'd done you a favour. You'd go in to ask for ten pounds and he was always there in his big chair, and you'd always sit in a low chair. And as soon as you went in he'd say, 'You've had a good season, you're playing well, I'm thinking of giving you a rise. As a matter of fact, I've got it in your pay packet this week, five pounds. How's your mum and dad? What have you come to see me for?' Well, what answer is there to that? He used psychology very well.

He not only knew his players but he also knew the players he wanted to play, so much so I would say it was a fault of his. He didn't like to change the players. He'd rather have you play with injuries than take a chance. He'd make you feel bad about missing a game. He'd whisper in your ear, 'Where were you on Saturday?' I'd say, 'What do you mean, where was I on Saturday?' He'd say, 'The fella who played for you gave their fella too much room, he didn't put himself in position, he didn't make himself last man. Tony Dunne would have. Can't wait to see Tony Dunne this week.'

You felt he was the schoolteacher. It seemed as though he was in control of your life. I'd come from Ireland and had never seen anybody like him. He'd been in the crash; he'd survived the crash; I mean, I thought he was like King Kong. I couldn't say – as I couldn't to my teacher at school – boo to him. I would never even tell him my thoughts. I thought whatever he thought was enough. Nobody really answered him back.

He might have been a good psychologist but he was dreadful with the names of opposition players, always getting them mixed up. He'd have centre-halves playing centre-forward. Nobody laughed, but everybody had a smirk on their face. No matter whether he got their names wrong, the thing was he had total confidence in you to beat them. He'd say, 'Tony, you know he's quick, you know what you've got to do. Just make sure you're the last man, because the fella in the middle is a bit quick, so just work on that for me.' And yet he could remember the names of people he dealt with. If there were 25 reporters in a room he knew each one's name. How could people think anything but nice things about him?

The atmosphere he created in the dressing room was such that if anybody was to shout, you would have had five heart attacks. It was just like that. He walked in, took off his hat, gave his bits and pieces, put his hat back on and said, 'Right lads, let's go out and play.' If you'd played badly up to half-time he'd come in and say, 'If you don't work as hard as these your ability will never come out. If you don't you'll come off the field beaten. I'm telling you now, before it happens.'

So they were all simple instructions, though not so simple to put into practice. But when you've listened to somebody like him telling you, then you think it's all possible. Whatever he says is possible. And anything that falls below is a failure on your part, not on his. His standards are right up there, and he's talking like it's expected. 'You're the best team in the world, but if you don't go out and work, what do you expect?'

As Dunne and others testify, Busby was not renowned as a tactician. The very idea of adopting a modern system of play was anathema to him. An uncomfortable experience reaffirmed his conviction. As Dunne recalls,

> He didn't like the League Cup. He didn't want to play in it. The FA Cup was a nice day out, but for him the best teams played for the League Championship and the European Cup. So we played at Blackpool in the League Cup and he said, 'We're going to try one of them systems everybody's doing. It seems to be the thing to do.' So we played 4–3–3. I think we were five down at half-time.

The flow of words is interrupted by Dunne's sudden fit of laughter. Eventually he is able to resume.

> We came in and he said, 'You can forget this sort of stuff. These systems don't work. Let's get back to normal.' We certainly didn't win the game but he made the point. He couldn't care less if we won or lost because the League Cup meant nothing to him. He tried this system but didn't go into any elaborate preparation and training for it, and afterwards, of course, he dismissed it totally because it didn't work.

Busby's psychological magic potion still had to counter Dunne's inherent meekness. The belief and sense of destiny that swept his colleagues into the European Cup final failed to penetrate the quiet, self-effacing little Irishman.

> I didn't think it inevitable we would win the European Cup. In important games the tension would be incredible. He would try to take the fear out of you. 'Why should you worry? He's frightened to death.' But that never took the fear away from me. He had that belief in you, but then when you made a mistake you were thinking, 'Oh, no.' It didn't give me confidence.
>
> Confident players are people like George Best. George didn't seem to worry. He took it slightly differently from anyone else. Early on I didn't think he was confident because he was quiet and shuffled along. But there wasn't another player in any game who really stood out as being confident

the way he did. They all had little things, little routines before a game. Some fell asleep, others would be jumping up and down.

Bobby was nervous. I'm sure he felt like me at times and his ability was 100 per cent more than mine. I always thought Bobby felt Manchester United more than anybody. He felt it if the crowds weren't up because the club might be losing money. That's how he felt for it. He was probably the best player England had at the time. Made for international football. And on the field he ran for 90 minutes. The enthusiasm! He would get frustrated because he always wanted to win. He wanted the club to rise, and I think that stemmed from the crash. He took an awful lot of things on himself. But he was quite a nervous man and if he could be nervous it was no problem for me to be nervous.

I didn't really enjoy the night of the final. There was too much at stake for me to enjoy it. I felt we were in control of the game but we had to put in a lot of hard work. When you're nervous before the game your mind focuses totally and you try to do it to 100 per cent perfection. That's what you're looking for because you feel that's what you've got to give The Man. Anything you do wrong is a little chink in your armour.

The fear is to come off having failed him. You've been geared for this. Everybody says you're a great team, and this is what you have to win. And we can win it. We are good enough to win it. But in football it's Sod's Law; it doesn't always work that way. You need the luck. We felt quite comfortable but it's no good you feeling comfortable in a game, because while you're doing well somebody else mightn't be and he will need your help.

We had a good team, a good footballing team. I had John Aston in front of me and he had a field day. So the more I could get it to John the better. He had sussed that the full-back was a bit square so if the ball was pushed past him he'd give him trouble. He was brilliant. Exciting for people to watch. But we didn't quite kill them off. We made an awful lot of chances and didn't put them away. And we knew they were a good team, and a good team can come back. We were uptight all the time.

At the end of the 90 minutes I was knackered. I had

cramp; my legs were absolutely tied up. Alex Stepney was pulling my feet. I was in terrible pain. But Matt came on, rubbed my legs and said, 'You're ready now. Let's get it together. We've had no luck.' That was it. There was no pain that could hurt you as much as seeing him if you'd lost. Because he was miserable. He had this face, like a dog. He'd put on his hat and say, 'All right, lads, it didn't happen for us tonight. See you. Enjoy yourselves.' And you felt like cutting your throat. You didn't want that to happen.

When we got to four, with just a few minutes to go, I thought, 'Come on, get it over with.' They shouldn't have been able to come back from that, but I wanted it over with. I was too tired to enjoy it. When he blew the whistle I thought, 'Thank God that's over.' It was a relief. We'd got to win it, and yet when we did it was a terrible anti-climax for me. I'm sure it was for other players too. Sometimes you win a game and think, 'yeah!' Not that. It's the winning of the thing. It's the crash, the history. You felt like you were going down a tunnel, and every time you lost you felt like a flop. But to win the European Cup, that was going to take a great deal of pressure off you. Because now you were there, and you know when you're there once you can be there again quite easily. Because you're good enough and suddenly the flowers are blossoming. You're now the top team and it's taken this great weight off your back and you've won it at last.

And at the end you're half running around and your legs are killing you. You see Busby coming towards you and you're walking through people and you're just not there. You're going through the motions of people talking to you, you're looking at them blank, you're saying things but it's as if your mouth's not moving. And I'm thinking I could just do with being with my wife and father, who was over from Ireland on the boat with his mates. I was frightened of doing anything disrespectful but I just wanted to be with them, listen to them singing, have a few pints with them, probably fall down drunk and they'd put me to bed. They'd accept me more doing that than trying to dress up to the 'image' for the official banquet.

I wasn't too good there. Quite a few of us couldn't get above it. Sitting with the wife, I must have been bad company. The beer didn't taste right. It didn't seem to be the pint it should have been. You didn't want to excuse yourself and go to bed. I brought my father and I knew where he wanted to be, with his mates, drinking. I woke up at six or seven o'clock in the morning, went to his room and he wasn't there. He was outside with his mates. They'd come round for him. They'd been up all night drinking. He'd missed that. If I'd had a few pints, then bed, I would have enjoyed it 100 per cent more.

Why I had that feeling, I don't know. Because I'd played in all sorts of games, and nothing like that had ever happened. I could see the supporters were enjoying every minute, and quite rightly, and I was thinking, 'I'd love to be like that. I'll have my day.' And I did, a couple of weeks later. Really loved it. But the night itself is not something I can look back on and say I loved every minute of.

I loved the winning of it because it was so important to me. I would have thought – and I'm sure a lot of us would have thought – we were failures if we hadn't won. And what would have happened I don't know. It wasn't a situation where I was worried about my position, because the manager thought an awful lot of me. It's just that everything was geared to it. I thought we would have won it a couple of years before. I thought we would have beaten Partizan because we were streets ahead of them, but we were a little naive. We'd wanted to win it too much and got carried away. The great thing about the team I played in was that it never played any differently, only if teams forced us to.

The team Dunne played in was blessed with the presence of the 'Holy Trinity', but much as Dunne bowed to their supernatural talents, he was comforted in the knowledge they had human feelings.

For a start, the important thing for me was to be in a team that was winning, but I always believed they could only feel as good as the rest of us could. Unlike the night of the European Cup final, I could enjoy the drink and the feeling after a game. If somebody said George was great, somebody else might say what about Bobby or what about Denis? But in the '60s we also had the likes of John Connelly and David Herd. They were exciting, top-class forwards. They were the ones who had to suffer. Also in the team we had Nobby Stiles, an England international, but he really only got recognised for his notoriety. Paddy Crerand was slower than anybody you've ever seen, but his skill wouldn't be out of place today when you have a touch and can pass a ball like him. Glenn Hoddle, who would have been a wonderful Manchester United player, probably had more about him than Paddy, but Paddy had the same ability to knock the ball high and low. Paddy and those others didn't really get a mention. People like me.

But Manchester United was built on the Stretford End, and all those who stood there were knowledgeable people. They'd seen great players before. And when you ran on the field they clapped and sang your name. And you knew that when you did something good they would appreciate it. 'Make Tony Dunne King of Ireland,' they demanded. I mean, they can say what they like about anybody else, but they are talking about *you* as the best. They make you feel like King Kong. They can only sing the same things to George. To play for them was unbelievable.

The realisation of the European dream was, Dunne knew, the beginning of the end of Busby's reign. And now the club had a problem.

It was impossible to follow Matt, in so much as he was who he was and what he was. But I thought Noel Cantwell could have done the job. He had a wonderful brain as a footballer and he and Matt seemed to get on smashing from what I saw. I think Noel went out to learn his trade, he knew Manchester United and I think he was ready. Why it didn't happen I don't know, because I would never have asked.

I thought Wilf was unfortunate. He may have done it but it wasn't the right time. Some players let him down and there was a great upheaval. I think it was the first time you could get to Matt. I wasn't the type to get to him. Others were and some played golf with him. As a manager he could deal with people. He was very astute, disciplined. People couldn't just knock on his door and walk in. But I think his door was open to certain people later, and I think people were looking for faults. They were saying, 'He's not doing this right.' But I did think the man I knew as Matt Busby would have closed the door. I think he'd changed. He'd won it, he'd done it. It was over. But he still wanted the acclaim.

And, really, it could have been so simple, with Matt as general manager and Wilf as his assistant. Wilf trains us all week, then Matt Busby walks in, takes his hat off and says, 'Wilf's told you how we should do it. You know you have to work. Get out and do it. Have a good day.' Puts on his hat and walks out again. And nothing would have changed. But he didn't. He left the door open, for people to talk to him. I would say he possibly didn't help Wilf, he hindered him. And he came back, and we won more games under him. Then Frank O'Farrell came and he went back to the way he was with Wilf.

By then the club needed changing. It needed someone to come in and acknowledge that Matt was a legend and listen to him, but make it clear the club would continue as Manchester United and that he was the manager. I got the feeling sometimes – and I hate to say it – that Matt was happy with failure, because that brought him back into it. I think he still liked to be part of the gloss, and then when the gloss shifted he liked to come into the fold again. I think he gloried a little bit in coming back. By the time Fergie brought success to United it had gone past him. His life had been football. His best pals weren't around him. There were no Jimmy Murphys.

For all he did and all he built, even he didn't open the door for old players to come back. But then that was possibly understandable because he didn't really need them and probably didn't want anyone to chip off a little bit of the shine that still shone. Maybe that's life. He built the empire and one would forgive him all these little things . . .

Dunne's emotions have been stretched these past minutes and now he hesitates. The hurt inflicted more than two decades ago is seeping from beneath a lingering, but fragile, sense of loyalty. He cannot tell all, but he cannot tell nothing. In doing so, he feels, he achieves an acceptable balance and kind of puts the record straight.

We fell out but that's something I wouldn't like to talk about. I wouldn't say I loved him. I was in awe of him. If he told me to climb a wall I'd climb the wall. I didn't play as many internationals as I would have liked because he wouldn't let me. He said he couldn't have me playing for Ireland because he couldn't have me injured. So I missed an awful lot of internationals simply because I thought he was right. And he was always on my back. He said I was the best full-back in the world. Very complimentary. He didn't have to say these things. He gave me days off. I had so much respect for him. Everything he said was right.

When the other players were getting all the headlines in the papers he'd say, 'You don't have to worry, you were the best player on the park. I know it and the fans know it.' He always used to tap me on the shoulder and say, 'Remember, I'll be there for you when you need me. I'm the man that's going to look after you.' And that used to embarrass me. And he'd say, 'How's your mum and dad? Are you bringing them over next week? How's the kids? Is the house all right? Windows need doing? Get Les [Olive, the club secretary].' And he'd say, 'I'll look after you.' In the end, I know he didn't. I probably built him too high. It was a great period of my life. I loved it. And he probably gave me the worst night of my life. Him and the club. It was my testimonial.

Dunne declined to elaborate but his grievance is familiar to his colleagues and others connected to United. He felt Busby reneged on an arrangement over his testimonial match, at a time when Denis Law's had to be accommodated also. It is understood Dunne made £7,500 from his game, £1,500 of which was consumed by expenses.

The wind of change, now generated by Tommy Docherty, blew Dunne out of Old Trafford at the end of the 1972–73 season. 'I didn't think I had to go. I thought I was quite capable. I could have gone to London when I left United but it was Jimmy Murphy who said to me, "Go to Bolton, I know they want you." So Bolton was the place and we went up to the First Division. Ian Greaves was a great manager, had a great way of playing.'

Dunne attempted to fashion a coaching career at Burnden Park but admits he was 'perhaps too aggressive and wanted to get at players'. The shy, self-effacing little Irishman?

I left thinking I might get another job. But that was the '80s and the game went dead. I went coaching in Norway. Had a good little team. Third in the League, and they also made it to the semi-final of the Cup, first time in their history. But you train three times a week, and do nothing else.

So I went scouting, and what happens is you go in the guest room after the game and I felt as though everybody in there was after the manager's job. I thought there had to be something else. I can't do this week in, week out. So I was doing some coaching with the schools when a fella at Trafford Council told me they were going to build a driving range. Then he said they couldn't afford it, and would I be interested? I saw it as an opportunity. There was nothing in football, so why not? It wasn't like now. It's Sky that's pulled it up again. Makes it look beautiful. And it's driving a lot of footballers off the streets, giving them jobs.

Now, though, the clubs are businesses with different objectives. It seems strange to talk about Manchester United as a business. It was a club when I was there. One time you could be nipping in there, round the back, to the tea lady and have a cup of tea. You could get Bill Shankly in there, old players in there. It was a place, and a football club. But now you need passport numbers.

I'm not really interested in going to watch them now. They're a very good team. Ron Atkinson had a wonderful team. I used to pop down and see them. But there's this feeling you have to ask for people to go with, rather than being invited. Some people can go and it's not a problem. I'm not like that. They're good, don't get me wrong. I get tickets. I write the cheque and the stamped addressed envelope and they send back the tickets. But you feel that's all you get. And you don't like to tell people because you feel it's more a knock-back on you than them.

I feel there's a terrible divide at Manchester United now. It's nothing to do with the manager, players or the people who work there. It's just that it's now this company. It's moved into a different time since Matt Busby. There were unfortunate times with Tommy Doc, and I would have to say he deserved to be sacked. You can't do things like that in the club. [Docherty left his wife for the wife of the club's physiotherapist, Laurie Brown.] Louis Edwards was a super chairman, a lovely man, and I felt there was something not quite right after he died.

Martin Edwards took over and now it's a business, and

businesses can dismiss anything, can't they? The players of
the past are recognised by everybody, but there are different
recognitions in life. One is where you can walk into a place
that you were part of and part of your life was there, a
wonderful part. I'm lucky to be a part of the history, a
member of the first English team to win the European Cup,
the only holder of Irish, English and European Cup-winning
medals. But I would have to say I sometimes feel like a
window cleaner there.

I have a feeling that if they could close the chapter on that
period they would. I think Brian Kidd and Alex Ferguson
would welcome you with open arms. How do you get to
them? Where do you go? There's no door you can walk in as
an ex-player. There's no seat. Every player's bum on a seat
costs that company money, and where's the loyalty in
business? I've done it, past my time. It doesn't really bother
me because life goes on and I do other things. But you're
aware of it. We have the old boys' dates and it's lovely seeing
some of the older lads, even though I'm not a great 'harper-
backer'. I'm lucky to have played for United in that period,
and then with that wonderful Bolton team. But if I went
down to Bolton Wanderers tomorrow I'd be as welcome as
anything.

Manchester United plc may not have Dunne's approval, but Alex
Ferguson has.

Fergie's done an absolutely fantastic job. He's a great manager
and must be a great manager to play for. He's looked after
them and pulled them into the fold. They're playing a
winning game and as at all times it's about confidence. They
really have it buzzing. I don't know what it's like there now
because I don't go, but it can't really be the same without the
Stretford End. That gave it something.

You're always going to get comparisons between the past
and present and there's one now, with Bobby Charlton and
this young lad [presumably he means David Beckham]. I
think the young lad will be under more pressure than Bobby
because Bobby would accept anything. I think comparisons
between Bobby and the lad today can't be taken seriously.
Bobby Charlton used to get the ball and dribble past people.

He used to drop his shoulder, he used to glide, then he'd whack it. And the leather balls were very difficult to hit. Now they are very light. If you are a good striker of the ball today and you are a clever little fella you can shift the ball sideways for a shot on goal and you can become a great player. Or maybe I'm wrong!

I think the present team can win the European Cup because it comes down to a one-off situation. Once you're in there, you're good enough to win it. They've got lovely stability at the back, and they've got players who can play.

But are they as good as his team? He thinks long and hard before responding.

There were so many in my team who could score goals, even before Kiddo came along. As a matter of fact, Kiddo looked like he would be better than Bestie. If he'd been a little bit quicker he could have been anything. We had quality players who played to the pattern. Busby would obviously have wanted Denis in the European Cup final team, although it wouldn't have made any difference because on the night we were wonderful. Four goals – you can't do any better than that.

But the forward line I always think back to was before '68. That was something. Connelly, Herd, Charlton, Law, Best – where do you go from that? It was the forward line we played at Benfica, in '66, when we won 5–1. They were all cut-throat merchants. They'd cut your throat to get their goals and didn't think anything of it.

Business is cut-throat at any level, but Dunne professes himself content with his lot, and here he is never far from the family embrace.

My son, Anthony, works with me. I've got two daughters, three grandchildren – marvellous. And the good lady. Thirty-six years we've been married. The job can be hard work, but if business is up it's the best job in the world.

An awful lot of people who come here want to talk football. Not just Manchester United supporters. They're Manchester City supporters, Everton supporters, all sorts. They all care about football. But there's a bit more animosity in football today. In my day you didn't want City to go down. You hoped your team was doing better than them, but just a few slots. And it's a big town. I think it's very sad City are down.

At least his customers recognise him, then?

Some do, some don't. Some say, 'Are you . . .?' I say, 'I used to be.'

4. PAT CRERAND

Born: Glasgow, 19-2-39
Debut: v Blackpool (h), 23-2-63
United career: Football League – 304 appearances, 10 goals;
FA Cup – 43, 4; Football League Cup – 4, 0; Europe – 41, 1.
Total – 392, 15.

The Holy Trinity will forever be exalted above all others, but the popular maxim of the time was that when Pat Crerand played well, Manchester United played well. That was some burden to shoulder, but then little intimidated Crerand. His defiance was as conspicuous as his visionary football. He was a paradox: at once a slow, ungainly-looking player, indifferent in the air, scored relatively few goals for a midfield man and had a dangerously short fuse – and an orchestrator of the most refined, classic football.

Crerand was granted his mantle of responsibility for United's fortunes after the 1963 FA Cup final. He had overcome a difficult first few months with a team that seemed as likely to be relegated to the Second Division as win a trophy. However, as the severity of that infamous winter abated and United worked their way through the backlog of fixtures, they arrived at a delayed final with their First Division status preserved and their minds cleared. Here was a Manchester United team playing with rediscovered joy and self-belief, and at the hub was Crerand, given licence to exploit his rare passing technique. United won 3–1 to complete their first post-Munich success, and the Crerand connection was forged.

The roles of wing-halves and inside-forwards were being redefined and Crerand, although a robust tackler and fearsome competitor, excelled when able to give free rein to his creative and expressive attributes. So it was that Busby released him from more defensive duties and provided him with the perfect foil in the combative Nobby Stiles. Their complementary functions – the battler and the passer – would produce the heartbeat for the '60s revival.

Crerand's competitive instinct was a product of necessity. He was raised in Glasgow's notorious Gorbals district from Irish stock and developed not only a sense of self-preservation but also a social conscience. He would declare an ambition to be Prime Minister and few doubt he would have made an unforgettable impact. He has never been reluctant to proffer an opinion or expound a theory. And always he would deliver his dictum with passion and conviction.

The orator in Crerand would blossom as a media pundit, but in those formative years he had to play as well as talk a good game in order to garner any street cred. The shipyards offered the most secure passage in life for the youth of the area, yet young Patrick Timothy was intent on steering a course in football. He went to school early in the morning so that he could play football before classes started, and took every other opportunity to exercise those fledgling skills.

The word on the street was that Crerand had a chance and, to his astonishment, intelligence to that effect reached one of the Old Firm clubs. The Catholic one, of course. He signed for Celtic along with the player who would captain Britain's first European Cup winners, a year before Crerand and United lifted the trophy. Unlike Billy McNeill, Crerand has little to show for his Celtic days, only a Scottish Cup runners-up medal in 1961. He was to find fulfilment south of the border.

Before he left Celtic, however, he represented the Scottish League against the Italian League, whose side included compatriot Denis Law. In the summer of 1962 United rescued Law from his Italian purgatory and the then British record transfer fee of £116,000 proved a bargain. Law made a further repayment by recommending Crerand to United. Matt Busby was torn between Jim Baxter and Crerand but, although Law rated the former the more gifted player, he felt the latter's more durable game would better serve the club in the long run. So, in February 1963, Crerand went to Old Trafford in a £56,000 transfer, making his debut against Blackpool. It was another of Busby's outstanding deals.

Three months later Crerand had an FA Cup-winner's medal, followed by Championship medals in 1965 and 1967, and then his European Cup prize. A total of 16 full caps represents scant recognition of his ability, although he had to contend with strong competition and perhaps a lingering prejudice. Crerand's opponents had to contend not only with his velvet touch but also with the iron fist and, as with Law, the fighting impulse was a mixed blessing. Again in common with Law, however, the volatile temperament was a symptom of burning commitment.

Crerand carried that enthusiasm and determination into a coaching job at Old Trafford before his ill-starred appointment as assistant to manager Tommy Docherty. The Celt cocktail proved too potent for one club and Crerand joined the exodus of the '68 team. He was given the manager's chair at Northampton Town but found it too uncomfortable. He left the game to try his luck in the pub trade and public relations and, after causing a characteristic stir as a television panellist, made a niche for himself on local radio as a professional United fan.

* * *

It is a few minutes before kick-off at Old Trafford and most members of the working media are settled into their seats in the press box, which is positioned in the heart of the old main stand, albeit a little to the right of the halfway line. To the left is the directors' box and on the other three sides the paying customers, ensuring a sample of the great theatre's atmosphere. One or two latecomers bustle up the stairs, among them the familiar figure of Wilf McGuinness, bald of head, wide of smile and expansive of pleasantries all the way to his United Radio commentary position.

Another familiar figure and another former United player has yet to bustle his way to another radio commentary position and his colleague from Piccadilly 1152 glances anxiously towards the bottom of the box. His expert summariser is at least in sight and the commentator need not be concerned. He should know by now that this is part of the pre-match ritual. The chances are it will be re-enacted at half-time and at the end. Paddy Crerand is trapped in conversation with a gaggle of punters who have lain in wait. He appears a consenting captive, one hand scribbling an autograph, the other seemingly being wrenched from its socket by an over-zealous admirer as he engages the self-appointed exclusive audience in excited banter.

The referee's final check with his fellow officials is the sign to break free. One more round of laughs and the beaming, self-satisfied faces turn to view the action. Crerand, also sporting a glowing countenance, bounds up the steps at a remarkable rate of knots. 'You were never as quick as that on the pitch, Paddy,' some wag at the back shouts. Was that Wilf? Anyway, it strikes a chord and everyone enjoys the crack. And Paddy long since ceased to take offence at jokes about his tardy pace. It almost became his trademark.

But what he lacked in speed he managed to make up for with other qualities, among them enthusiasm. It is instantly apparent that the passing years have done nothing to dull that. In fact, he has changed comparatively little since he was shuffling around down there in the middle, confounding visiting defences with a perfectly measured, threaded pass into the path of Law or Best or Kidd. He is still lean and, yes, you imagine he could still be mean.

The old combative edge comes across in his comments. He is fiercely loyal to United, effusive in his praise of the home team, scathing in his condemnation of the referee when a borderline decision goes the way of the away team. The fire and aggression go down well with the listeners. This is vintage Crerand. It's what they want to hear.

Crerand is part of the family, always has been. He was estranged after falling out with Docherty but his heart was always here. He was one of Matt's boys, hand-picked to do a specific job, and he responded. He was comfortable with Matt. Another Scot, another Catholic. He had unshakeable self-belief and the patter to match his swagger. He was engaging, if at times too opinionated, and Matt felt he brought spirit to his family.

Busby, ever mindful of creating a homely, welcoming first impression (remember Stepney's experience?), took Law and his wife along with him when he met Crerand at the airport. Crerand would be further impressed by the patriarch's personal interest in his growing family. The club was almost an extension of the players' family life.

Crerand says of Busby, 'We had great respect for him. He was loved by all his players. He was fair and honest. You knew exactly where you stood with him. There was never any in-between with him. He was a very good-living man, very religious, never used bad language, never anything crude, and he didn't let his players do anything that wasn't right, either.'

It was five years to the day after Munich when Crerand joined United, and he was sensitive to the trauma Busby had endured in losing so many of his 'Babes'. Crerand reflects, 'It must be very difficult when you grow up with all those kids and know their families, and suddenly all those kids are killed. It must have been horrendous for him.'

The welcome at United may have been warm, but the reception from English football was distinctly chilly. The League and Cup programme had been thrown into chaos by the worst freeze since 1947 and clubs were seeking desperately needed match practice in more clement climes. United went to Ireland and gave their new wing-half the chance to acclimatise. It would, however, take more than friendly exercise to eradicate the malaise that threatened to drag them down to the Second Division. Even the brilliance of Denis Law might not have been enough to spare them that ignominy.

Crerand would have wished for an easier introduction to the English game. His imagination was stifled as he was deputed to help United battle their way out of trouble. Somehow they did, finishing an inglorious but safe 19th in the First Division table. Somehow, too, they managed to avoid the tricky draws along Wembley way, squeezing through the congested schedule almost before Crerand could find his feet.

At Wembley, however, he stood firm and imperious. The pressures of fending off relegation removed, United revelled in their new-found freedom, and no one more so than Crerand. The underdogs outplayed Leicester City, the 3–1 scoreline scarcely reflecting their superiority. United were on the up again, and Crerand had established himself as an integral force in their ascent.

Championship successes gave the boy from the Gorbals a view of the game's loftiest peaks. He first glimpsed the summit after United's momentous 5–1 win away to Benfica. Crerand feared he had undermined the cause by smashing a mirror in the dressing room while playing with a ball before the game, but any superstitions were swept away by the majesty of United's football. The Scot was sufficiently becalmed to register his only European goal.

> I really thought we were going to make it all the way after that. I can't believe we didn't. That night in Lisbon was our best ever. I'd seen Real Madrid beat Eintracht Frankfurt 7–3 in the 1960 European Cup final at Hampden Park and they were absolutely magnificent. And I think our performance at Benfica was up there with that. We produced a lot of fabulous football over the years, but that 5–1, on Benfica's home ground, that was something else. Especially after our 5–0 hammering by Sporting Lisbon two years earlier, when Matt said our performance was an insult to the people of Manchester.
>
> We should have gone on from that win in '66 and won the Cup, but we had injury problems. George missed the second leg against Partizan and it all went wrong for us. But we should have had it that year. We all knew that.

Crerand, sent off in the second leg against Partizan, and his team-mates focused still more clearly on their objective two years later. He savoured the build-up to the finals, the journey to Wembley and the atmosphere of the great occasion, but wondered whether they might be punished for squandering opportunities.

We missed a lot of chances and should have sewn it up well before they equalised. When it was 1–1 I was sure George's goal wasn't going in. From where I was, it looked as if their keeper's dive was going to keep the ball out.

It was unusual in that the teams knew each other so well. The Portuguese, as they always are, were all very friendly and extremely sporting, particularly the captain, Coluna. At one point he kicked the bottom of my boot in a tackle. He was down to my pace – and worse – from then on. After the game we tried to break with Wembley tradition by getting Matt to come up and accept the trophy, but he refused. He was never a showman. If Munich was the low point of his career, then this was the highest. He was like a little kid of five years on Christmas morning. Like Bobby, I was ill at the end.

There are still some poignant memories. Of going to the all-night banquet at the Russell Hotel, and seeing Duncan Edwards's parents and Eddie Colman's parents. All the parents of the Munich victims were invited. I didn't know what to say to them and there were a lot of tears. It was very sad. I kept thinking that if he had been alive, Duncan would have been playing instead of me.

The more feisty side of Crerand's character can obscure a sensitive, perceptive, compassionate nature. He willingly shouldered the responsibility of being Best's 'minder' and dismisses much of the adverse publicity about the Irishman as 'newspaper talk'. But he also recognises, with obvious sadness, the self-induced element in the decline of a genius.

The biggest thing that damaged George was that he lost his fitness, and the way he lived didn't help. I think he lost a bit of appetite when he stopped playing with the players he'd been brought up with. George today would admit that he himself was the problem, not the club or anything like that. The problem Matt had was that he couldn't go home with George. If you are a single lad you don't sit in the house every night, do you?

Crerand accepted Best as a house guest in an attempt to curb the instincts for extra-curricular activity, but the forces of time would not be repelled. Although Crerand is adamant that United were unjustly dumped out of the semi-final of the European Cup in 1969, signs of their demise loomed large and ominous.

The club felt Crerand had a role to occupy beyond his playing days and he duly joined the coaching staff in the summer of 1971. He survived the 'Night of the Long Knives' that accounted for Frank O'Farrell, Malcolm Musgrove and John Aston senior, and became assistant manager to Tommy Docherty. It would be described as a 'marriage made in hell' and, sure enough, it did not last. Busby, the club patriarch, was distinctly more enthusiastic about the appointment than the new team boss.

Crerand departed, having come to the conclusion he had stayed around too long anyway. In 1976–77 he had a six-month spell as manager of Northampton Town, which did little to rekindle the spirit. He changed direction as a public relations officer for a Manchester engineering company and followed a traditional route for an ex-footballer as a licensee, in Altrincham. To a new generation of United followers, however, he is the unrestrained, caustic, outspoken, ever-devoted champion of the club on Piccadilly 1152.

'Fergie's done a magnificent job,' he tells his audience a thousand times. And at the end of the match against Crystal Palace, which United have won with two first-half goals, he sustains the high-intensity chatter with his listeners, bouncing back excited questions with his forthright comments. Suddenly he whips off his headphones to bellow a suitably abusive message to a current United player, Gary Pallister, who appears to be having some difficulty negotiating the seats in the centre of the stand after conducting an interview. The amiable big defender smilingly shares the joke and resumes his precarious course.

Crerand returns to his listeners, secure in the knowledge the flow of his words will never be constrained. 'His tongue was always faster than his legs,' some wag at the back reckons. Was that Wilf?

5. BILL FOULKES

Born: St Helens, 5-1-32
Debut: v Liverpool (a), 13-12-52
United career: Football League – 563 (3) appearances, 7 goals;
FA Cup – 61, 0; Football League Cup – 3, 0; Europe – 52, 2.
Total – 679 (3), 9.

Even the most elaborate tapestry needs a wall to hang on. Manchester United had Bill Foulkes. Solid, dependable, durable – all those labels were stuck on him. But his was not merely a physical presence and support. His was a psychological, perhaps even spiritual vinculum with the cause that rose again from the ashes of Munich. He and Harry Gregg were the only survivors of the crash who carried the torch into the FA Cup tie against Sheffield Wednesday. Foulkes was the captain. He was still there at Wembley in 1968, and although the captaincy, and so much more, had passed to Bobby Charlton, Foulkes alone had made the full journey.

He had none of Charlton's elegance or skills, yet such was his importance to the crusade that he defied injury, at Busby's behest, to play in the second leg of the semi-final at the Bernabeu – where he emerged the hero in an improbable guise – and the final. For all Busby's devotion to the game of the angels, he demanded of his centre-half an earthy, no-nonsense resilience, and if that meant peppering the punters in row Z then so be it. Foulkes was just the man for the job.

In his earlier days he was a right-back, though no less compromising and no more indulgent. He came from the pits – yes, many have suggested he was mined – of South Lancashire, born in the rugby league town of St Helens. His father and grandfather played for that famous club. Only when he was picked for England did he feel confident he could hold his own with the Babes and make a career in football. He played through United's pre-

Munich Championships, FA Cup and European campaigns and was the obvious choice to lead the team after the crash. More conspicuous personalities would ease him out of the skipper's role, but he remained the guardian and protector, a John Wayne-type figure who enabled the others to rest easier simply by his being around.

He won four Championship medals and an FA Cup-winner's medal before accomplishing his own mission in the European Cup. He played on with United for another two years, by which time he had made 682 appearances for the club, and then joined the coaching staff. He subsequently had coaching posts in America and Norway, and more recently forged connections with Japanese football, in managerial and then in scouting and consultancy capacities.

* * *

He now qualifies for a pension, but he still cuts an impressive figure. The slight gait and grey hair cannot disguise the familiar cowboy image. The old gunslinger is in his city civvies, immaculately turned out in blazer, collar and tie. He strides not into some main-street saloon, but the United museum café, and the greeting is genuine rather than sycophantic. He offers to pay for two coffees but the man behind the counter will have none of it. This customer contributed more than most to the creation of the United empire, an Old Trafford now comprising executive lounges, restaurants, bars and stores. No member of the '68 side has seen greater change. This softly spoken, gentle man recollects his early days at Old Trafford.

> I came here as a boy, although I worked in the pits until I was 23. I had three years playing in the first team and working full-time in the coal mines. I became assistant to the under-manager, quite a good job and well paid. I did quite a bit of overtime, as well. I didn't really want to turn pro because I was getting twice as much money from the Coal Board as I was getting here. To be honest, I never thought I could really make it because there were so many great players here. I didn't think I'd be good enough. But Matt said if you want to be a professional you've got to be a full-timer. Then I was picked for England and he said, 'Don't you think you should sign full-time now?' I played against Northern Ireland, at right-back. We won 2–0 and Billy Wright congratulated me on how well I'd played. So I said 'okay' and signed.
>
> I was getting married and pointed out to Matt that in the

mines I was exempt from National Service. He said they'd
take care of that, as they did for Mark Jones and David Pegg.
So I got married and within two weeks I was on my way
down to Aldershot for two years' National Service! It was
arranged I'd have three days a week at the Officers' Training
School down there and the rest of the time here. But I
couldn't always get the passes I needed, so I had to go in
disguise – big overcoat, trilby hat and briefcase – to get past
the MPs. That was actually the CO's advice. He said it would
get me through and it worked every time. Nobody ever
stopped me on the station.

That little subterfuge captured the spirit of the time. Foulkes and his
colleagues were adventurers and achievers, carefree, gifted young
troubadours who took their show around the land and then beyond,
beguiling their audiences and mesmerising their opponents. Munich
claimed more than the lives of eight friends and team-mates. It claimed
some of that spirit forever, leaving in its place a demon that will not be
exorcised. The voice softer still, he recalls the team of 1958.

The Munich team was such a great team. Brilliant players,
young players. You realise even more now that we had so
many world-class players. The team that died would have
been, I think, European champions that year and maybe for
many years to come because they were that good and they
were still growing, still learning. You could see the
confidence in the team.

I never really spoke to Bobby or Harry about the crash
afterwards. The only thing I discussed with Harry was about
how he nearly took Jackie Blanchflower's arm off with a
tourniquet! But about the crash, no. I think we all prefer to
keep our thoughts to ourselves. I've suffered badly from it
because I do a lot of travelling and it affects me when I fly
even now. Even before I fly.

I don't think Bobby enjoyed his football as much after
Munich and that applies to me, as well. I remember in
particular playing away in Estudiantes, in the World Club
Championship, and after it I felt I never wanted to play
again. I mean, I didn't want that sort of stuff after the career
I'd had. Before Munich it was a different game and there was
a different atmosphere in the team. We were all young

together, growing up together, and didn't realise the talent and the stature of some of the players.

It was very emotional leading the team out for the first time after the crash, against Sheffield Wednesday. I would hate to go through it again. I felt a bit sorry for Sheffield Wednesday. Albert Quixall, who was Wednesday's captain, was shaking with emotion. He was nearly crying. The team we put out was a mixture of kids and over-the-hills and whatever, but we still came through. I think it was mainly due to the crowd and the emotion. How could Sheffield Wednesday have won that game?

The emotion could not sustain United's momentum all the way to FA success that year, and Busby had to negotiate one of his most difficult and perhaps defining periods, on the field and in the dressing room, before his reshaped team reached Wembley again in 1963. They disposed of Leicester City with the kind of panache that was to become their trademark in the seasons ahead. Foulkes recalls that time with lingering alarm.

In '63 we could very easily have gone down. We got a draw at City with a dubious goal scored by me! But it kept us ahead and we didn't go down. There were arguments in the camp around that time, Matt acted and it wasn't long before Noel Cantwell and Maurice Setters left the club. It was a critical period for Matt, to have to sort that out, a test of his strength. But he was a strong man and a great manager. He appeared to be a very nice man, genial, a sort of father figure, and he lulled people into thinking that about him. But there was another side to him. He was a Gemini. He was two different characters. He could be ruthless, tough, and at times he had to be.

I remember a pre-season jaunt in Austria. We played two or three games there. One of them was against an Austrian national XI and I was left out because of a calf injury and sat on the bench. There was quite a big crowd but it was very quiet on the bench. They weren't happy with what was going on. We were being beaten four or five-one. But Matt was very calm. Harry did something and Matt said, cool as anything – you could feel the ice coming from him – 'That's the last game you'll play for this club.' He cut off Johnny Morris in a similar way. When he decided, good God. That's the way he was.

He collared me and threw the leather at me a couple of times. When I was on the staff, semi-player but reserve-team coach, I saw Brian Kidd at a dinner at the Piccadilly Hotel one Christmas time. Players weren't supposed to be there and, of course, as soon as he saw me he was away, or so I thought. My wife and one or two others saw him again. I came in as usual the following morning, very early, getting ready for training. Matt stepped out of the shadows and said, 'Why didn't you tell me about Brian Kidd?' I didn't know what the hell to do or say. I said I had seen him but I thought he'd gone home. He said, 'Don't do that again. I rely on you.' That gives you an insight into him. He was a tough man, a hard man. He wasn't a softie. But he was also a nice man, a considerate man, a family man. You always knew, though, that there was the other side.

Tales of splits in the camp and over-zealous training games are part of the United lore, but Foulkes, another fundamentally nice man known to have had a harder side – he has even been called a bully – is adamant there was no rift between him and Gregg.

I was always pretty strong-minded. I knew what I could do and I knew how to do it. I was known as a strong, physical player, but I was fair. I tried to be, anyway. Yes, there would be one or two set-tos, but that happens at every club. This talk of Harry Gregg and me not getting on is absolute rubbish. Harry and I are good friends and always have been. I heard about the story so I tackled Harry about it at a dinner we had in Ireland. He said he was going to ask me the same thing. We had arguments, we could belt each other to hell, but then it was forgotten. That's football. But there was no undercurrent or anything like that.

The Championship successes of 1965 and 1967 confirmed a unity of purpose as well as abundant talent within the camp. Deep into that 1967–68 European Cup campaign, however, Foulkes feared the dream was beyond realisation.

We should have won it in '66 and two years on I thought our chance had gone. The team we had in '66 and '67 was a great side, but we had injuries just at the wrong times, with Best

EUROPEAN CHAMPION CLUBS' CUP

BENFICA F.C.

MANCHESTER UNITED

FINAL

**ORGANISED BY THE FOOTBALL
ASSOCIATION ON BEHALF OF THE**

UNION DES ASSOCIATIONS EUROPÉENNES DE FOOTBALL

WEDNESDAY MAY 29th 1968

Kick-off   7·45 p.m.

OFFICIAL PROGRAMME   **ONE SHILLING**

WEMBLEY
EMPIRE STADIUM

The day of destiny arrives

Captains Charlton and Coluna exchange pennants while referee Lo Bello makes the most of the photo opportunity

Best shows Jacinto a clean pair of heels as Charlton looks on approvingly

Charlton's header puts United in front

Out of camera shot and out of reach for Benfica. Best's goal restores United's lead

Kidd heads United's third at the second attempt

Charlton completes the demolition

Birthday boy Kidd celebrates his goal

The heroes and the people, United in triumph

Charlton and Foulkes
get a close-up of
Stiles's famous fangs

Busby's dream is realised

John Baumann and Great Fosters today, and (inset) the author (second left) rubs shoulders with Pat Crerand before United's 5–1 victory at Benfica's Stadium of Light

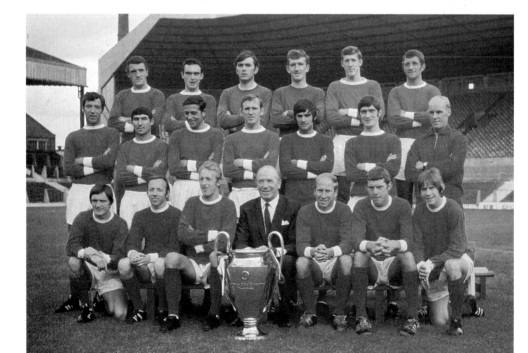

The 1968 European champions

and Law and David Herd. Then, in '68, we had injuries again. Denis was having more problems and, remember, he had done a fantastic job for the club. As soon as he came in he was unbelievable. I had a knee ligament injury that season and, to be honest, I thought it had finished me. I refused to play in Gornik and Matt was very annoyed. David Sadler played and was great, but we lost 1–0. Then Matt took a gamble, bringing me back for the second leg against Real Madrid.

I hadn't played for about four months because of my knee, but he played me in the last League game, against Sunderland. He gave me a test in a practice game and put Alan Gowling against me. Alan knocked me around a bit and I came through it, but my knee blew up. I had the fluid aspirated off the knee and played against Sunderland. We were still in with a chance of winning the Championship but City won and we drew 1–1. I wasn't tested, really, which was just as well. I could hardly walk. Again I had my knee aspirated and played in Madrid with it strapped very tightly.

Nobby Stiles and Tony Dunne were absolutely brilliant. They covered me. All I had to do was stand there. But it was a big gamble. We were just 1–0 up from the first leg, when George scored. There was no explanation as to why I was playing, he just said I was playing. And then, of course, I scored that goal, which was incredible. I can't explain it, and nobody else can explain it.

But also like everybody else, he recollects it vividly.

At half-time we were a bit despondent because they had murdered us. They were brilliant. But at 3–1 they were only a goal up on aggregate and if we pulled that back it would mean a replay in Lisbon. As Matt reminded us, we'd beaten Benfica 5–1 there and we would stay at Estoril again. We didn't need the replay. First David scored, though I don't think he knew much about it. The ball hit him on the shoulder or somewhere and just went in the net.

Then I remember Nobby shouting to me, 'Where the hell are you going?' Now I couldn't give Nobby enough credit for the way he covered for me that night, in front of me and behind me. I just got on the end of everything in the air and hit everything. Anyway, he was shouting at me because Pat Crerand had picked the ball up for a throw-in on the right and was looking for someone to give it to. At that stage of the game everybody, including Madrid, had frozen. George was marked very tightly and nobody seemed to make a move, so I made this run and shouted to Paddy. He looked and decided against it, and threw it to George.

My idea of making a run was to pull one of their players off George and it worked. George went down the line, beat two or three players, looked up and, of course, I was the only player in the box. He had a second look, as if he couldn't believe it, and I thought he wasn't going to part with the ball. I thought he was going to shoot and he feinted to drive it to the near post. The centre-back left me and George cut the ball back beautifully. I couldn't have missed. I just swept it into the other corner. The fact that I shouldn't have been playing in the first place made it all the more incredible.

No more, his team-mates might say, than his assertion he couldn't have missed. Depending on how you read that, he is either extremely modest or revealing delusions of goalscoring grandeur. Since the latter option is totally out of character, we should accept the former. Either way, Busby was now intent on patching him up for Wembley.

After that game he just told me to get myself ready for the final. I don't think it was an emotional thing. I think he thought I could do the job and had the experience for the occasion. I don't think he would have taken that sort of risk. Munich and everything else didn't come into it because this was his ambition, to win the European Cup. He wouldn't take any chances. He thought he had a better chance by playing me. I was at the training ground on my own, then having treatment afterwards, building up muscle strength. I couldn't stop, I couldn't turn, but I worked at it to get myself fit enough and played in the final. In fact, I played on two years afterwards with it.

But come the final we're talking Torres, and, of course, when you've got a cruciate ligament injury you can't leap, and here's a guy of six foot four, brilliant in the air. But I managed. Just inspired, I think. In the build-up I was a little nervous I would let the team down, but not as nervous as I had been in the semi-final. I didn't really want to play in the semi-final, but once we got to Wembley I was hoping he'd pick me.

On the day of the final I just whiled away the hours at that big, rambling hotel in the country, and relaxed. I just went for a stroll through the gardens, beautiful gardens, and went down to the bottom of the field and back. I went into the match in a really relaxed manner. I couldn't get to the ground fast enough, even though I was limping. As soon as we went out on to the field I knew we were going to win. In Madrid, when everybody was kissing each other, I said that was it, we were going to win the final. And now I knew it. We *had* to. It was our last chance and it was Matt's last chance.

Even when Eusebio broke away I wasn't worried. It's incredible and it's happened to me very rarely in my life, perhaps a couple of times, but I knew we would be all right. Normally you would think, 'Oh no, Eusebio!' But as he shot I just knew it would go straight into Alex. I just felt it. We *had* to win that match. And then George scored and we all started flying.

The team wasn't as effective as it had been in the past, although in saying that I'm thinking of myself, really. George was great, Nobby was still there, and people like Tony Dunne. Johnny Aston came in and played out of his skin. Brian Kidd was just 19 years of age. Paddy took a lot on his shoulders as well. But, to be honest, it was nothing like the side we knew, nothing.

Stiles's role, as Eusebio's jailkeeper, was crucial to United's game plan and Foulkes's faith in his little partner was unflinching. He concedes, however, his methods would probably not be tolerated by modern referees.

Nobby wouldn't have got away with it these days. I think he would have been off. He took him once from behind and, well . . . But to be fair they were the same. They were a bit naughty as well. And Real Madrid. Kicked us all over the bloody place. This may sound ridiculous, but Nobby was not a dirty player. Nobby was a brilliant footballer and was never given the credit for it. He was physical, obviously, but I think a lot of his mistimed tackles were because his eyesight wasn't too good, and I think his optician was to blame for that. I'm sure he was given the wrong lenses and was out of focus most of the time. Lenses and dentures! That was Nobby.

He was small in stature but so intelligent and good on the ball. Our combination and the understanding between us was incredible. It was like telepathy. He knew exactly what I was doing; I knew exactly what he was doing. The other aspect was his enthusiasm and his spirit, but that had a drawback. He was shouting non-stop, and his language wasn't too clever, but once you got to know him you just ignored it.

It was a worry being without Denis that night because he was such a big influence, but he'd had a knee problem for a couple of years, so we were accustomed to not having him. Having won it, I thought Matt may have had enough, emotionally. I wouldn't be surprised if it wasn't the same for Bobby. I didn't feel the others were outsiders, but we had a different purpose. I think they were worried about being so overjoyed. I didn't show any elation because I just felt relieved. I wasn't jumping about or anything. I just stood there. I was so relieved we had done it, and I looked at Bobby and I could see the same thing with him – he was drained. The feeling of, 'That's it, we've done it.' Bobby was crying. I've never been as emotional as Bobby, but I felt it just the same, just as much.

I played on for a couple of seasons after the European Cup final. I wanted to retire. To be honest, I wanted to be a pro golfer, but Denis talked me round and Matt told me to go and get a coaching certificate. So I went to Lilleshall and got really interested in the coaching side. I'd never really dreamed of staying in football as a coach, but it fired my enthusiasm and I became reserve-team coach. Whether I became too enthusiastic I don't know, because I had my hard days, as I did when I was a player. Being strong-minded helped me.

The will made him persevere across the globe when his time at United was finally over. He went to Chicago Sting, Tulsa Roughnecks, returned to England as manager of non-League Witney Town, then was back on his travels, to San Jose Earthquakes and to Stenjker, Lillestrom and Viking Stavanger in Norway, before trying his luck in Hiroshima. He has retained working contacts with the Japanese but has returned to his home in Sale and the embrace of his three children and six grandchildren.

I'd been abroad for so long – 17, 18 years – but I kept my house here. I belong here. It's home. In a way, Old Trafford is my second home. I think there was a certain bond between the players we had, almost a family feeling.

I wouldn't say the game has changed all that much since then, but the finances have. Money plays a big part in the game now. I would love to have had some of the salaries being paid these days. I do envy the modern players. These guys are secure for the rest of their lives, most of them. I'm not bitter but I just feel we were exploited a wee bit. Over a five-year period we made a real impact. We reached the pinnacle. We won the European Cup. I also got to four Championships, three Cup finals and numerous semi-finals. The fact that I have had to sell my medals is sad.

Sad and, alas, not a unique course of action for one of the game's old soldiers and heroes.

I needed some cash, not for myself, and decided this was what I should do. I think there were nine medals in all. We only found out afterwards it was a record. I don't like to disclose what they raised, but it was quite substantial. It was hard to do but my wife was relieved, because with my moving around so much it was a responsibility for her. Although I was sad to see them go it's nice to know they are here, at the museum. They are sort of within the family.

The new generation at United have matched Foulkes's achievements in the Championship, and now endeavour to retrace his steps to the pinnacle of European football.

You shouldn't really compare teams from different eras but people do, and I am always asked to make comparisons. The Munich side was brilliant, full of young, world-class players. Our team in the '60s had three European Footballers of the Year. How many teams can say that? In '68 we actually won the European Cup. This team is good, but it can't be as good, can it? They've got to be in Europe for a while, and they've got to win the European Cup. Alex Ferguson has made fantastic strides here and he's going the right way, but whether they are ready I don't know. I don't think they are skilled enough yet.

There's a lot of talent, young talent, which is again the strength of the club. Beckham is a bit like the old Bobby with his shooting. He has the confidence to shoot from 25 and 30 yards, as Bobby had. He's an exciting player. Giggs still has talent to develop. It's there, no question. Keane is a very important player. He's got to curb his enthusiasm just a little bit but not lose any of his game. Like Paddy and Denis, he's very fiery. He's a Celt, just the same. Central defence has been a problem. The nature of the game is changing. Possession is important now. You've got to keep the ball in your own half as well as theirs and help create space. Pallister can do that but his fitness is suspect. You also need people in there who intimidate the opposition.

I'm pleased to see Solskjaer doing so well because I sent a fax to Japan two or three years ago recommending him. I knew him from my time in Norway. He's got loads of talent. He's cunning and an instinctive goalscorer. It's no surprise to see him coming through. But he may need a physical player, a Mark Hughes-type player, to take the weight off him. I think the experience of recent seasons will help them this time. It was our experience that pulled us through. We'd been there so many times we knew how to cope with it.

A few customers have come and gone from the café. Some threw inquisitive glances the way of the big, amiable man cradling the coffee mug. Eventually two members of staff approach him and ask for autographs. He signs them with a gracious smile and great deliberation. 'I think it's nice if people can actually read your name,' he says. 'I got Eric Cantona's autograph for some Japanese people and, to be honest, you couldn't tell what it was. Don't get me wrong, though, they were very pleased.'

It would be difficult to get Bill Foulkes wrong. 'He's like that all the time,' the man behind the counter says as the old cowboy heads back to the ranch. 'He'll talk to anyone but never in a big-headed way, you know? He's very polite, very quiet, really quite shy, you know? And when you think what he's done, what he's gone through for this club, you know?'

6. NOBBY STILES

Born: Manchester, 18-5-42
Debut: v Bolton (a), 1-10-60
United career: Football League – 311 appearances, 17 goals;
FA Cup – 38, 0; Football League Cup – 7, 0; Europe – 36, 2.
Total – 392, 19.

The United side of the '60s conjures all sorts of images: players with elegant strides and explosive shots; players with quicksilver reflexes and predatory instincts; players with incomparable ball control and audacious self-belief; players with inventive compulsions and radar passing. And there is another image, equally vivid, equally enduring, equally significant: the image of a player with menacing fangs and snarling challenges. It is the image that intimidated opponents across the spectrum of the game. It inspired that busload of Benfica fans to dub him 'The Bad One'. And yet that was only half the player, half the image. He read the game like few others and infected everyone with his boundless enthusiasm, capturing the childlike joy of ultimate success with his Wembley jig after England won the World Cup in 1966. That image was revived for a new generation circa Euro '96, but for a certain generation that and the many other images of Nobby Stiles were always in the consciousness.

Stiles was a United man: born, bred, besotted. He was a Collyhurst Catholic, ripe for United's picking. Or at least that is the way folklore would have it. A small, scrawny kid, he learned how to look after himself. Courage and tenacity were essential, not least on a football pitch against much bigger lads. To flourish, rather than merely survive, required still more. It demanded skill and perception. Young Norbert had the mix, which is why he emerged from the throng of hopefuls in schoolboy football to play an integral role for club and country as they accomplished the game's greatest goals.

He was a genuine wing-half, which he effectively confirmed when that traditional position was rendered obsolete. For United he settled into the back four, supporting, covering and sweeping up for the recognised centre-half, Bill Foulkes, with whom he developed a symbiotic relationship. For England he was a 'midfielder', supporting, covering and sweeping up for the recognised creators, who included his club-mate Bobby Charlton. He operated in either job with efficiency and intelligence, breaking up the opposition's attacks and swiftly supplying Charlton and company.

Stiles left United in 1971 for Middlesbrough and began a career in coaching and management at Preston. His new life took him to Canada and West Bromwich before he returned to Old Trafford for four years as Alex Ferguson's youth-team coach. More recently he has rekindled the 'hard man' image for the benefit of insatiable dinner audiences. But with tongue, not boot, firmly in cheek.

* * *

Bill Foulkes's words spring to mind the moment his little partner comes into view. 'Lenses and dentures,' the big man had said, with an affectionate giggle. Off the pitch the lenses always gave way to chunky spectacles, while the dentures filled the gaps on his gums, and here he is now, with familiar large-framed glasses and a smile revealing a full set of ivories. He has three layers of protection against a fresh spring breeze and, not surprisingly, is content to sit out in the open, drawing on a cigarette.

He lives just down the road, barely a hoofed clearance from Old Trafford. 'In fact, we're in the next road to where we lived after we got married,' he says. 'I was 21 then, so this is an area I've known a long time. A lot of the lads went to a pub called the Quadrant, near the cricket ground. If they'd been in for treatment on a Sunday they'd go on there for a game of cribbage or whatever – Maurice Setters, Shay, one or two others. That reminds me, I've got to get that sod [Shay, that is]. He's always giving us these stupid questions and the last time I saw him he asked me, "Who was the chief baddie in *High Noon*?" I went through all the names, all wrong. Anyway, I've got it now, somebody I'd never heard of. I'm telling no one till I get Shay.'

He chats easily, almost cosily. An unassuming grandad and man-next-door, a typical lad from Collyhurst, just the other side of the city centre. Can this be 'The Bad One' from Wembley? He went to St Patrick's School, another institution in United lore, and yet Stiles remembers more Blues than Reds among his pals in those distant, sepia days.

In the playground you always played United–City, and we were outnumbered two to one. It was only a few years after the war, and although United had won the Cup in '48, City had Frank Swift and all those players. They were a big team. In our area your team was passed down to you, generation to generation, father to son, and I was always a United supporter.

Kiddo went to St Pat's as well. I played football with his older brother, Jimmy, who was a year younger than me. His next brother was Bernard. I played cricket with him. I can remember Kiddo as a little kid. He was only tiny and he used to join in with the big lads. He had a lot of go about him.

In the playground the young Reds and Blues would emulate their idols. For young Norbert, that meant the United team led by Johnny Carey.

I remember going in '52 to see them in a League match against Chelsea and Johnny Carey scored one of the most fantastic goals I've ever seen, and they won 6–1. I'll never forget it. At that time there were seven or eight from the 1948 FA Cup side and they won the League in '52. Then Matt said, 'Right, the youngsters are coming in.' It's often said Stein and Shankly were the ones who won things and then changed the team, but Matt did that as well.

In doing so, Busby introduced a new set of heroes to the infatuated Collyhurst schoolboy.

That was the start of the Babes: Duncan Edwards, Eddie Colman, all of those great players. In those days you'd got no television, no videos, so you went to watch them. My idol was Eddie. Snake Hips, he was called. I tried to do some of the little things he did, but I couldn't. That's what we did, though. We went to the games and then came back and tried to copy what we'd seen. For me, as a United fan, to join United was a dream.

And the European games filled impressionable young minds with more fantasies.

One of the greatest nights I've ever known was United playing Bilbao. That night, at Maine Road, was fantastic.

The one I missed, because I was playing that night for the school and couldn't get back in time, was the 10–0 against Anderlecht. So for me, as a Manchester lad, the European Cup was very, very special.

Also as a Manchester lad, he felt the pain of Munich almost as acutely as a family bereavement. Stiles was by then at the club and he recalls the poignant moment when he was instructed to tend to a duty familiar to all groundstaff boys.

We used to clean the boots, and when the skips came back after Munich, the kit caked in mud, Bill Inglis, who was the second-team trainer at the time, said to clean the boots of the lads who had survived. I said if I cleaned them, could I keep Tommy Taylor's. So I put them in my mac, took them home and had them for years. Then I gave them to an old school pal, who became a United scout, and eventually he gave them to the club. They're now in the museum.

Obviously Matt didn't have the base to build on, as he had in '52, so he had to bring in the likes of Noel Cantwell and Maurice Setters, and bring on the younger lads as well. And that's where Jimmy Murphy was so good, not just in that period immediately after Munich. He taught me the game was simple. It took a while to drum it in, but he did. It was so simple you couldn't see it. You were looking to do difficult things which weren't necessary. All the great players knew when to keep it simple. Jimmy was brilliant for me.

Johnny Giles reminded me of what Jimmy taught us some time later when he said Pele would do the simple thing when it was on to do the simple thing, but when he had to perform a miracle he could do that. The point he was making is that it's not all about miracles. The great players can perform them and I don't class myself as one, but Jimmy Murphy didn't tell me what I *couldn't* do, he told me what I *could* do. He told me to play to my strengths, which were winning the ball and giving it early. Five- and ten-yard passes. Bobby couldn't win the ball. I won the ball. But I couldn't do what Bobby did with it. So that's where you get the compromise.

We had great players in the '60s side, Bobby, Denis and George, and when you think about them you think of the

great games they had. But they didn't always have great
games. They couldn't, because week in, week out, they were
being man-marked. That's why we, as a side, would
complement each other. You'd have somebody else turning it
on, like Paddy. At Wembley Johnny Aston was the best
player on the park.

Man-marking was another of Stiles's strengths, a resource harnessed by
club and country with crucial effect. That, however, is not the only role for
which he would like to be remembered.

Everybody says that's what I did, especially on Eusebio, and
of course it's nice that they remember that. But I did that job
only five or six times in my career. The first time I had a
man-marking role as such was in '62, in a Cup semi-final
against Spurs. I marked John White and got the biggest
chasing of my life. They beat us 3–1.

When you are an attacking side you want to join in, and
if you do that it only takes a second for them to destroy you.
So what you've got to do is sacrifice your urge to join in and
attack and have the discipline to say, 'I'm staying with you
wherever you go.' I next did it in '66, against Benfica in the
European Cup, when I marked Eusebio. I did it for England
in the World Cup that summer, against Argentina and
Portugal – again marking Eusebio – and then for United in
'68 against Madrid, on Amancio, and, obviously, in the final.
But these were the only times I played in that role.

With England I played in the middle. At the back, of
course, we had Bobby Moore, the best reader of the game I
ever saw. Mooro was absolutely brilliant. At Old Trafford I
played at the back, alongside Bill Foulkes, who would attack
everything. We had two quick full-backs in Shay and Tony,
and we had a good understanding between us. I was the
reader, slotting people in, talking and whatever. That was the
strength of my game, but people seem to think I was always
a man-marker.

The fact is that I came to Manchester United in 1957,
when all those great young players were there, and you don't
get invited to a place like that if you can't play. So no matter
what people remember, I never underestimated myself. To
me it was a great honour anyway, but to be coming to a club

with the likes of Eddie and Duncan, it has to be because they think you can play a bit.

Stiles's colleagues, to a man, will testify there was more to his game than the terrier-like attention he lavished on Eusebio and the others. They will also concur with his observation that he was a 'talker', although they might argue that is a euphemism for a communicator of a less agreeable nature. Hence the bestowal of the sardonic nickname 'Happy'.

He confesses, 'It was certainly not because I had a nice nature or anything like that. Quite the opposite. I got christened that because they said I was a narky so and so on the pitch, always moaning at my own players. But off the pitch I'm a completely different character, not like that at all. In fact, people say I'm easy-going.'

Eusebio and the other chosen few would doubtless receive that message with a wry smile. Or is that a grimace? The contention that he would not get away with his interpretation of man-marking in today's game provokes a characteristically spirited defence.

> I don't agree with that. People complain now that they've taken tackling out of the game, so what do you want? Bill Foulkes and I were always told, 'Don't let your front man come off you.' If you were playing against Jimmy Greaves or Denis Law and you went diving into them, they'd be off, they'd be round the back of you. You watch Italian football – they don't let forwards come off them. So you had to learn to stand up and know when to tackle. That's the way I played Eusebio, not whack, whack, whack, because he'd see that coming. But tackling at the right moment.
>
> My father used to talk to me about this. When I was young and we watched Johnny Carey playing at right-back, even on the heaviest of pitches, my father would say, 'Watch him go in at the end of the game, never a mark on his shorts.' As he told me, that was because he didn't go down on the ground; he stood up, and that's what tackling is about. I took that in as a small boy. Jack Crompton later told me the same thing about Johnny Carey. He didn't sell himself and go down; it was all about timing the tackle.
>
> When I'm told these days I wouldn't last five minutes it makes me laugh. You would change and adapt to the times anyway, but I think a lot of defenders these days, faced with a one-to-one situation, don't know what to do. They don't

know whether to tackle, whether to hold or what. That's because they're used to playing this tight thing where they're looking for offsides, and so the tackling starts to go. Mind you, I've got to admit, when we look back now at some of the things which they sometimes show on television, my wife says, 'Oof, did you do that? They don't do that now . . .'

The words trail off in a giggle. But can he share the laugh with Eusebio?

Oh, yeah. He was a great player, and he's a lovely, lovely man. A gentleman. He came over for a function Bobby was involved with a few years ago and he was great.

I remember in the final he hit one which whistled just past the post. The thing you couldn't do with Eusebio was let him get set. You had to keep pushing him, pushing him on. He had only a short back lift and he could whack 'em, so you had to keep him going, keep him going; pushing him, pushing him. But obviously he got through that time when Alex made the save.

We'd been attacking – that's Manchester United and Matt, still attacking so close to the end – and Shay had gone forward and was out of position. They broke, with Simoes, to the halfway line. There was me, Eusebio, Torres and Bill. Tony was out wide, with Augusto, I think, and I thought, 'We're in trouble here.' Simoes was very fast and I thought, if he pushes in too far I've got him. As I went for him, Torres made the run out and Bill went with him, as he had to, but I didn't know that at the time. Simoes toe-poked it and I thought Bill was still behind me, but by then he'd gone and Eusebio was right through. Alex made a terrific save.

People talk about how well I marked Eusebio in '66 and '68, but I don't think they would say that if it hadn't been for Alex. He was a great keeper. He never bragged about things; he was never flashy. He was a great keeper to play with because he always knew what he was doing. He told you when he was coming and that was it. To Alex it was just a save.

What Matt said to us before extra-time was more or less what Alf said before extra-time in the World Cup final. He said we'd been playing not to lose the game instead of playing to win it. They both said, 'You've won it once, go out and win it again.' And that meant, 'Keep the ball, don't be trying to hook it into the stands.' Mind you, when Mooro pulled the ball down on his chest Big Jack [Charlton] and I were screaming at him to knock it out. But, of course, he played that great pass and England had won the World Cup. We'd not had that composure in the last ten minutes of either game and I thought it was great for both Alf and Matt to have that coolness in such a situation. I know I couldn't have done it if I was the manager. Matt got us to do it, as Alf had, and I think we did it more for the boss than anything in '68.

At the end of that final against Benfica it was just fantastic. Manchester lad, United fan – and now I'm in the European Cup-winning team. That made it special to me. Very special. The only sad part was the following day. All my life I'd wanted to come back with the Cup in an open coach, through Manchester to the Town Hall. I didn't in '63 when we won the FA Cup because I didn't play in the final. And I couldn't in '68 because I'd gone off with England the next day. That was a big disappointment, missing that. I'd have loved it.

In '69 we should have won it again, and perhaps I would have got my coach ride then. We were unlucky. But I think in a lot of our minds it was a case of, 'Yeah, we've done it.' It was ten years after Munich and we'd done it – the lads who grew up in the club, like Shay, Bill, Bobby and myself – and I think we did, in a way, subconsciously, let down George and the younger lads. I remember George saying in a television interview that should have been just the start for him, and I think he felt let down. At the time I didn't agree with him, but when I look back now I have to say I think he was right.

It was difficult for Wilf to come in but he was very unlucky. To take over from Matt was hard, and yet he got us to several semi-finals in the cup competitions and there's a fine line between that and success. For me it was also a difficult period. I had two cartilage operations, so I was basically looking on at that time.

Stiles left his beloved United in 1971 and joined Middlesbrough, where he would link up with Jack Charlton. Later he was reunited with Bobby Charlton at Preston, and then he became manager at Deepdale. He worked with his brother-in-law, Giles, at Vancouver Whitecaps and West Bromwich Albion, and had been assistant manager, manager and coach at The Hawthorns when, in 1989, Alex Ferguson brought him back to Old Trafford as youth-team coach. In 1993 he left his beloved United a second time.

Inevitably, there were tales of discontent and we were reminded Stiles had not had a testimonial. Whatever his inner thoughts may be, he has no inclination for recrimination now. Life has dealt him a hand he could never have hoped for, making him an unlikely star of the after-dinner circuit. Above all, he has his family and he has his memories.

I don't want to talk about the times I left United, and, in any case, there was no problem the second time. It was good of Alex Ferguson to invite me back in the club and I enjoyed it, working with the kids. I'd been travelling to West Brom all those years so it was nice to be back in Manchester. That period was great. It got me back in touch with people. Now I'm settled again and, touch wood, I've never been happier.

I enjoy doing the after-dinner stuff. I meet so many personalities from other sports. I work with Tommy Smith and Norman Hunter. Tommy's a good pal. We do the 'hard men' thing. Those who know me will tell you I'm not like that, but we have some fun and people seem to get a laugh out of it. I never dreamed I could do anything like this but it just goes to show. I dreamed I would play for United when I was a kid. When I went to the games with my brother and uncle I dreamed that the man announcing the teams over the Tannoy would say, 'And at No. 4, Norbert Stiles.' It's true. In doing that, and winning the European Cup on top of it all, I lived the dream.

But this is something I never imagined doing. People around the country are lovely. They remember me with no teeth, the dance with the World Cup, and say they remember where they were on that day. And all that seems to have passed on to kids and grandkids. When the old clips were shown at the time of Euro '96, kids were asking 'who's he?' and wanting to know all about it. I've got four grandkids and the eldest has begun to pick up on that sort of stuff. He's a United fan, of course. Absolute Red. It was lovely going to Old Trafford for a match with him and my son, three generations of us there. I don't go very often because I'm usually working on a Friday night and don't get back till three or four o'clock in the morning.

I think this team have learned an awful lot from their experiences in Europe, and it is a learning process. We saw how Dortmund were happy with a one-goal lead at home [in the 1996–97 European Cup competition]. Over the years United supporters have come to expect their team to play a certain way; there's a tradition of attacking football. United would rather play for a 5–4 than a 1–0. If United had been 1–0 up at home they'd have been going for another.

But I think United will do it soon. It's a similar situation to the one we had. Matt took United to the semi-finals in '57 and '58 and I believe they would have won it but for Munich because they had learned. But over the next few years Matt made sure we played Real Madrid every year in friendlies because they were the best side in the world. The first year they beat United 5–1 at Old Trafford, the next year in Madrid United lost about 6–3. Next year Madrid came over here and I played. We drew 2–2 after leading 2–0 at half-time. And the next year we went over to Madrid and beat them 2–0. Now we knew we were starting to come of age. And that was because Matt had kept us playing the best.

After five years out of Europe because of Heysel all English clubs have had to catch up, but gradually you get there. We should have won it in '66 – everybody says so – but we missed George. We got there in the end, though, and this team is getting there. There's quality and blend. But you've got to be strong at the back as well. People like Gary Pallister, young Gary Neville and Denis Irwin are very important. Irwin is one of the unsung heroes. Like Tony and Shay. When people talk about the '68 side they don't mention Tony or Shay, but the other players know how important they were.

We won the League in '65 and then again in '67, scoring 100-odd goals, but we conceded only 35. We won a lot of games 1–0. People don't realise that. Tony and Shay were very quick, and gave the ball early and simple to George and the others. To win leagues and trophies you've got to have that strength at the back. We had that – and the rest.

So how does he respond to Peter Schmeichel's proclamation that the '68 side would not live with the present team? With a quip worthy of an accomplished public wit and raconteur: 'He's quite right – but then most of us are well into our fifties!'

Stiles wonders, by way of doubled-edged riposte, whether Schmeichel and his chums have as much fun on their European jaunts as the '60s boys had.

> It seems to me to be a very different scene now. But then we were able to relax and have a drink without having to watch out for the press. In fact, the press lads were often with us. There was that trust. I don't think that's there now. One of the great football writers and characters of the time was Frank McGhee, and he could be a cantankerous so and so when he'd had a drink. He used to rev up Paddy and, well, we all know what Paddy's like. Paddy got up one night and said, 'Right, that's it,' but just as he walked over to Frank to chin him, Frank's head tilted over as if he was fast asleep. Ah, good days.

So are these. The old nickname has become appropriate in a more literal sense. And now he has to go, to pick up one of his grandchildren. He leaves not by car but on foot, heading for the tram. 'Yeah, it's only a couple of stops.' So off he goes, just another grandfather in three layers and large glasses. Somehow you cannot imagine the current players taking the tram. Or some of the other '68 players, come to that.

7. GEORGE BEST

Born: Belfast, 22-5-46
Debut: v West Bromwich Albion (h), 14-9-63
United career: Football League – 361 appearances, 137 goals;
FA Cup – 46, 21; Football League Cup – 25, 9; Europe – 34, 11.
Total – 466, 178.

That 14th day of September, 1963, roused like any other match day in Manchester. The bustle of shoppers and people going about their business fused with the familiar swell of anticipation among those merely marking time before heading for Old Trafford. Those converging on the city's Central Station – since deemed obsolete and then regenerated as the G-Mex exhibition centre – for the short train journey that deposited passengers on the very doorstep of United's ground eagerly checked the early edition of the *Manchester Evening News* for any word on the team to line up against West Bromwich Albion. There was. A 17-year-old from Belfast would be making his debut at outside-right, in place of the injured Ian Moir.

The instant, gut reaction was one of mild dismay. This was the season when United were supposed to be re-establishing themselves as the best in the land. They had just won the FA Cup and now they were back on the trail of the League Championship. That meant fielding a settled, proven side that would instil fear in the opposition. This selection smacked of problems, even panic. Of those dark, confused, indecisive days that were supposed to be consigned to the past. And when he trotted out on to the pitch we were convinced problems, even panic, had set in. The kid was little, skinny and might have been aged 12.

What happened in the following 90 minutes of football depends on your memory, imagination, romanticism or source of information. One of the most distinguished writers of that or any other time, Arthur Hopcroft, considered it one of the two most memorable first appearances he had seen in League football. Others were more sceptical. To many of us standing in the Stretford End Paddock, this was another kid brought in for the ritual try-out. A kid with a few nice tricks but who was not ready yet, and who, like so many before him, might never be ready. He was marked by Graham Williams, the Wales left-back, and given an inevitably uncompromising reception to the grown-up game. In the second half the youngster was mercifully switched to the other wing and played better, though not well enough to figure in the first team for another three months.

The legend, like the boy from Belfast, needed a lot of developing yet. He had arrived in Manchester, the son of a useful amateur footballer and outstanding hockey player, in 1961, only to return immediately to Belfast along with his travelling companion, Eric McMordie, homesick and terrified. Fifteen-year-old Best was persuaded to come back to Old Trafford and give it a go, while McMordie would try his luck at Middlesbrough. Glowing communiqués about Best's talent had preceded him, but here he was, five foot three inches tall, weighing seven stone ten pounds and apparently as timid as a dormouse.

He was entrusted into the care of Mrs Mary Fullaway, a landlady whose name would also pass into Manchester football lore. She and the club fed him and built him up sufficiently to enable his gifts to take their natural course. Busby was one of those who evidently felt his protégé required more time after that baptism against Williams and West Bromwich, and probably had no intention of exposing him to the rigours of a second League game until well into 1964. Then problems, even panic, brought a change of plan.

United were thumped 4–0 at Everton and 6–1 at Burnley over the Christmas period. Best, so far out of contention for a first-team place he had been allowed home for the holiday, was summoned for the return fixture with Burnley on 28 December. Making his debut on the other wing was a 16-year-old called Willie Anderson. The younger winger was terrific, spearing the heart of Burnley's defence with his crosses and corner kicks. The 'senior' partner was a revelation. He destroyed Burnley's defence and scored his first League goal in the 5–1 victory. This was the day we knew something special was happening at Manchester United.

Anderson was one of those who never quite made it in the major league, but Best had arrived and over the following decade would subject United's management, players and supporters to the gamut of emotions. They would be beguiled, inspired, sometimes exasperated and occasionally feel betrayed. But they would never be bored. Best on the ball was an art form, a thing of beauty. His mastery of it was something they had never seen, even at Old

Trafford. Duncan Edwards is immortalised as the greatest, the complete player, his stature sacrosanct. But Best flaunted something else on the senses: the images of a wizard, his willowy frame bending round defenders and over flailing challenges, always balanced, and always with the ball at his command. He was impish, inventive and utterly self-assured. He played to the gallery and he played for the team, scoring goals – 32 in the 1967–68 season – and creating goals and tackling back. He could shoot with either foot and was excellent in the air for a player of his height.

He won Championship medals in 1965 and 1967 and scored the pivotal second goal in the European Cup final, which effectively sealed his European Footballer of the Year award. But perhaps even more memorable and certainly just as defining in his own career was his mesmeric display at Benfica's Stadium of Light in 1966. His two early goals propelled United to an astounding 5–1 victory and had all Europe talking about the 19-year-old 'Beatle'. Best, with floppy dark hair, irresistible smile and a taste for trendy clothes, was a young man of the '60s, projecting a public way of life more familiar among pop stars than footballers. He moved into a futuristic house and dated actresses and beauty queens.

There were, however, voids in his career. He never had the chance to strut on the World Cup stage because the rest of Northern Ireland's team were not up to it, and he never experienced an FA Cup final. Even so, he left his impression on the grand old lady of football competitions by scoring six goals in United's 8–2 victory away to Northampton Town in a fifth-round tie in 1970. During one of his 37 international appearances, against England, he deployed his speed of thought and movement to steal the ball from the great Gordon Banks as it left his hands bound for his boot, and nodded it in the net. The goal did not stand, but the magic did.

Alas, he also left marks of a different kind. He began to make headlines for his drinking, gambling and womanising. And then a new idiom came into the game: 'Best goes missing.' United were falling apart and his disenchantment pushed him over the edge when, at the age of 26, he announced he had quit football. He returned but his halcyon days could not, and he walked out on United for the last time early in 1974. The legend remained a draw for many years thereafter, and he took his one-man show on the road, around Britain – enjoying a particularly acclaimed run with Fulham – Ireland and the United States, where he scored what he considers his greatest goal, and, finally, Australia, in 1983.

His playing days had ended but his penchant for attracting headlines had not. His marriage broke up, he made several visits to clinics and Alcoholics Anonymous in an attempt to beat the booze, he was declared a bankrupt and he served two months in jail after a drink-driving charge accelerated out of control. He failed to turn up for the court hearing, then resisted arrest and was accused of assaulting a police officer.

From that nadir he has made a seemingly remarkable recovery, even if his friends still worry and the sceptics still sneer that he remains susceptible to drink. He has developed an after-dinner and theatre club act, has regular employment with Sky television, promotes a number of business ventures – including his own wine label – and is involved in plans for a film about his life. He is married for the second time and lives in apparent new order and bliss in Chelsea.

* * *

You would expect him to live in Chelsea. Near the King's Road. And you would expect his watering hole to be hip and decorated with long-legged creatures. This part of Chelsea, however, even so close to the King's Road, is not what you would expect. Nor is the watering hole. It is discreet, reserved, unpretentious, unsophisticated. Almost village-like.

He is just another regular, popping into his local. A couple of other regulars nod; a more presumptuous patron greets him with an enthusiastic 'Hi, Georgie boy'. Their salutations are acknowledged politely, though not ostentatiously, and he perches himself on a bar stool. He is wearing black tracksuit bottoms, a black sports shirt and trainers. The long-established beard is greying and he pulls out a pair of glasses to tackle the newspaper. A couple across the bar try to make out what he is drinking. 'Looks like a spritzer,' one says to the other.

The legend is alive and looking well at 51, even if the eyes are not as sharp as they were. He is carrying more weight than he did that night in blue, but not as much as people have made out. And you are soon reminded of what his team-mates and confidants say of him: that he is demure, respectful, friendly. Even vulnerable. He is also a doting husband and father. His wife, Alex, is half his age and by all accounts has taken years off him. Calum, his 16-year-old son by his first marriage, is over from America and dad is as proud as dads should be.

When George Best was 16 he could belittle grown men with a ball at his feet. Clever ball-players landed on the doormat at Old Trafford as regularly as the post, mostly to be discarded like junk mail. This kid was different, and on the training ground and back at Old Trafford, on the tarmac between the stadium and the railway line, where private scores were settled and cocky recruits were cut down to size, his talent ranged beyond their constraint and comprehension.

As Best recalls those days, a flicker of mischief returns in the smile.

I was the new kid on the block and all these other players were big names, internationals. We played at the Cliff or in the car park at the side of Old Trafford, amongst broken glass and bricks and all sorts, and it got a bit tasty. They didn't like it when I nutmegged them, especially Harry Gregg. Harry was crazy, but usually in a nice way. He was such a pro. He'd come through the disaster and then went through a terrible spell with injuries. But even in practice matches Harry was so serious about his game. You didn't score against Harry. You were risking your life if you did.

When it came to the real thing there were obviously doubts about me, but the club realised that with proper training and proper food, living in digs and getting looked after, I was going to get bigger. I never got massive but my legs strengthened. The upper body didn't matter that much. In those days we didn't do weights. It was a worry for me, wondering whether I could make it at this great club with all these other lads.

Busby, wrestling with a few injury problems early in that 1963–64 season, decided to gauge the development of the skinny kid from Belfast in the home match against West Bromwich Albion, coincidentally also the opposition when Denis Law had made his debut for United a year earlier.

It was a test all right. I was up against Graham Williams, the Welsh international full-back. Off the pitch he's the nicest bloke you'd ever want to meet. I've bumped into him many times over the years and he's a lovely man. But when you were out on the pitch playing against him you knew you'd better realise there were no prisoners taken. That was my introduction to the First Division. He gave me a couple of smacks and dear old Sir Matt moved me over to the other wing in the second half to get away from him. Funnily enough, I made my international debut against Graham, as well.

To be honest, I didn't find it any more difficult playing in the first team than in the reserves, but then I didn't play that many reserve-team games. I played mainly in the A and B teams. After that first-team game in the September I was back in the junior teams. I was actually at home in Belfast that Christmas when they called me. They'd just been to

Burnley and got stuffed well and truly, and they sent a telegram asking me to come back. I told them I wanted to be back home in Belfast after the game, and they booked me the flight. So I played the game, we beat them 5–1, I got my first goal and that was it. I was in the side for ten years.

It sounds so simple. To Best it was, at that stage of his life. He had made a natural progression from the streets of Belfast to the glass- and brick-strewn initiation ceremonies at Old Trafford to the grand stage of English football. He represented a fresh, invigorating and successful period at United.

Other kids were coming along as well. People like Willie Anderson, who was younger than me. He was 16 when he first played. He was on one wing, I was on the other, and there was a lot of controversy about playing two young kids. I remember a Cup tie at Southampton, who had a good side. We both played in that game and we won 3–2. We were a bonus for the boss because he had so many top players and it was developing into a terrific side again. He had Bobby, Denis, Paddy and Bill. Noel Cantwell was the captain, and he had Shay and Tony, Maurice Setters and Nobby. Then later came Alex Stepney.

To achieve fame and distinction at home is one thing; to bewitch Europe is quite another. Best accomplished that second feat in 90 of the most memorable minutes in football. United arrived at the Stadium of Light in March 1966 with a fragile 3–2 lead over Benfica in the quarter-final of the European Cup. Busby, for all his reputation as the unsullied purist, was pragmatic enough to demand containment in the early stages, to frustrate their opponents and turn down the volume of the towering stands. As Nobby Stiles would say, 'Nobody told George what the plan was.' Best scored twice in an extraordinary opening burst and the strategy of containment was rendered redundant. United were on an irresistible course to a 5–1 victory. Best recalls,

Domestically I was starting to do it, but the big thing, especially for this club, was always Europe. Benfica had never lost at home in Europe. They had almost a full team of international players. But we went there and produced an unbelievable performance. I've always thought the two club

teams closest to perfection were the great Real Madrid of the
late '50s and 1960, and the Tottenham side of 1960–61. But
I think that night we got as close to perfection as you can get.
We played a terrific side and absolutely demolished them. It
could have been more. I think we had a goal disallowed in
the first half, when John Connelly scored.

United had a place in the semi-finals of the European Cup, and George
Best had a place in the consciousness of a world beyond the white markings
of a football pitch. Overnight, this lean young man with the dark, floppy
hair, pictured returning to Manchester wearing a sombrero, was 'El Beatle'.
Iberian tongues may have been crossed, but no matter. It was a great
headline and Georgie, the Belfast boy, was no longer merely a footballer.

The El Beatle thing actually makes me smile, because when
you look back, my hair wasn't that long. But for those days
it was, of course, and it was the time of the Beatles, so that
was it. I was just a kid, enjoying myself. I was 19 and I was
getting paid for doing something I loved doing. I'd have
played for nothing. But I was able to buy nice clothes and I
could afford nice cars when most of my pals couldn't. I was
into music because that was just massive in the North.
Fashion was changing. Hippies were coming in. Everything
in that period was just special.

Football was the thing for me above all else, but I realised
something different was going on when I came back from
Lisbon. I bought a sombrero for a friend and wore it as we
came off the plane, for a bit of a laugh. Pictures of me
wearing the sombrero actually appeared on the front page as
well as the back page of a national newspaper. Footballers
just didn't appear on the front page. Not in those days. It just
snowballed after that and the next few years were terrific.

For a few years, too, he seemed able to balance his football with his
celebrity status, the boutiques, the personal appearances and the glamorous
girlfriends. He had an agent to handle his business affairs and secretaries to
deal with the daily mountain of fan mail. On the field, he could take care
of himself.

Best's performance in the Stadium of Light was perhaps too dazzling for
his and the team's good. Busby risked him in the first leg of the semi-final,
away to Partizan Belgrade, despite a knee problem. Their relatively

unknown and generally unfancied opponents won 2–0. Best missed the second leg – and the rest of the season – and Stiles's late goal was not enough. Another Championship, however, gave them another chance in 1967–68.

> Although I got a goal in the home leg against Real Madrid it was going to be hard over there, and sure enough we were 3–1 down at half-time and it might have been all over. I'd been marked closely and hadn't really done much. But a fortunate goal got us back in it and then, after one of the few times I got past the full-back, I knocked it back to this red shirt. When I realised it was Foulksey I thought, 'Oh, no.' But he didn't half stick it away. It was unbelievable.

But Bill says he couldn't have missed. Best stifles his guffaw to respond.

> He had a lot of choices. He could have stopped it, he could have walloped it. Instead he side-footed it in. It was brilliant. At 3–3 we knew it was ours.
>
> I think we might have relaxed a little too much after Madrid, because that was some result. There was a danger of thinking we'd already won the final. We'd beaten Benfica twice two years previously and the final was virtually a home match for us. Nobody said publicly that we thought it was all over, but we did think we couldn't really lose this one. In the end, the script couldn't have been written better.
>
> I don't remember anything about where we stayed before the final or what happened afterwards [it can be safely assumed he had a good night], but the two hours of the match I can see almost perfectly. I do remember I just couldn't wait to get out there. I've never been superstitious about anything, so playing all in blue didn't worry me. I was never physically sick before, during or after a game. I loved it so much, I suppose I was able to take it in my stride. It didn't matter if it was a five-a-side, an international in front of 120,000 or a European Cup final.
>
> Shay Brennan insists he made my goal. He passed it back to Alex, who cleared it. Brian Kidd flicked it on and then I stuck it through the legs of the centre-half, who was the last defender. I get a bit annoyed when I see the goal now because they only show the end of it, never the whole of it. There was

a bit of work to do, especially sticking it through his legs. Then the keeper came out. I always dreamt that if I was in a position to do it, I was going to stop the ball on the line and head it in. But the keeper was a bit too sharp, so I thought I'd better not risk it. Kiddo and Bobby finished it off in style.

Sir Matt realised his dream that night but, remember, we had a pretty special side over a number of years, and the more successful you are the tougher it becomes. Every week was a battle for us because we were Manchester United and everybody wanted to beat us. That made the job even harder for Matt.

You just had to see the respect people had for him to realise how special he was. He knew how to get the best out of his players. He was always paying us compliments. He'd tell me I was the best tackler in the club. Coming from him that was brilliant. He gave you such a lift. But he knew how to bring you down to earth as well. He didn't call you in to his office and tell you that you were dropped, he'd call you in and ask you, 'How do you think you're playing?' You would have to say, 'Not very well, boss.' After that you had to be dropped. And that was the way he did it.

He was like a father to me. Remember, I left home at 15 and this great man treated me as if I was a son. When I was going through hard times he never lectured me. He talked to me. I came back from Spain in 1972, after announcing I was retiring, with a thrombosis, and he was the first person to come and see me in hospital. He stayed for about 20 minutes, we talked about old times, and as he walked out of the door he popped his head back in and just said, 'Don't you think it's about time you were back playing?' And that was it. He was no longer the manager, but he was still the Great Man.

The trouble was, it was never going to be the same. Those ten years were just magic, but the King was no longer on the throne. The fact that the club went into the Second Division just six years after being the best in Europe was a disgrace. It doesn't matter that they came straight back up.

We all know what should have happened. The team should have been strengthened before it was too late. But the club signed a lot of players who weren't good enough. It was as simple as that. I was still quite young. If I was lucky I had another seven or eight years. At first I didn't think there was extra pressure on me after Wembley, but there was. I was coming back to the dressing room after getting stuffed by teams who a couple of years earlier couldn't have lived with us.

It was like revolving doors with the different managers. Some would come in and hardly say two words to anyone and they were gone [an obvious allusion to Frank O'Farrell]. And some of the team-sheets! Some of the players who were putting on the red shirt . . . well, it was an insult to the great players who'd worn it in the past. When you think of Bobby and Denis, Paddy and Nobby, and, yes, me, there's no comparison. Good players could and would have signed for the club. Mike England and Alan Ball were two who should have joined us. There weren't too many players who didn't want to sign for Manchester United. In that respect the fans were let down.

I'll probably never know whether that pressure on me led to my problems. Nobody will ever know. But I knew one thing: that something I loved more than anything apart from my family had been taken away from me. It was something I'd been doing since I was a year old and the only thing I'd ever wanted to do. And all of a sudden it had been taken away from me.

As we shall hear from Bobby Charlton, he felt Best let down the fans and his colleagues when he went missing in those later years. Some observers maintained the differences between the two men extended to disdain and even jealousy. Best sees it differently.

I never let anyone down on the field. That's one thing no one can say against me. I suppose I can understand the accusation that I let down my team-mates in terms of training, but I would go back and train in the afternoon with Bill Foulkes and Paddy Crerand. I was top scorer in the League for five years in a row, playing on the wing. That's hardly letting them down.

I've never felt people were jealous of me. Not then, not today. I see Bobby now regularly and we get on great. We were just different characters. He was a real family man. After training he'd be off to his family, whereas I went with the lads

123

for a game of snooker, and at night maybe had a few drinks. Sometimes we'd lay a few bets. Bobby was different, that's all. But on the field, we were part of the same team and we wanted the same thing, which was success for the club we both loved. And still do.

Denis has the same feeling, but is a different character from Bobby as well. I'm a different character from Denis, though probably closer than Bobby is. If you've got a squad of 15 or 16 players, you are going to get differences of character, differences of opinion and fall-outs. We had some punch-ups in training and rucks and arguments. But it's forgotten as soon as training's finished and you get on with things. And come the Saturday, we all did the business.

David Sadler was my room-mate, a really quiet lad who kept himself to himself, and we got on well together. I was also shy and quiet – but I came out of it a bit later! David's never changed. He's the same today. Different class. He's always sending me messages about old boys' get-togethers. I try to get up when I can. Denis and Shay became two of my best friends later. Our relationships developed after we finished playing, really after I came back from the States, in '81. Since then the three of us have become very close, regularly seeing each other in twos or threes.

We had a team get-together for the 25th anniversary of the final and it was very special, because they can't take away from any of us what we achieved in '68. Some players have maybe fallen out with the club, for whatever reason, and some maybe aren't seen as regularly as others, but there is still that feeling within the team. And when we sat down together to watch a rerun of the final, I think some of us realised we'd forgotten how good we were. Some of the football was fabulous, and you could see the confidence running through the whole team.

We never went out believing we were going to lose, home or away. When we won the Championship in '67 we went to West Ham and knew we could finish it there. But they were a terrific side. It didn't matter. We went to Upton Park and stuffed them 6–1. That's some way to do it. Other teams would have gone there and had their backs to the wall. We just thrashed them.

By 1972 the days of virtuoso football had gone. United were the team on the wrong end of thrashings. Best quit, then returned; then the club announced there was no future for him at Old Trafford and Tommy Docherty succeeded Frank O'Farrell as manager. Desperate for a spark of inspiration to ignite his fading team, Docherty sanctioned another comeback by the Ulsterman and Crerand brokered the deal. Even 75 per cent of Best, even in a more withdrawn role, had to be better than most of the rest had to offer. He played a dozen games, the last on New Year's Day 1974, a 3–0 defeat at Queen's Park Rangers. Four days later Docherty dropped him for the third-round FA Cup tie against Plymouth Argyle at Old Trafford and Best walked out on United for the final time.

Best gives his version of the closing scene.

> There were stories that I had hit the booze again that weekend, but I had not. Those stories are always going to come along. The Doc had said to me that if I ever missed training, for whatever reason, it would be kept quiet. I'd take my punishment and do extra training. And I'd been training really hard, doing extra work with Paddy and Bill. I think we'd played Spurs the week before and I'd scored, and it was the first time I felt I was getting there. I was starting to get past players and away from them.
>
> On the Wednesday I went out with some friends and had a late night, and I missed training on Thursday morning. So I came in Thursday afternoon. I came in on the Friday morning and trained, and nobody said anything to me. I turned up on Saturday with the rest of the boys and the Doc took me in the referee's room with Paddy. He said, 'I'm leaving you out today because you missed training Thursday morning.' That was it. I said to myself, 'If I can't play today, it's over.'
>
> What might have happened after that we'll never know. But I don't regret walking out because I realised it wasn't going to work. I'd worked my socks off to get back into it, and I still wasn't happy about the team and the sort of players that were playing. So I think it was just a matter of time anyway. I just figured it would be best for all concerned to do it there and then.
>
> Even to this day I sit and wonder whether it really was the best thing to do. It was like being with a woman you loved, knowing it was going to end sooner or later. It was probably braver to make that decision sooner rather than let things

carry on. I couldn't have achieved any more at Manchester United, the team being as it was. And after those fabulous years, when we won everything, I didn't want this. And anything after United would have been second best. I didn't want second best.

I could have gone to another club and started anew. I had a lot of offers. I could have gone abroad. There was talk about Chelsea, which might have been a good move for me. In London. Then again, that might have been the worst move I could have made! But the bottom line was I didn't want to play for anybody else. So the next few years I was a maverick, and I played everywhere in the world.

His wanderings took him to some unlikely watering holes: Dunstable, Stockport and Bournemouth, to name but three. He revived the soul with a cameo spell at Fulham, teaming up with fellow showman Rodney Marsh and Bobby Moore. He maintains he performed his real show-stopper, however, playing for San Jose Earthquakes in 1980. 'Yeah, I enjoyed that, going round five players and sticking it in. When you score a goal like that it's a bit special, no matter where you're playing.'

Best always had a yearning for that special something and he weaned his public on to the drug. He remembers how, as a youngster, he was mesmerised, along with Sheffield Wednesday's exceptional goalkeeper Ron Springett, by Pele's penalty for Santos in a friendly at Hillsborough.

He dummied three or four times and the poor keeper was just bewildered, rooted to his line, as Pele eventually smacked it in. Pele made ten the magic number, and since then it's been a symbol for some of the great players – Platini, Zico, Maradona – and, I must say, I enjoyed the game I played with it on my back. Yeah, that has to be the number to have. I've been eight, but, of course, more often seven, which I had in the final, and 11. I suppose really I think of myself as 11 and my son wants 11 on his shirt.

Unlike Pele and the rest, as well as several club colleagues, Best never had the opportunity to demonstrate his talent on the World Cup stage, but he maintains,

I don't really regret that, because dear old Northern Ireland were never going to make an impact at that level. Sure, I'd love to have played with a great team, with ten Brazilians, but we were never going to have a great team.

As his football prowess ebbed, the booze flowed evermore freely. Best was in a twilight zone and in danger of being sucked into eternal darkness. That he has emerged in daylight seems a minor miracle. He has learned his lessons the hard way, yet appears none the harder for the experience. Cynicism has mercifully passed him by. He is simply grateful to be able to tell the tale.

I have to be thankful for the way I've ended up. When you consider what I've been through, I've got to consider myself lucky. I've been in prison, I've been in clinics, I've been treated three or four times for alcoholism, I've been bankrupt and I've had car crashes, fights and all sorts of dramas with women. And yet I couldn't be happier than I am today. I go to bed at night and I sleep. For years I couldn't. I'd got that many things going round in my head.

My life is under control now. Brilliant. Totally different from when I came back here from the States in '81. Calum was a year old, I was getting divorced and I'd had to leave him over there while I came here to get things sorted out. Today it's a nice family and Calum is over here with us for a while. I say to my wife, Alex, 'Isn't it nice we don't have a nine-to-five working life?' We don't know from one day to the next what we're going to be doing, but there's always plenty for us to do.

For the past three or four years I've been working with Sky. I'm on the after-dinner circuit, although I cut down on that a bit because I was doing too much. I do some with Rodney, some with Denis and quite a few on my own. I'm involved with a few companies and businesses, basically to make personal appearances, and there's a movie in the pipeline. It's really my life story and it looks like it could be a biggie.

One of the places I got involved in was Bobby Keetch's 'Football, Football' restaurant, in London. Poor Bobby died not long after it opened and I was supposed to speak at a memorial dinner organised as a tribute to him. I was actually going to read a letter he wrote me just before he died but I freaked out. I couldn't do it. I had to get Marshy to read it.

Keetchie's death, and Bobby Moore's, not so long ago, have made me think a lot about myself. I was the one who had all the problems, I was the one who wasn't supposed to be around much longer, and yet I'm still here, feeling as fit as a fiddle. A lovely old doctor did some tests on me and said he must have got them mixed up with somebody else's because as far as he could see there was nothing wrong with me. I don't do any sport now because one of my knees is really bad, and I have my circulation checked following the thrombosis. I go to a health farm about four times a year, just to relax, and I feel great.

I'm thankful because I think I'm lucky. I'm travelling the world first-class, I stay in the best hotels, all paid for. I'm married to a beautiful lady and I'm madly in love. And I've got a terrific son. And you know what's really nice? That despite all the trouble I've been in and the scrapes I've had and all the bad publicity, people remember me above all as George Best the footballer. That's lovely.

I took Calum to 'Football, Football' for lunch and there must have been 50 or 60 kids who came up and asked for my autograph. I've spent three hours signing autographs in New Zealand and even then had to be dragged away. Sometimes on the theatre tours I'm amazed how many youngsters are in the audience. I haven't kicked a ball at top level for 25 years, but they know about George Best the footballer.

There was a time when being George Best meant a lot of hassle. About 50 per cent of the time, in fact. Now it's maybe 10 per cent. I tend to have regular haunts, where I know I'm going to be looked after. You still get the odd idiot and that's never going to change. I don't know whether I'm getting smarter or just too old to fight, but I tend to walk away from it now, whereas a few years ago I wouldn't have done. I was up at the local pub for some charity do and this guy wanted to be Jack the Lad. He's with half a dozen of his mates, all having a few drinks, and he starts effing and blinding. I'm there with my wife and in-laws and I'm tempted to walk over and smack him in the mouth. But that's probably what they want, and then, of course, they're the first to complain and it's 'George Best in brawl again'. Unfortunately that's how certain people look on you, but the kids don't.

You can imagine what Alex's mum and dad said when she

told them about me. She's half my age and they've heard all these stories about me. But I went to meet them and we've become good friends. When her mum said to me, 'I've never seen my daughter happier,' it made me feel pretty good about life. My relationship with Calum is great. He's football-daft. A United fan, of course. The team he plays for have just won their championship. He fancies a career in the game, but he'd need to live here. He's got an American accent but hates to be called an American. He says he's half Irish and half Scottish, because his mum's got a Scottish background.

The doting father has arranged time off from his Sky commitments to take his son to a match at Old Trafford, the first of two trips to his old club in three days. He explains,

We've got a box organised at the game against Coventry and we're getting there nice and early so Calum can go to the megastore. I've also got to go up there to interview Alex Ferguson for Sky. This is a bit of a first for me and I'm looking forward to it. Fergie's done a terrific job, no question about that.

You've got to say this team does compare with ours, except in one important respect. They haven't won the biggie, and until they do the comparisons are only words. Cantona was the one who brought back the style and flair, and I think every team at this level needs a genius, with ten good players around him. What he's left behind is the confidence, and you can see that in the kids. We had that with kids like Kiddo and Johnny Aston coming in. They have that same feeling that they're not going to lose. Domestically they are the side to beat, and they should have got to the European Cup final last season. But that's where they've got to do it.

Having said that, the European Cup's not really the European Cup any more. It's not the Champions' Cup it used to be. I think it has been devalued by allowing runner-up teams into it, but at least United did qualify as champions.

Best would be similarly resistant to change in his own life. He is adamant, in fact.

I wouldn't change anything, because although I have had bad times, the good times outweighed them. I had those fabulous years in the game, which the older fans remember and the younger ones can see on video, and I've certainly no complaints about my life now. I have to smile when people talk about 'poor old George'. I wouldn't swap places with anyone.

The respect people show me means everything. When I go to Old Trafford I always get respect, even from the present players. I went to Coventry to kick off the celebrity game at David Busst's benefit and Peter Schmeichel, who was warming up for the main match, came sprinting over to me. He shook hands and said he wanted me to know that business about the present team walloping our team 10–0 or something was all a load of rubbish. The thing is we did it – and you have to respect that.

8. BRIAN KIDD

Born: Manchester, 29-5-49

Debut: v Everton (a), 19-8-67

United career: Football League – 195 (8) appearances, 52 goals;

FA Cup – 24 (1), 8; Football League Cup – 20, 7; Europe – 16, 3.

Total – 255 (9), 70.

If Busby's story was the main theme of the fairytale, there was also a sub-plot to intrigue the romantic: local boy, United fan, called up to the first team at the start of the 1967–68 season and, on his 19th birthday, scores in the European Cup final victory. And, by way of a further sentimental twist, he is back at Old Trafford today, assisting Alex Ferguson's endeavours to reclaim the club's position as the continent's No. 1. Brian Kidd, like his original manager, has his heaven right here.

As a youngster raised in a Catholic family in Collyhurst, Kidd followed Stiles to St Patrick's School and developed the same devotion to United. At the time of the crash, however, he was only eight and his heroes would be those of the next generation. Of Stiles's early teams. His idol was Denis Law, so imagine the pride stirring inside Kidd when a fan ran on to the pitch and 'crowned' him the new King in succession to the Scot.

Kiddo had been in dreamland since joining the United fold as a schoolboy. Two years on he was an apprentice and beginning his rapid progress through the junior ranks. When the 1967 Championship-winning side went on tour to Australia, Busby added Kidd to the squad. He needed a replacement for David Herd, who was recovering from a broken leg, and had been impressed with the youngster's performances for the reserves. Like Herd, Kidd possessed a venomous shot. He was particularly strong on his left side but the right foot was no mere 'swinger'. He was big enough to be a physical handful yet mobile enough to exploit exceptional close control.

Kidd returned from the trip with his graduation certificate. He played in the Charity Shield game against Tottenham Hotspur and made his League debut the following week. He appeared in 38 of United's First Division matches that season, scoring 15 goals. He also played in all nine European Cup games, culminating with the Wembley final and that birthday goal.

He was unfortunate his arrival coincided with the erosion of the great '60s team. Like Best, he was blossoming as others were wilting. The years of turmoil can scarcely have eased his development, and yet his powerful displays devastated opponents and captivated subjects yearning for their next King. It was a short reign. There was no future for the old monarchy in Tommy Docherty's republic and Kidd left relegated United for Arsenal in the summer of 1974 in a £110,000 transfer.

The move resuscitated Kidd's career but he seized the opportunity, two years later, to come home. Home to Manchester, anyway. He had to withstand some ribbing from his old pals when he signed for City, as well as a few scrapes with the authorities. The seemingly shy, humble demeanour hid a wicked inclination to mischief and a sharp temper. He joined another major club, Everton, before completing his regular playing career in England with Bolton Wanderers. Considering the stature of his employers it is perhaps surprising his only club honour was that European Cup winner's medal. He won his two full England caps – after international Youth and Under-23 appearances – as a United player.

Kidd followed the trail of the prospectors to America, panning for gold in Atlanta, Fort Lauderdale and Minnesota, before trying his hand at management with Barrow, Swindon and Preston as first or second in command. But he remained a Manchester boy at heart – a United boy, in fact – and he revelled in the opportunity to forge links between the club and the community and to activate Ferguson's desire to bring the best of the local talent to Old Trafford. Kidd's work with the School of Excellence and as youth development officer convinced the manager he had the ideal No. 2 on his doorstep.

* * *

Less than 45 minutes to kick-off and the bars and kiosks inside the stadium are humming to the familiar tune of brisk business. The moment the customer is released from the turnstile into the concrete cavern beneath the stands, he or she is assailed by earnest invitations to buy half-time draw tickets. Programmes are sold by the bunch. 'Must take one home for little Jimmy. Oh, and I bet your Fred would like one.' Groups gather to sip from plastic cups, master the art of excavating a pie from its container one-handed and listen out for team news. Few have yet taken their seats. Early arrivals in the top tier of the new stand (what time did they set off?) are distant specks.

Down on the pitch, however, there is activity already. Peter Schmeichel, the United goalkeeper, has begun his warm-up routine in front of the old Stretford End, fielding short-range shots from a man once hailed in these quarters as 'King Brian'. Today Kidd is slightly chunkier, but he still has a good head of hair and those boyish features, and that trusty left foot looks as lethal as ever. The right one is still no mere swinger, either. Schmeichel asks for crosses and the assistant manager obliges. From left and right, they stretch the magnificent Dane, who has been given the captaincy in the absence of the injured Roy Keane.

We have a delicious irony here. It was Schmeichel who told the press his team would have demolished Kidd's European Cup-winning team. It was later dismissed as a tongue-in-cheek, throwaway, not-to-be-taken-seriously wind-up. But rivalries cross the generation time zones, and here are two fiercely proud and competitive characters. Should we discern a little extra venom in Kidd's shots now? And a steely determination by the goalkeeper to defy him? After 20 minutes of entertaining sparring Schmeichel is satisfied, and they conclude the session with a ritual handshake. Schmeichel, whose stature here has grown in every sense, leans over the perimeter fencing and gives his gloves to a thrilled youngster, then walks back towards the dressing room accompanied by warm applause.

Kidd now turns his attention to the other players, who are into their final preparations: stretching, sprinting, juggling, passing. Kidd is joined in the arc of the penalty area by an apparently self-appointed lieutenant, Brian McClair, and together they supervise the mosaic of moving patterns. There is an air of confidence and control, as you might expect from players who have just won a third consecutive match in the Champions League. The flicks, tricks and smiles are those of young men utterly sure of their course. Giggs and Beckham, the crown princes, trot out together, sprint together, laugh together. Kidd, an earlier product of the United nursery and symbol of the club's faith in youth, maintains a paternal watch, occasionally reaching out a guiding hand.

For all it is an easy, happy atmosphere, but this is another day at the office and Kidd ensures they go about their business. At 2.45 he winds up this part of the proceedings and herds the players back up the canvas-covered tunnel, conveniently positioned at this end of the ground. He, too, looks content and relaxed, proffering a thumbs-up sign and wave aimed in the direction of the players' and staff guests' enclosure. In a few minutes Kidd will re-emerge and take his place alongside Ferguson on their pitchside platform, and hope he is still content and relaxed after the game against Barnsley.

Kidd has not always been able to hold station on the sidelines. One of the abiding images of him is his delirious celebration when Steve Bruce plundered a crucial and improbable victory against Sheffield Wednesday in 1993 with a goal some six minutes into stoppage time. Kidd leapt into the air, then sank to his knees, fists clenched, paying homage to the One responsible for divine deliverance. Manchester United were never merely a football club to Kidd, and in moments of extreme emotion he was never afraid to show it.

As a player his passionate reactions sometimes brought him into conflict with the game's officials and authorities, but it was usually the tantrums of childlike innocence rather than premeditated cynicism. Kidd by name . . . And yet, when he was entrusted, at the age of 18, with a man's job, he responded with a stoicism and maturity even Busby cannot have anticipated.

Herd's injury in 1967 appeared to have secured David Sadler a permanent place in the attack, but by the start of the new season Busby's perspective had changed. Sadler's versatility had provided new options. If anything he was a better player in midfield or at the heart of the defence. And, in any case, the young boy Kidd was looking the part. He would be given his chance in a forward line that also comprised Best, Law, Charlton and Aston. It is a measure of how well he took the chance that he woke up on the morning of his 19th birthday contemplating the European Cup final.

By then his more experienced and renowned colleagues had come to admire his talent and muse at his taste for mischief. As David Coleman recalls, he found ready-made material in the Stiles family trade. It was Collyhurst Jack the Lad humour, a chattering Mancunian parody. He would always play the humble, self-deprecating boy-next-door role for public consumption, but here was a young man not out of place with Manchester United and not out of place at club football's showpiece event. He tells the story in an accent as authentically Manc as it ever was.

> It was my first season in the first team, and to be involved in the European Cup final, I don't think anything could have topped that. You had every type in that team. Bobby, so graceful. Bestie had everything, so explosive. Paddy, what a passer of the ball. You go to Tony Dunne, who for me was the best full-back in Europe that season. Bill Foulkes, who'd seen it all and what a great servant he had been to the club.

You go through to Johnny Aston and myself, the local lads. It must have been nice for John because his dad was youth-team coach here. We'd Dave Sadler coming in as well; he was a young lad. Nobby, again, we went to the same school, St Patrick's, Collyhurst, so it was another double, two lads from the same school playing in the European Cup final. And then Shay and Alex. It was a really nice mixture of talents.

With the great players in the team we had, nobody from Benfica was worried about me. My marker wasn't. He didn't kick me as hard as I expected! I remember reading in the *Daily Express* about Eusebio saying, 'Who's Kidd?' So obviously nobody knew me. I was only an 18-year-old that season and nobody was really worried about me.

Equally obvious was his relishing the opportunity to introduce himself. He had no doubts about his value to the team. He had held his place on merit and, for all the politically correct tributes to the 'great players' around him, he felt comfortable in their company. By the end of the long evening the Portuguese had been made aware they ought to have done their homework on the other lad from Collyhurst. Kidd not only headed his birthday goal but also played supporting roles for United's second and fourth.

Because I'd played all that season it really wasn't as much of an ordeal being the youngest member of the side as some might imagine. It probably seemed odd to see us in our blue away kit when they were in white, but as we both usually played in red we both agreed to change, which seemed fair. The 90 minutes was really a non-event. It was only the first 15 minutes of extra-time when it came to life. We possibly lost our way near to winning the game. We were 1–0 up and really, subconsciously, we tried to protect it. Obviously it didn't work out that way but we were never going to be short of legs.

Memories of my goal are vivid. It was pretty straightforward. It came from a corner and I got a double header in. A lot of people think I hit the bar with my first header but I didn't. Henrique, the keeper, made a save and it came back out. I just lobbed it over his head. It was a soft head, really; I can see it now, just going over his head into the back of the net. Then I was away and running, like the greyhounds round Wembley. No one could catch me. Because, obviously, I couldn't believe it. It was a dream come true.

At 3–1 it just gave us that bit of a buffer. And then Bobby went on to get the fourth goal, which I was involved in on the right wing. My right leg was for standing on, but I could see the defender coming in to kick me and I just managed to kick it past him and go down the right wing. I didn't hit it well but you don't have to with Bobby. Hell of a strike. Rifled it in.

We had the reception back at the Russell Hotel, with Joe Loss and his orchestra. Joe Loss presented me with a birthday cake. That was nice. My mum and dad were there. Three or four of the lads were emotionally drained. I think it had all come to a head for them. To be honest it was a bit of an anti-climax, but for a local boy it was still a wonderful experience.

Like Best and the other young players, he anticipated many more wonderful experiences with United. The scoring touch deserted him the following season – he managed only one League goal in 28 starts, and that in the 8–1 thrashing of Queens Park Rangers – but he was more productive in 1969–70. He also felt inclined to be more assertive and when, midway through 1970–71, Wilf McGuinness was sacked, the Kidd from Collyhurst angrily turned on his illustrious team-mates, accusing them of letting down their manager and precipitating his demise.

Supporters warmed to the local boy's commitment and loyalty. He was one of their own, a surrogate wearer of the red for each and every one of them. To Kidd passed Law's crown. Alas for Kidd, and United, he was not as prolific a goalscorer as the Scot. He was capable of spectacular strikes, the type Law admits he was incapable of. But not the quantity of goals the old King delivered; the scraps and six-yard stuff the great goalscorers fed off.

United were relegated to the Second Division at the end of the 1973–74 season but Kidd did not go down with them. Instead he went south, to Arsenal. He talked of the wrench leaving his club, yet accepted he did not figure in Docherty's plans. The new environment invigorated Kidd, but the chance of a return to his roots was irresistible, even if it meant wearing the sky blue of City. The Maine Road fans made him feel at home, especially when he became their top scorer. He helped them to second place in the 1976–77 First Division Championship. There were, however, bouts of frustration and brushes with opponents and referees. 'You know me,' he would plead with that wide-eyed local-boy-misunderstood-and-picked-on expression. 'I'd never kick anybody.'

He had almost three seasons with City before moving on to Everton, and from there to Bolton. After the then regulation sample of football Stateside he came back to England to mould a career in coaching and management, although he never envisaged circumstances conveying him to the No. 2 job at Old Trafford. Kidd went back to the family circle as community officer and extended his influence to luring youngsters to the club and coaching. City's scouting and coaching system had outmanoeuvred United in the area and even Oldham were having more success with the local talent. Kidd's name, enthusiasm and dedication were hugely instrumental in changing the trend. Many of his discoveries have made it all the way to the first team.

Ferguson had seen enough in Kidd's work to be assured the 'United man through and through' should become his assistant in August 1991. Kidd reluctantly accepted the promotion, but since then United have won the Championship four times and been runners-up twice. They have also twice completed the League and FA Cup double. Ferguson has no doubt about Kidd's contribution: 'He's been fantastic for this club. His heart's in the club but also he's dedicated to the job he's doing. He's loyal to me, and his commitment to the players is great. His training sessions are excellent. He takes a lot of care and consideration over his training.'

Kidd has formulated those training sessions after scrutinising methods used by leading clubs in Europe. His brief also includes monitoring possible transfer targets on the Continent and beyond, and future opponents in European competition. His assistance to Ferguson has encompassed extra-curricular duties, such as dragging the volatile Scot away from confrontations and potential trouble with referees, and keeping the boss's feet on the ground with a few well-chosen wind-ups about European Cup glory. Little wonder Ferguson has resisted overtures from other clubs – notably City – for Kidd's services as manager. Ferguson has indicated that when he stands down, the club would have to look no further for the perfect replacement.

Kidd himself is adamant he has never encouraged such approaches and that he never wants to leave Old Trafford for another club. As No. 2 at United he has the emotional attachment, the satisfaction, and none of the media attention a No. 1 must endure. He remains, for public consumption, the humble, self-deprecating boy from Collyhurst, happy and grateful for his role and his life.

At the end of the match against Barnsley he is palpably still content and relaxed, making his way back towards the tunnel. United have won 7–0.

9. BOBBY CHARLTON

Born: Ashington, 11-10-37
Debut: v Charlton Athletic (h), 6-10-56
United career: Football League – 604 (2) appearances, 199 goals;
FA Cup – 79, 19; Football League Cup – 24, 7; Europe – 45, 22.
Total – 752 (2), 247.

Pele apart, no greater ambassador has served football; no other former player is more instantly recognised, more loved or more revered wherever the game is played. That, even more than the century of caps and record 49 goals for England, the World Cup winner's medal, the European Cup winner's medal and a knighthood, is the measure of Bobby Charlton's impact and stature. His fame and appeal reached the remotest outposts not merely because he was one of the finest players of all time (in fact, his ability has been understated in some quarters), but also because of his manner and sportsmanship.

Those who have endeavoured to undermine his reputation by focusing on his non-existent tackling and dubious heading prowess, and suggesting he was moody and inconsistent, are, frankly, whistling in the wind. Tackling was certainly not part of his game and did not need to be with so many expert practitioners of the craft about him, and yet in an international when injuries reduced England to nine men and a state of emergency, he performed splendidly at left-back. Two of his most important goals – a winner for England and the opener in the European Cup final – were headers. If he had moods they provided confirmation he was human after all and reflected how much he cared about his club, a commitment his team-mates confirm. Inconsistent? He had the odd erratic spell, particularly when he was isolated on the left wing, but, as Stiles says, no player is great in every match.

The reality is that Charlton maintained a standard of excellence over a 15-year span probably unparalleled in the English game. His graceful, flowing style belied the awesome ferocity of his shooting with either foot. A dip of the shoulder could send a whole defence the wrong way; his sudden surge could carry him within range of a terrified goalkeeper. He could drop the ball on a colleague's little toe from 50 yards. And artist though he was, he did not consider it demeaning to lather his skills in sweat. As one eminent writer observed after a match at Derby County's notorious Baseball Ground, 'This man could play good football on a ploughed field.'

This rare talent emerged in the North-East, renowned for its productivity in coal and footballers in roughly equal proportions. He was the nephew of Jackie Milburn, a Newcastle icon before anyone knew what an icon was. He was the younger brother of Jack, the Leeds United and England centre-half who was everything Bobby was not. Bobby was a natural. The progression from East Northumberland Schools to England Schoolboys to United was natural, too.

He was a member of United's FA Youth Cup-winning team in 1954, 1955 and 1956 and made his League debut, ironically against Charlton, a few days before his 19th birthday. He scored twice in the 4–2 win. By Munich he was a recognised first-team player, alongside the tragic Babes. After the crash he shouldered the responsibility of inspiring the rebirth of United. Soon England, too, turned to him for the first of his 106 international appearances.

Charlton dutifully switched from inside-forward to left-wing for club and country before returning to more familiar territory as a deep-lying No. 9 or central midfield player. His goals against Mexico and Portugal were beacons that lit England's path to World Cup triumph in '66, his goals against Benfica a fitting contribution to United's finest hour.

He retired at the end of the 1972–73 season to begin a career in management with Preston North End, but he resumed active duty in an attempt to rescue the cause and had a brief spell with Waterford. He became a director of Wigan Athletic and stepped into the breach when the club had a managerial crisis. In 1984, however, he was back at Old Trafford as a director and he has since combined an obvious ambassadorial role for club and a range of worthy causes with his business and television enterprises.

* * *

A group of Porto supporters are gathered, as arranged, at reception, awaiting their conducted tour of Old Trafford. Later they will doubtless plunder the megastore and later still sit on the edge of their seats for the first leg of the European Cup quarter-final tie against United. Suddenly, their meticulously planned agenda is interrupted. Their guide is abandoned as they spot the bald, bespectacled gentleman, wearing a suit and raincoat and carrying a briefcase, stepping from his car. Legends are unmistakable.

Sir Bobby Charlton CBE is swallowed up by the adoring visitors and smilingly poses so that every member of the group may take a photograph of him with the rest of them. He is polite and modest. He has no need to flaunt his greatness. He radiates it. Autographs collected, hands shaken, the beaming Portuguese respectfully form a phalanx as he turns towards the door of the building. He makes his way up the stairs and through a labyrinth of corridors connecting offices, restaurants, bars and suites. Finally he unlocks a door and announces our arrival in the 'inner sanctum'.

It is the directors' private lounge, sculptured within the structure of the old main stand. It is impeccably appointed and decorated. A huge table dominates the central area, settee and armchairs offer comfort in a corner. Pictures of matchstick footballers hang on the walls. The eye, however, is inexorably drawn above the fireplace to the imposing roll of honour. It lists only United's wins. Runner-up places do not belong here. The most treasured entry is in the top left-hand corner – 1968 European Cup.

So much of Charlton's life had been dedicated to the pursuit of that simple inscription, and after so many lives had been lost it was almost as much his crusade as Busby's. He oozes pride. Not on a personal level but on behalf of his club. No hint of the moody player here. He is warm, buoyant, effusive.

> I've been here since the start of it all. Sir Matt had been to see a few matches in Europe and came back saying it was the only place for the best players, a different world. We had to go there. The Football League were against it, complaining there were already enough matches, but I think their concerns were more financial. They got more of a cut from fixtures here. It was a bit of sour grapes. But the Old Man was always progressive. He'd come back from the Giants Stadium in America talking about the corporate thing, people enjoying much more than the match. His plans were in place. So we went into Europe.

United had always held an exotic attraction for the quiet miner's son from Ashington.

> I was first drawn to United when I listened to the 1948 Cup

final on the wireless. I remember wanting them to win when everyone else wanted Stanley Matthews and Blackpool to win. I think I must have been reading about them and made my mind up I wanted United to win.

Charlton's native instincts took him to matches at Newcastle, and the Milburn genes, augmented by the encouragement of his mother, Cissie, created another future star in the fair-haired boy. He sharpened his appetite for the game and prepared himself for its earthier characteristics on visits to another of his footballing uncles at Chesterfield. 'I learned all about swearing when I went to see Uncle George,' he chuckles.

Newcastle must have cursed when they watched Charlton's development in Manchester. The young player, however, grew restless for his chance to graduate in the Babes academy and defied an injured right ankle to make his debut. Fortunately for him and United, he had already worked on improving his weaker left foot, so much so that many became convinced that was his favoured side. The club, meanwhile, had embarked on its maiden European voyage. Charlton recalls,

I missed the first European matches. I wasn't in the first team regularly and I was doing my National Service, stationed in Shropshire. When any little aeroplane flew over I used to think it would be the lads going off, to Dortmund or Bilbao or wherever. It was just a great adventure, so exciting for the fans and the players, something totally different. You were seeing players you'd only read about. The atmosphere at the matches was sensational. It made what you'd call exciting cup-ties pale into insignificance. They were all midweek games, at night, and people were having to rush from work to get there. And we had the advent of floodlights. We didn't have lights here at the time so we had to play at Maine Road.

And you were going to all these places, playing all the really great teams. We knew we had really great players and we weren't afraid to play anybody. The best way to show how good you are is to play against them. I wouldn't have liked to have played against our team at the time. It was the best we've had – Duncan and all those others. There were times, when George and Denis performed at their peak, that the '60s team was sensational. But regularly the team prior to Munich was great.

When you think that now we're restricted to crowds of

55,000 and at that time I think we could have got 200,000
in, it is amazing. It wasn't like now, when you see the stars all
the time on television. Then your only chance was to go to
the games, and here were Puskas and Di Stefano and Rivera.

The excitement was extinguished on 6 February 1958, and no one did
more to rekindle it than the young man suddenly elevated to leading player.
Recovered from his injuries, he returned to steer a patchwork team to
Wembley, only to collect his second successive FA Cup runners-up medal.
The European adventure almost inevitably ended that year in Milan.
Charlton offered his soul to the crusade and insists he was willing to make
the switch to outside-left.

> I didn't have any difficulty with that. All I wanted to do was
> play, so if it meant I played every week on the wing, that was
> okay. The Old Man explained he didn't have any wide
> players. Albert Scanlon, an orthodox left-winger, had gone.
> United teams were always expected to play with wingers. We
> had plenty of midfield players but nobody left-sided, so he
> asked me if I'd play there and I said yes. I preferred the
> freedom of the middle of the field, but I did quite well on the
> wing and played a lot of times for England there. Because I'd
> done quite well he kept me out there. But I was frustrated at
> times because I had to depend on other people to get the ball
> to me, whereas in midfield you can go and impress yourself
> on the game. Once I came back inside it was better.

By the time Charlton had his FA Cup winner's medal in 1963, he was
having to share top billing with Denis Law. Come the first of their two
Championship successes, in 1965, George Best was up there too. Charlton
was very different from the other two, in character as well as playing style.
He was more of an introvert, more sensitive. It was his club, and he had
gone to hell and back with them. United watchers sensed friction, even
envy, between them. Charlton now proffers his version of their relationship.

> The only criticism I would ever have of George is that he
> didn't give the people what they wanted in his later years at
> the club. He was a young lad and he could do whatever he
> wanted in private as far as I was concerned. All we were
> interested in was winning the games. He was a really
> sensational player and all he had to do was come and train

and play. When that stopped I think he was on a downward spiral.

He denied the public seeing him at his best. To stop at 26 was nonsense, really. He knows that. But at that particular time I don't think George listened to the right people. It was very frustrating for me and the other players. All the other players were coming down training when sometimes he wasn't. When you're doing six-mile runs and you don't know where he is, it isn't right. We were all pros and we expected everyone to behave as pros. The lads were complaining about it and as I was captain I had to go and see the boss about it. He took it in but, at the end of the day, nothing really changed.

There was, though, no friction between me and George, or between me and Denis. George was in a different age group to me, that's all. I didn't go out to night clubs. By the time George came on the scene I was married and we'd started a family. I was settled. My night-clubbing was over. I used to hear about some of the things he'd got up to and I couldn't believe it [his laughter emphasises the incredulity]. But, as I say, if he played, that was okay by me. I think one thing which perhaps didn't help George was the fact he played for Northern Ireland rather than England, and he never got on to the world stage. That always frustrated him.

I had no problem with Denis, other than when he didn't get the service he wanted. Denis was an out-and-out goalscorer, and if you didn't give him the ball in the 18-yard box he would argue with you. And if you tried to score . . .! If I got in a good position and didn't give it to him, he would have a right go at me. But that's the striker's way. Denis and I are fine. In fact, we play golf together.

It's the same with George. No problem. Honestly, I'm really proud when people talk about 'the three' of us, about the 'Best, Law and Charlton era'. Somebody came up to me at a function and said he'd got a great picture of us in some match. I've never really seen an action picture with the three of us together, and I asked him if he'd let me have it. Because that's how I feel about us. They were great players.

Nobby Stiles was a great player as well. I don't have any hesitation in saying that. In people's minds he's probably that dirty, argumentative, irritating little sod. In reality, his defensive qualities were just sensational. He was an unbelievable reader of the game. He could sense where danger was coming from. If it was coming from the side, he'd be over and nip it in the bud there. His timing was amazing. Technically, he was brilliant. If you turned round and saw him there you'd feel at ease. He'd tidy up for Shay, for Bill and for Tony if necessary. He was an instinctive, natural defender, and when he went into coaching I think that took something from him. But when people ask me who were the great players I played with I always include Nobby Stiles. No question.

Charlton toes the party line that it was the club's destiny to win the European Cup after the great escape at the Bernabeu.

We were fated to do it that year. Having been 3–1 down and overrun for 45 minutes by Real Madrid there was no way we should have got back, but we did. Half-time was the turning point. Jimmy Murphy, the Old Man and all the staff were stunned. The players were. Gento had gone on a couple of runs and they were just alive. The goal we got in the first half was an own goal, scored by Zoco. You'll see him now, standing next to Real Madrid's manager on the touchline at matches. It turned out to be vital.

The Old Man said, 'Come on, keep going,' but there was no great conviction. Then we realised another goal would give us a replay in Lisbon, and I remember going down the tunnel behind the Spanish players and they were strutting as if to say, 'Only another 45 minutes and we're in the final.' But they obviously didn't train like we did and they played in bursts – and they'd had their burst. We just kept plugging away and you could sense after five or ten minutes that the spark had gone out of them and that there was something for us.

Nobby started shaking up a few people. We didn't feel our goal was under any threat and started pushing forward a little. David Sadler somehow got one in and there was silence from the home fans. We had about 10,000 there but, obviously, they were greatly outnumbered. You could tell then that they'd gone. They started arguing among themselves and little fights were breaking out between them.

That's when there was a little incident I'll never forget. The ball went out of play and I wanted it quickly because time was running out and we felt we could win the tie. This chap in the front row picked it up and went as if to throw it down the line. I thought, 'Keep calm, don't panic,' and just walked over to him and put my hand out. He put the ball into my hand. I couldn't believe it.

Anyway, not long before the end George went past his man, which you always expected him to do, and got to the dead-ball line, and I was thinking, 'What's he going to do?' Well, instead of trying to beat somebody else he pulled it back, as you would hope, and I could see a red shirt coming on to it. Then I thought, 'Oh . . .' I was really depressed, you know? It was Bill Foulkes, and he never crossed the halfway line unless it was for a corner. Ever. But he was obviously caught up in the thrill of it all and just slotted it, side-foot, like any professional would, into the bottom corner. We'd come back from the dead. I'd never been in a match where we'd gone from such absolute depression to perfect happiness.

I broke down because it was such a hard slog, and it meant so much to win the European Cup for all sorts of reasons, all that had happened before. We'd had a couple of attempts at it and failed, and most people thought this was possibly going to be the last chance. I probably thought so, too. We had a lot of players at their peak and I felt if it wasn't going to be this year it was never going to be.

So when the whistle went it was really emotional, and I remember the United fans coming on and all the excitement. What made it so much better was that we'd done it in Real Madrid's stadium, a great stadium, maybe my favourite. I loved playing there. And now we'd won the semi-final there was no way we were going to lose the final. There was no danger of complacency. I knew we would be stronger and that the longer the game went on the better we would be. Playing all in blue wasn't a problem either. We had no superstitions about that. We were all focused.

What we didn't expect was that it would be so hot. It was so humid. It was pumping out of us. And they didn't throw water bottles on in those days. Players suffered. It was a cracking game, though. They had shots at goal, Eusebio hit the bar with about the only shot he had apart from the one at the end, and Torres was a real problem because he was so big. If you allowed crosses to him and allowed him to have a run he could do damage. But Bill Foulkes was great against him and we nullified most of the things they had, all the other dangerous players they had. And we were at Wembley. We knew it well and you could feel the will of the crowd helping us.

The fact that Charlton's opening goal was so uncharacteristic – it was stamped with the Geoff Hurst trademark – reinforced the belief that fate had decreed this would be United's year.

I didn't score many headers, and, to be honest, I went to the near post as a decoy as much as anything else. You go to the near post, as you are taught, to take a player away. I went, but David Sadler didn't knock it to the far post, he knocked it in to me, and I literally just helped it on its way. It didn't need much of a touch, but it was quite wide out and if the goalkeeper was positioned properly it was going to be difficult to beat him. It went just inside the post, into the bottom corner, almost impossible to stop.

We'd had some chances in the first half – David Sadler missed a couple – and I think their defence panicked. They weren't very big and the Latins were used to getting plenty of notice when people went at them. They didn't like people coming at them too quickly – and coming again. We pressurised them, they left a few spaces at the back, but we didn't take advantage. Having got the one we were on our way, but physically it was still a slog because we were drained and we had to keep forcing ourselves. Then they scored and it was the big man there, knocking it down, and Graca popped it in, good right foot.

When Eusebio was going through I thought that was it. We hadn't done anything wrong but it was a good pass, good run, and there's not much you can do about it. It was unlike him to miss that. If he'd placed it or taken it a bit further he would have scored, but I don't think he knew who was behind him, so he hit it a great blow and Alex Stepney, well, it just stuck. Unbelievable, really, but the thing about Alex was he had good hands.

Fate was showing its hand again, too.

We thought then that if we got to extra-time we would be okay. You are trained and prepared in the English game to push yourself through the pain barrier. Our record in extra-time had always been good and our record against Portuguese teams had always been good. They didn't like extra-time. Latins generally didn't like playing one game soon after another. I remember Chelsea drawing against Real Madrid in, I think, the Cup-Winners' Cup, and the Spaniards didn't want to play again in three days, as they were told to. They wanted a week. The Latins are much more professional now, but at that time they didn't like playing too often and they didn't like extra-time. Really, Benfica never had any sort of chance in extra-time.

We overran them and when George went through and popped in the second that was it. There was no way they were going to score again, and they collapsed psychologically. There were loads of goals to be scored. If we'd gone at them in the second period of extra-time we'd have got more, but it was over anyway. Brian knocked in the third and then rolled the ball in for me to score the last one. Again, I went to the near post as a decoy and it wasn't really a shot, but he wasn't a very big goalkeeper and it just looped over him.

When I picked up the Cup the first thing I thought was how heavy it was, because at the end I was physically drained rather than emotionally drained. I've never known humidity like it in this country before or since. I couldn't go to the reception. I lay down in our hotel room and every time I tried to get up I started to pass out before I reached the door. I suppose had I drunk water, as they do now, I would have been all right. But I was completely dehydrated. Pat Crerand was the same, sick as a dog even before we left Wembley.

And there were so many people I wanted to see. Some of the old players were there – Harry Gregg, Kenny Morgans, Johnny Berry, Jackie Blanchflower – and parents of lads who died in the crash. And I never saw them. My wife, Norma, had to go to the function on her own. She came back and said it was a pity I didn't make it because the Old Man had stood up and sung 'What a Wonderful World'. He'd lost his team at Munich and he always said it would take a long time to get anything like that sort of team together again. He used to say that in memory of the lads who had died it was right and proper that one day we should win the European Cup.

The lads in the '60s team never asked me about Munich. Even now there isn't a day goes by when I don't think about it, and, of course, I've since flown there many times. But it was always a private thing, and they respected that. They were obviously aware of the history and the significance of the European Cup. They were aware of their responsibilities, as well. But they were good players in their own right, so why shouldn't they win the European Cup? We were never really going to be a *proper* football club until we won it.

Winning the World Cup was very different, and didn't mean any less to me. But that was a six-match competition. We didn't have to qualify, and that's a lot easier than having to play over two years, win the Championship and then go and beat the rest of Europe's champions. That's hard. The quality at international level was obviously higher, but it's not a slog. I wouldn't have liked to have played out my career and not had the World Cup and not had the European Cup. I'd lived through the gamut of emotions for the European Cup, right from when we first played in Europe. It had been a long and painful journey. But we made it.

Above all, Busby had made it. That is how much of the world saw it, and some within the camp would have you believe that is how he saw it. Charlton, his ever-loyal lieutenant, maintains Busby was never so egotistical.

He never talked about himself as the manager, it was always him and Jimmy. We've seen it elsewhere in the game. The great Liverpool sides were led by Shankly and Paisley, then Paisley and Fagan. Derby and Forest had Brian Clough and Peter Taylor. There were always two. You need two. You bounce ideas off each other. We had Sir Matt and Jimmy. Jimmy was the coach. Sir Matt was never the coach. He was a motivator, but he wasn't a technical coach. He didn't work on you day to day on how to do things. Jimmy Murphy was the one who did that and the one who got me from being a schoolboy amateur to a professional player. For about two years he worked on me as an individual, getting all the bad things out of my system and teaching me the professional things.

But Jimmy didn't like it when he had to do things Matt did, because he wasn't good at it. Jimmy was good at working with the lads. After Munich we seemed to be at Blackpool all the time, because Jimmy wanted to get away from all the pressures in Manchester. He's always held in high esteem here. His family, I think, are still looked after and they are always welcome when they come.

The end of the Busby–Murphy era left United in apparent free-fall to mediocrity and worse. Even recalling that period appears to pain a man who symbolised the club's triumphal parade.

I have been presenting a series of programmes on *Sky* featuring some of our matches from the early '70s, and it reminds me how awful it was. It was a period of transition, when people like me were coming to the end of their careers, and to try to maintain the quality players were drafted in, but they weren't really good enough. It was a bad time for us. But it was obvious after 1968 that everyone would want to beat us, and there was a lot of good competition. The Bill Shankly era had started at Liverpool. It became much more difficult and we weren't able to go along with it. It was obvious it just couldn't continue. These days you would make it continue because you would have the money to go into Europe and buy the best players.

Charlton, having drawn an astonishing 60,000 to his testimonial match against Celtic, played his final game for United at Chelsea in April 1973. He was 35, had made 754 appearances and had scored 247 goals. A month later he became manager of Preston and discovered, as many of the greatest players do, that natural talent does not easily rub off on others. One of his charges at the time confided, 'He was trying to get us to do things that were nothing to him but beyond us. The fact is that even at that age he was twice as good as the rest of us.'

The old skills were dusted off in a forlorn attempt to revive Deepdale's glories. This, alas, was one crusade too many. Charlton parted company with Preston in a dispute over transfer policy and would return, via Wigan Athletic, to his spiritual home in 1984 to join the board of United. A decade on he was knighted for his services to the game, a game he again enjoys thanks largely to the success of the Ferguson–Kidd regime and the sight of a new generation experiencing the incomparable thrills of the European adventure.

It's really great being around the club now because you sense the same feeling and hunger that we had. I listen to some of the younger lads, like Gary Neville, and they've got so much enthusiasm for European matches, just like we had. Gary was saying how he heard the old, great players talking about Europe and never realised how much of an achievement theirs was until he actually sampled it. He now realises how hard it is, what a great challenge and adventure it is, how it demands total concentration and performances of the highest calibre. Anything short of that will not be good enough.

Gary's a really intelligent and sensible lad, as well as a terrific player. He reads the game so well. He is a leader and I think he will be captain of England one day. David Beckham is another tremendous player for this club and the country. He's a bit like me. He likes experimenting. He likes short passes, he likes long passes. He likes shooting, he likes all the glamorous parts of the game. That makes him exciting to watch. He's not afraid to have a go. He's not afraid to miss. Too many players are. And he can hit a ball. He concentrates on his technique. We've also got Phil Neville, Nicky Butt and Paul Scholes in the England set-up. They all want to be the best.

The young lads talk to you about Europe all the time, and they're very keen to show they are up to it. They put a lot of work into it and it's a great spur to them to think that one day they might be able to achieve greatness. We've had one or two stutters in trying to get there again, but then not being able to play the full team was a bugbear for us. The team is better equipped and prepared for it now. It's not just the young ones who are hungry for it, of course – although they're all young compared with me! The likes of Peter Schmeichel, Gary Pallister and Denis Irwin want to be the best in Europe as well.

I think winning the European Cup would have been the icing on the cake for Eric Cantona. He was a great player for this club, but I don't think from a satisfaction point of view you can call yourself one of the really great players unless you win the European Cup or the World Cup. You have to be seen to do it on the big stage, in the big pressure situations.

If Busby was the Father of Manchester United then Charlton appears to have accepted the responsibility of fostering the flock. His daughters, Suzanne, who is making a name for herself as a BBC weather expert, and Andrea, will feel they have a whole dressing room of brothers in red.

For me it's great to be involved with the club again in these exciting times. This was the only place to play and it's still the only place to be as far as I'm concerned. I've no ambitions to be chairman or anything like that. My ambitions are for the club to keep going forward. I want to see us win the big one again, and knowing Alex he'd want to keep winning it. But there is something else beyond that – the World Club Championship. We didn't manage to beat the South Americans and that would be the target for us. I'm sure that's in Alex's mind as well. There's no end to his ambition. You need good management, good coaching and it is, to use the old cliché, a team game. We are all part of it here and can't win without each other.

I've never felt as sick as I did when Fenerbahce won here in the last five minutes. Losing the unbeaten record to them was bad enough, but I just felt there was no justice because they were clearly inferior to us. Having said that, you have to be good enough to break them down and not make a mistake to let them in. That's the game. Juventus was a different matter. They are a great side. But they can never have had as many shots on their goal as they had in the second half here.

This, though, is why winning the European Cup is such a fantastic achievement. It's hard – harder than winning the World Cup. That's what keeps you going at it. And I love it as much as I ever did.

10. DAVID SADLER

Born: Yalding, Kent, 5-2-46
Debut: v Sheffield Wednesday (a), 24-8-63
United career: Football League – 266 (6) appearances, 22 goals;
FA Cup – 22 (1), 1; Football League Cup – 22, 1; Europe – 16, 3.
Total – 326 (7), 27.

If Shay Brennan is the most-loved member of the '68 club, then David Sadler is probably the most respected. Intelligent, level-headed, conscientious and organised, he has always provided the ballast for a ship that might otherwise list beyond control. Little wonder he runs the United old boys' association. On the field and off it, he was ever 'Mr Dependable'.

Sadler's calculated course took him into a career in banking before the professional game and, at the tender age of 16, he became an England amateur international. He played for Maidstone United, in the Isthmian League, and news of a potentially sound investment reached Old Trafford. Business concluded, he joined the club in January 1963 for £750. He made his debut for United later that year, still aged 17, at centre-forward.

That remained his role through much of his early period at the club and he scored a hat-trick in the 1964 FA Youth Cup triumph. However, establishing himself as a regular forward in the senior side proved a formidable task and it was to the considerable benefit of player and club that he emerged as the versatile answer to almost every eventuality. He could operate in a range of midfield guises but found probably his most effective post as a central defender. Here his composed, discerning style contrasted with the orthodox stopper approach and earned him accolades as one of the most polished players in the land.

Sadler won a League Championship medal in 1967 and then played his full part in the European Cup success, somehow improvising the goal that revived United in Madrid and then delivering the cross from which Bobby Charlton opened the account in the final. That year he made the first of four appearances for the senior England team, thereby completing a treasured international collection. He also played for his country at Youth and Under-23 levels, and represented the Football League.

The exodus of the Docherty era carried Sadler away and he joined Charlton at Preston for a still-reasonable £25,000. Their return was more than 100 matches of elegant football. Since no obvious routes opened up for him in the game after his playing career, he retraced old steps and became branch manager of a building society. He linked up with Charlton again as a financial consultant before developing a corporate hospitality business. He chips in a few comments to the media pot and still finds time to keep his hand on the old boys' tiller.

* * *

The exterior of the brick building in Chorlton is much as you would expect David Sadler's workplace to be. It is imposing rather than grandiose, dignified rather than ostentatious. Behind the door . . . things seem to be listing. Still getting things sorted, someone explains. David? His is the room at the top. Watch the boxes. Sorry. The stairs reaching ever upwards towards the attic negotiated, more evidence of disorder paves the final steps to his desk. Beneath the folders it is a simple piece of furniture, in keeping with the modest office. Organisation will doubtless ensue; flamboyance is unlikely to. A few sporting trophies give a clue to the occupant's line of interest, but nothing flaunts his involvement in Manchester United's greatest night.

Sadler's play with Maidstone had been more conspicuous and he was whisked into the fold before the big clubs of the South could convince him the 'Frozen North' was no place for such a refined boy. He settled into the 'family' with Mrs Fullaway and was in the first team three weeks before his new house-mate, George Best. A less likely pairing is unimaginable, as Sadler hears constantly.

> Yes, that's what people say all the time. But in fact we got on
> fine together and George was nothing like the image some
> have of him. It wasn't night clubs and drinking and wild
> goings-on, nothing like that. George was just a pleasant,
> quiet lad. We'd play cards or read at our digs, maybe go for a
> game of snooker or bowling. He was the greatest player I ever

played with, and brave with it. But he was a normal lad and we had the normal life of young footballers.

United are not readily perceived as a normal football establishment, but players come in much the same mix wherever they land and Sadler found life comfortable. The shadow of Munich was never overbearing, the ghosts never intimidating.

As a young player coming to the club after Munich I was obviously aware of what had happened and I was with people who had gone through it: Gregg, Foulkes and Charlton. But it was something we would never raise and talk to them about, and in a sense we didn't need to. Nothing was thrust upon us in that regard. People still talked about the players, about Duncan Edwards, Tommy Taylor and Roger Byrne, but not in a depressing or morbid way, just about what great players they were. Obviously it came up in the build-up to the big European games, and especially the final, but it wasn't something that was hard to bear.

Things went pretty well for me, anyway, as soon as I went to the club. I'd been playing in senior amateur football with Maidstone and there were strong leagues in the London and Home Counties region. Wimbledon, of course, came out of this environment. I scored a few goals, played for England amateurs, came to Manchester as a centre-forward and very quickly got into the team. I did reasonably well for two or three years without really establishing myself as a regular, playing my part in the first-team set-up as stand-in for the likes of Denis and David Herd.

The likes of Law and Herd, and then a youngster called Brian Kidd, represented an impregnable barrier to Sadler's long-term aspirations. There is a school of thought that suggests his versatility undermined his lasting stature, but Sadler is honest and pragmatic enough to acknowledge the switch from centre-forward effectively resuscitated his career at United.

It all came about by accident, really. At the end of training we'd have little kick-abouts, five-a-sides, eight-a-sides or whatever, and you'd get people wanting to play in different positions, goalkeepers at centre-forward and that sort of thing. I would play in defence. I enjoyed it and found I could play there. Anyway, at some particular point I got moved back and played for a junior side at centre-half. I also started to play a bit in midfield and I was into a period where I played centre-half or midfield according to the team's requirements, and that was around the time of the European Cup run.

We had Nobby Stiles and Bill Foulkes at the back, and in midfield we had Bobby Charlton and Paddy Crerand. There was clearly a need for somebody to do the defensive duties for players of that sort. Nobby did it and I did it. So I played all over the place, but I suppose at the end of the day I failed as a centre-forward and that's what it came down to. I didn't score enough goals. Equally, it suited me better. There's no question that by playing in more defensive positions I was able to develop my game and my career. Playing in either role enabled me to secure as permanent involvement as you are likely to get bearing in mind the sort of team we had, and I was happy with that.

The club should really have won the European Cup two years earlier than we did. I wasn't quite as regular a player in the side but I have to say it was probably a better side then. People who were near the end of their careers when we won it were two years younger in '66 and were expected to win it, but they blew it. Had it not been for that failure a lot might have changed, even to the extent of the George Best situation and how things developed with him. Because we didn't win it, the team remained much the same.

We won the Championship in '67 and it was a Championship-winning side, but it should have been fairly clear – although perhaps not to us, because it's never that clear when you are involved in it – that changes were going to have to be made. You have to think Matt must have been looking to make changes in that side. Bill was of an age when he might have been contemplating finishing and Denis was struggling with his knee, but for whatever reason the team stayed together and we won the Championship and went on to win in Europe. For me it was great. I was just happy to get in the side.

The final was actually a bit anti-climactic. We'd been to Gornik and conditions were really dreadful there. They were a very good side and we really had to battle to get through that one. We played very well against Madrid at Old Trafford and really should have taken a better lead over there. But we didn't and we got absolutely slaughtered in the first half. Of course, as everyone knows, we were only 3–2 down on aggregate, so the game was still there for us. But it didn't feel like it. We felt as if we had lost the first half 6–0. The one we got was an own goal. And then, of course, in the second half . . .!

All these years on, having rerun it a million times in the mind, this bit still seems the stuff of fantasy.

We obviously played better in the second half, and we worked much better, but I wouldn't claim enormous credit for my goal. I'd started in a defensive role again, supporting Nobby and Billy, but come the second half we had to take every opportunity to go forward, so I was starting to get more in touch with the front players and even getting beyond them. And that's really what happened. The cross came in, Bestie went for it and I sort of followed in. I don't know whether he got a touch or somebody else did, but the ball eventually found its way to me and I just stuck my foot out, in passing almost, and in it went. It was one of those situations where you take a bit of a chance, you see something, and it comes off for you.

It was quite strange then because you had this massive crowd – you read all sorts of figures as to what it was, 125,000 or whatever – and they'd been so noisy in the first half, and all of a sudden it was as if somebody had turned a radio off. For a minute I didn't really understand what had happened. It was unreal. But, of course, the ball had gone in and that was it. We were then on top of the game. I can't remember what the situation was in those days with relation to draws, but there was never any thought we would settle for that. And then we had this situation where Bill Foulkes scored the winner, which makes the story all the more incredible. When you consider everything Bill had been through with the club, for him to get that goal was amazing.

So after all that the final itself was probably a bit of an anti-climax. You have to remember there was a special relationship between Madrid and United. Matt and all the people at Madrid were very close. And Madrid, of course, had been the great European side, the team to aim at. Benfica, too, had a great record by then, but I think Madrid had a special place up there for Matt and United.

United's special place in the build-up to Wembley holds memories of walks through the grounds and bets on the Derby. Typically, Sadler's recollection focuses on something else.

Horse-racing didn't interest me very much anyway, so I don't recall too much about the Derby. But I do remember watching David Coleman as he was doing the TV programme from the grounds of the hotel and thinking how professional he was in terms of the way he handled it. Apart from that I just remember wanting to get off to Wembley.

Benfica were a side not dissimilar to us. They had one or two players, like Coluna, who were getting towards the last throes of their careers, if not actually over the hill. It was a hot day but I don't remember it as being unbearable, and I think the game was good, it flowed. I realised that when we got together for the 25th anniversary and watched the match in full.

My overall recollection, though, remains, and that is that the game had a strange look about it. I was really a centre-half-type player then, and it was hard to see how we would play with Bill, Nobby and me. Nobby was really marking Eusebio but at the same time we didn't want Eusebio pulling Nobby all over the field. After '66 it had become a bit of a battle between them and Nobby, of course, had done pretty well against him. But we knew he would try to drag Nobby all over the place, so the idea was that I would be the anchor-man in midfield, and if Eusebio pulled away from Nobby I would pick him up rather than have Nobby go chasing him. The tactics worked reasonably well, and I also had to look after people like Coluna.

Bestie had a fairly free licence, but Johnny Aston, of course, was really the star player. If Denis had been fit, Johnny almost certainly wouldn't have played – which is ironic, because he had such a magnificent game. By that time we were almost certainly going to play with Brian Kidd because he was a strong, up-front player, though still fairly

inexperienced. Although I was in a fairly defensive situation
I had chances in the first half and in the second, when
another goal would probably have made it safe for us. If Alex
hadn't made that save when we were rocking a bit, it might
all have gone wrong. The fact is I had two or three good
chances which I should have taken. I didn't, but we still went
on to win and I felt I had contributed anyway.

That save by Alex got us through to extra-time and it was
the best opportunity they were going to have. Matt and all
the coaching staff came out on to the pitch to us before extra-
time, just saying, 'Come on, come on, we can do it now.
We've got 30 minutes.' We were tired and lay all over the
place. Matt didn't change any tactics or anything like that, he
just urged us on. But it just so happened that we scored fairly
quickly in extra-time and then ran away with it. We just
overwhelmed them.

It was a marvellous win and a marvellous night for all of
us, but I think if the truth be known, some of us, the
younger ones or those who had come into the club after
Munich, did feel slightly like interlopers, a little bit out of it.
We were all in it together, it's a team game and we were all
elated with the victory at Wembley, the achievement and
significance of it all. But at the same time we were aware it
was about Matt, Bill and Bobby, in particular, because of all
they had been through. Bobby was drained. So was Matt,
and for the first time he looked old, and you wondered what
was left. That's why you can look back now and use words
like 'crusade' and 'destiny'.

Sadler was not among those approaching the end of their careers and his
prime coincided with the period of turmoil that followed the abdication of
Busby.

I was involved in the aftermath of the European Cup and
probably played my best football at that time. I'd become a
central defender, got England caps and was part of the
England set-up in the build-up to the 1970 World Cup in
Mexico, although I didn't actually make the 22. So this was
very much my peak. But there were all sorts of problems at
United; finding a successor to Sir Matt and all of that.
Looking back, it shouldn't have been a surprise, the problems

the club had. It probably needed somebody as great as Busby, and when you consider the time he was at the club and all he went through, it's inevitable it would take time to find the right man to follow him.

Liverpool maintained their level of success exceptionally well for a period of time with Shankly, Paisley and Fagan, but then they had their problems with Souness and Dalglish. I just hope there isn't a problem for United following Alex. You accept this situation as a player. Managers come in and managers go; or managers come in and players go. I experienced that at Old Trafford. When Tommy Docherty came in I was initially part of his plans, then I was no longer part of his plans, and that, as a professional footballer, is something you have to accept.

I did make mistakes, and one I made was at the end. I was under contract and should have sat it out there, but pride comes into it. You want to play first-team football and you're not getting treated as you think you ought. But then we all think we should be treated better. The fact is I'd had a great time and a great career at United. I had the best part of 11 years at Old Trafford. But having played for England two or three years before and not getting matches, I had to be interested in an opportunity to move on.

Bobby had gone to Preston and I was always quite close to him – or as close as you can be – and he asked me to join him there, so I went. It was quite a dramatic change and it would be fair to say it was something of a culture shock going to Preston. When you've played at the top and travelled and done everything first-class, you have to get used to different realities in the Second and Third Divisions and at a club like Preston, a club that was losing money and having all the associated problems.

Bobby himself wasn't used to it, and could never really come to terms with the problems. Bobby, as you would expect of him, was something of a purist and an idealist in terms of wanting to keep his best young players, bringing them on and building a team, all the things he had experienced at Old Trafford. At Preston the attitude was that if you produced a good player that was fantastic because you could sell him on and buy off six months' debt. That's the nature of the game there. Bobby didn't see it like that but then, fortunately if you like, recognised it and got off the managerial merry-go-round.

It was very difficult for me to adapt when I first went there. I got an illness – mumps, of all things – which was not very pleasant for someone of 28 or 29, so that was a bit of a setback. Then I had a good spell and enjoyed it, but by then I was having trouble with the knee and I was advised to stop playing when I was barely 31. It was the sort of knee ligament job they would do something about now, and really it didn't compare with the injuries Paul Gascoigne and others have had. I tried to play on and didn't train for the best part of a year, but you can't go on like that because you risk really bad problems later – and you've got a lot of life to live after football.

I had thought about doing something in the game, although the idea of coaching had never done anything for me. Working with players was something that never interested me. I did feel that if I had something to give it would be on the management side, perhaps running a club like Preston and having a coach who would work with me. But football never made any efforts to keep me, nobody asked me to go and manage them, and I never made any efforts to stay in football on the other side. Instead I got involved in one or two things outside football, and made myself another life. Now I've got links with sport in general through the hospitality and entertainment business.

The link with United and his old colleagues is also intact. As secretary of the Association of Former Manchester United Players, he is the axis of an organisation that reunites the Reds, rekindles the spirit and, in the process, helps replenish the coffers of worthy causes.

We've been going for about 12 years and it followed on from organising a bit of a charity team, having the odd game here and there and then a glass of beer. It was just a social thing, a nice way of seeing one another again. It's not elitist or just for first-team players; it's for any ex-Old Trafford player. A lot of my pals never got near the first team. It's broadened out and we do a fair bit of charity work, but first and foremost it was about catching up with players you hadn't seen for ages, enjoying a pint together and getting into the football chat.

We basically hold four events, including a golf day, a year. Most of our dinners are back at Old Trafford. Over the years we've probably raised more than £80,000 for charity. We support a charity Jimmy Murphy got involved with, leukaemia research, after his son-in-law died. Jimmy was such a big part of our lives, as of course was Matt.

There is really a bit of a bond with the European team, but it depends on who you speak to as to how secure that bond is. It depends also, a fair bit, on who's in power down there. By that, I really mean the manager. Certainly Alex Ferguson has been great with us. He's never been scared of the old boys, if that's the right word. Some people have been, and that's probably understandable. One who was not comfortable with it was Frank O'Farrell, though of course he came immediately after Sir Matt. The next problems will arise when Alex goes.

The question is, who's going to be big enough to take that on? They'll come in, as managers did after Sir Matt, with their own ideas about how to do it. Some of them decided the past was the past and they should leave it there, and they didn't want anything to do with it. They wanted their own men around them, their own players in and all that sort of thing. But nobody quite succeeded Sir Matt until Alex, although there were people along the way who did reasonably well. Big Ron [Atkinson] had a pretty good time there, and Tommy Docherty had a great relationship with the fans and got things moving again. Even if Fergie doesn't do anything else from here on in, he's going to be up there and he's going to take some following.

You do sense the same desire in Alex to pull off the big one. United have no divine right to win anything, and they went 20-odd years before they won the Championship again, so that became an enormous pressure for managers. Some coped with it, some didn't. When finally they pulled it off it was an enormous relief to a lot of people. To a certain extent it sort of pushed us to one side at last. There were times when it was embarrassing for some of us to be at the club, being members of the last Championship-winning side. And it got worse as the years went by. The whole thing became a bigger and bigger issue.

I never actually wanted to put the past away. If it's in the right place it should never be intimidating. It should be some sort of inspiration, something special. When they did eventually win the Championship that was great. Liverpool went on to achieve more than we did in Europe, but the fact we were the first English club to do it remained a landmark, and even Alex must have realised that winning the European Cup was unlikely to be accomplished straight after his first Championship. They'd got rid of one millstone only to find another hanging round them. But all English clubs had suffered by not being in Europe for five years. Europe is a different matter and the rest of Europe had opened an enormous gap between us. I think, though, the gap is closing, and the more experience our players get the better chance they will have.

It's difficult to make comparisons because so many things are different. The format is different for a start, and I'm not in favour of it, but then, as we know, it is money-orientated. The current side has evolved, and there have actually been two or three sides over the last six years, starting with the one that won the Cup-Winners' Cup. Older players are always moving on, younger ones coming in. The trick is to catch them all at the right time. This should be a good time for the team, providing Alex doesn't have too many injuries and can pick his strongest line-up.

I certainly never look at the current team and think, 'Oh, only two of these could get in our team,' because the game is so different. And what I admit with regard to myself is that you become a much better player than you ever were the older you get and the further away from it you get. I know I was a reasonable player, but time glorifies things to a certain extent.

What you can say is that we had some undisputed great players in our side – Charlton, Best, Crerand, Stiles and, although he didn't play on the night, Law. And then in Tony Dunne we had the best full-back around. If you could beam them to another era, they would have been part of the present-day team. Equally, you have to say that people like Schmeichel, Keane, Giggs and maybe Beckham would have been great players in our period. Cantona certainly would have been.

Sadler and his wife Christine, a Stretford girl, have long been settled in the North Cheshire belt that houses many of Manchester's footballers, past and present. Ironically, their son, Nigel, took the opposite career direction to his father, heading for London and the bright lights. Literally. He works in the theatre on lighting and special effects. Establishing a work base here in Chorlton is appropriate for his father. 'Our digs were not far from here,' he says.

He passes another reminder of a cherished past every time he climbs or descends those stairs: a concocted picture of the 11 players who won the European Cup. 'As far as I can remember that 11 never actually played together again and no photograph was taken of the complete team on the night, so I suppose that's the nearest we're going to get to a picture of the winning line-up.'

Even if they are in red, rather than blue.

11. JOHN ASTON

Born: Manchester, 28-6-47
Debut: v Leicester City (h), 12-4-65
United career: Football League – 139 (16) appearances, 25 goals;
FA Cup – 5 (2), 1; Football League Cup – 12 (3), 0; Europe – 8, 1.
Total – 164 (21), 27.

He was the last name on the team-sheet and somehow he always gave the impression he felt he was the last in the affections of the club and its supporters. It was evident in the body language and in the sentiments he confided to friends and colleagues. It is evident, too, in the few words he is now willing to express about his career with Manchester United. An apparent sense of family betrayal impelled him to sever all physical and emotional ties with the club and seek a new life in self-imposed exile.

The feeling of treachery is doubtless compounded by the acclaim for his performance in the European Cup final. He was the man of the match. Everyone says so. It was the night his uncomplicated wing play destroyed one of the Continent's most sophisticated and successful teams. He sucked in his marker, then left him dead for pace and invited colleagues on to his constant supply of crosses. He did not have the sublime skills or charisma of other forwards in the side, but then neither did he carry any egotistical baggage or enrage the rest with unpredictable intent. There was never any doubt where John Aston was coming from.

He had been brought up in the United household, not merely a local boy but the son of the John Aston who played for United and England in the post-war years. Aston senior was a powerful, versatile player who would answer the call to bail out a depleted forward line with gusto and goals. He was a similarly effective wing-half, assured in the tackle and on the ball. But it was as a left-back that he excelled and was renowned, partnering Bert

Whalley and then, more famously, Johnny Carey. He collected an FA Cup winner's medal in 1948 and a Championship medal in 1952. Illness curtailed his playing career and he joined the staff as junior coach. He switched to scouting duties and was chief scout from 1970 to 1972.

The young player he monitored with particular interest was John junior, who advanced through Manchester Schoolboys and Lancashire Schoolboys to an apprenticeship at Old Trafford. A boy called Best worried about his own future because Aston was ahead of him in the pecking order for the No. 11 shirt. He turned professional in 1964 and was a member of the FA Youth Cup-winning team that year. A year later he made his senior debut as the club closed in on their first Championship post-Munich. He played a more regular and influential part in the title success of 1967 and duly picked up his winner's medal.

The following season he featured in the cast not only on the domestic stage but also, and more crucially, in the grand arena of the European Cup. He was on one wing, Best on the other. Both scored in the hard-earned victory against Gornik, and Aston created the goal converted by Best in the home leg against Real Madrid. And then came Wembley. Aston, aged 20, was like a man possessed. He terrorised a defence that had expected most of its problems to come from the other flank. Best will always be remembered for his critical goal, Charlton for his double, Kidd for his birthday goal, Stepney for that save and Stiles for his shackling of Eusebio. But John Aston junior outshone them all.

And yet John Aston junior was the whipping boy of United, the player the fans turned on in less exultant circumstances. When his direct, orthodox play was neutralised he did not have the options more gifted team-mates possessed and became an easy target for the disgruntled. He was never a shirker and always tracked and tackled back, but sometimes it seemed the harder he tried the more he was ridiculed. If Best fought back it was another dimension to his genius; if Aston fought back it was a giveaway sign of his desperation and inadequacy. Some said he had an inferiority complex and a propensity to sulk which dragged his chin to the floor. Little wonder.

Aston's confidence can scarcely have been buoyed when, three months after his and United's greatest night, he was laid up with a broken leg and Busby signed another winger, Willie Morgan. McGuinness endeavoured to restore Aston's faith and brought him back into the side, but that injury had caused his career at United irreparable damage. He moved to Luton Town in the summer of 1972 for a fee of £30,000 and had five productive seasons with the club, helping them gain promotion to the First Division in 1974. He went on from there to Mansfield Town before returning to the North-West and finishing his playing days with Blackburn Rovers.

He would not, however, feel inclined to return to his original football home. His father was discarded, along with the manager, Frank O'Farrell, and the coach, Malcolm Musgrove, in December 1972, and, according to his colleagues, he could never forgive the club for that. He turned away not only from United but from football, seeking his new world and his new life in the pet shop business.

* * *

Stalybridge is one of those small towns on the fringe of Manchester that like to cling to a notion of independence. The locals tell you they will never consider themselves part of a metropolitan sprawl but will always live in a secluded corner of Cheshire. As if to underline their devolutionary zeal, they have a football team, who play in the Vauxhall Conference, called Celtic. There is a comfortable, self-sufficient rather than affluent feel to the town centre and part of the main street has succumbed to the compulsion for pedestrianism.

Down on the left-hand side, beyond every other familiar frontage of a shopping centre, is the focal point of John Aston junior's working world. Pets World. The first thing that strikes you, considering his aversion to United, is that the lettering is white on a red background. The window beneath is a kaleidoscope of colours, crammed with dog baskets and mattresses presumably designed for sundry furry creatures. The second thing that strikes you about the place is that there are no furry creatures. 'Foods and accessories,' the lady assistant explains. It does actually say that outside!

The shop is of modest dimensions, yet every conceivable form of furry creature comfort, entertainment and sustenance seems to be available here. Now if Benfica had afforded Aston so little space in '68 it might have been a different story. The narrow path between the boxes and toys leads to a back room and stacks of cages and pens.

This is probably as far removed from United and football as you can get. It is almost inconceivable it is run by the star of a European Cup final, the man we see in the mind's eye skipping over another despairing challenge and haring for the line. It is an almost anonymous little shop in an almost anonymous little town centre. That is perhaps appropriate, after all. Certainly it would appear to suit John Aston junior just fine.

Some years after United's European Cup win he talked of the 'strange night' that completed the reincarnation and fulfilment post-Munich. He consented also to give his recollections of the match and its significance to *The Independent* newspaper:

It was a particularly good night for me because there were a lot of world-class players on the pitch whose reputations preceded them. I was a bit of an unknown quantity. I think only Brian Kidd was younger than me. People say it was the best game I had for United and I think I'd probably agree. I'm not being immodest, but if they'd had a man-of-the-match award I think I would have won it. The game went very quickly. I remember half-time coming and thinking we'd only been playing for about 15 minutes. The atmosphere was tremendous.

It was the only time I ever played at Wembley. I was a Manchester lad and I'd always supported the team. I was about ten when Munich happened, so by 1968 it was half a lifetime away to me. It was only when I was older I realised how close they were to each other. My father played for United so I had the pleasure of knowing quite a few of the United side, especially Mark Jones and Tommy Taylor. I think if that team had lived they would have won the European Cup.

Now, as the 30th anniversary approaches and as United renew their pursuit of that giant trophy, Aston feels no desire or obligation to talk about the club or the cause. Indeed, he is openly and unapologetically hostile to the invitation. It is as if time has reopened rather than healed old wounds. It is as if he welcomes the opportunity to cleanse himself of the stains of hypocrisy and to be honest to himself, his father and the world. He will have no more truck with phoney magnanimity and threadbare platitudes. This is a man speaking his mind and heart.

I'm not interested in football any more and I'm not interested in Manchester United any more. It was all a long time ago, anyway. I played till I was 33 but I've not seen a game for, oh, I bet it's 15 years. I never go these days and I've no interest in going. I just wouldn't watch a game any more. Nothing against the club, but at the same time I just don't want to talk about it any more. That's the past, another life as far as I'm concerned.

I've said it all in the past and gone along with it. That's what people want to hear. They want to hear nice things said about Manchester United and about Matt Busby. They want you to say, 'What a great club, what a great manager, what a great night.' That's all they want to hear, the nice things. But they're all clichés, all sound-bites, and I don't want to say them any more. I'm not bothered about any of it any more.

Life goes on and I've got a new life here. I prefer to look forwards rather than backwards. I've got a business to run and no time for dwelling on the past. It's so long ago I can hardly remember it anyway. It seems like a different life, and that suits me.

The bitterness towards United is obvious and many would perhaps consider it understandable, but surely that should not sour the taste and satisfaction of the occasion and his contribution to United's success?

Of course it was a special occasion for me and I'm proud to have been a part of it, and to have played the part I did in the final. But that's my feeling and it's a private feeling. I don't see why it should be of interest to anyone else. I'm not a famous person. I'm an ordinary bloke getting on with his life and his business. That's all there is to it and that's all I want.

I look at some of the old sports stars doing the rounds these days, the likes of Fred Trueman, recalling stories from way back in their after-dinner speeches and so on, and, quite frankly, I find it slightly pathetic. I don't want to get into any of that. I think it's all a waste of time.

And so he recoils to his own preferred world, his business and his family. It is reported a third generation of Astons, Mark, made such a big impression as a midfield player he fully justified his selection for the English Universities side. It is difficult to imagine that did not reawaken John Aston junior's interest in football.

SUBSTITUTE: JIMMY RIMMER

Born: Southport, 10-2-48
Debut: v Fulham (h), 15-4-68
United career: Football League – 34 appearances, 0 goals;
FA Cup – 3, 0; Football League Cup – 6, 0; Europe – 2 (1), 0.
Total – 45 (1), 0.

The man who did not play because of injury springs readily to mind. The image of Denis Law watching the final through a haze of inebriety from his hospital bed is almost as vivid as George Best's shimmy round the goalkeeper to score that crucial second goal. But the man who sat on the bench? Not so easy. In fact, it may surprise many who remember the final that substitutes existed at the time. Aficionados, however, will have the answer to a popular football trivia question: which English player won European Cup winner's medals with two different clubs yet played only 11 minutes of a final? Jimmy Rimmer is that man.

Substitute goalkeepers only were permitted in 1968 and Rimmer sat on the sidelines at Wembley, waiting and hoping in vain for the chance to make an appearance. Fourteen years later he was in the starting line-up for Aston Villa against Bayern Munich in Rotterdam but soon gave way to the recurrence of an injury, and Nigel Spink, his understudy, became the star of another English success. Rimmer's medals, you sense, do not fully compensate.

Many consider Rimmer was equally unlucky to be released by United. Had he been born a year or two earlier, Busby might not have felt the need to sign Alex Stepney. Had he been born a year or two later he would have been the natural successor. Rimmer grew up quickly in United's nursery but had limited opportunity to claim a first-team place. By the 1973–74 season Tommy Docherty considered him surplus to requirements and, after a loan spell with Swansea, he moved to Arsenal.

He established himself as a regular in the side and did so again following his transfer to Villa in 1977. His consistent excellence earned him a full England cap – thereby matching Stepney's international achievement – and left a trail of 'I told you so's' all the way back to Old Trafford.

Rimmer played out his Football League career at Swansea, where he settled, and switched to coaching after an encore in Malta. A decade on, he lost his job and wandered in the wilderness until he received an unlikely offer he could not refuse: to help guide China through their World Cup qualifying campaign. He was off the bench like a shot.

* * *

Sunday evening at a hotel in Blackheath and Jimmy Rimmer is grateful for the chance to catch up with a couple of old pals. Still more appreciated will be the coming weekend at home, a short sojourn to be enjoyed after the Chinese uproot their English training camp. Then he is on the road across Asia and, he hopes, back to Europe for the World Cup finals in France. Beyond that, perhaps even the glow of the limelight in his own country. Rimmer's role with the Chinese squad has recharged his spirits and reawakened an ambition that took him to United in the '60s and through the junior ranks. He recalls,

> Everything started really well for me when I went there. Everyone was saying what a good prospect I was and I got a lot of encouragement. I played my way through the various teams and at 17 I was a regular in the reserves. That was at a time when they had the likes of Dave Gaskell, Harry Gregg and Pat Dunne, all highly rated keepers. The competition was very strong but I seemed to get promoted up the order and I was very happy. Even in the reserves. I was still very young and keepers always mature later than outfield players.

It was a lively environment. While the Holy Trinity and other revered figures maintained their sacred status, and with it an inevitable distance, the tyros gathered on the cathedral steps with due respect, but also a sense of fun, a mood of optimism and an appetite for adventure. Rimmer found a soul-mate in an even younger player who would make an indelible mark on the European Cup final.

That was a great time to be at the club because they won the Championship twice, all the great players were there and, of course, Matt Busby was there. There was a real excitement about the place and you felt proud to be part of the club, even if you were a young reserve. The senior players were all fine with me – Bobby Charlton, Denis Law, Nobby Stiles, all of them. But the younger lads naturally stuck together more and I always got on well with Brian Kidd, who of course also went to Arsenal.

He had a terrific talent, a tremendous shot, and when he got his chance in the first team he grabbed it. When I travelled with the first team I tended to stick with Kiddo and he was always good for a laugh. He was good fun and always up to something. I remember once when he was all cool and sophisticated, ordering steak tartare. When it arrived he wanted the chef to cook it! After it was explained to him this was how it was supposed to be, he decided he'd better just ask for an ordinary steak. Typical Kiddo.

But he did brilliantly, and to be in the European Cup final team on his 19th birthday was amazing, really. Then he went and topped it all by scoring. John Aston was another of the lads I mixed with, and it was good to see him have such a great game in the final. It showed that even at the biggest club in the land there was a chance for lads coming through the ranks. I was pleased to be part of the final squad. I felt time was on my side and was confident I had a future at United.

So Rimmer sat out the match in near anonymity and completed the first part of his trivia question. He now admits, however, he watched the unfolding drama, and Stepney's full part in it, with churning emotions. He shared the anxieties and the tensions, then the elation as United mugged Benfica with those three goals in the first period of extra- time. He even had his winner's medal at the end of it all. And yet . . .

I remember sitting on the bench and going through it all with the rest of them. I had just a plain jersey. No number on the back of it. Jimmy Murphy and Jack Crompton were there, and Sir Matt. Sometimes he sat up in the stand but at Wembley he was down on the bench with the others. I was delighted, just like everybody else, that we came through it all, the ups and downs, and won it. I knew how much it

171

meant to the club and especially to Sir Matt. And my medal was just the same as all the other players'.

But in a way I felt a bit of an outsider that night. I've got to be honest: I would have given anything to have gone on. Just for a minute. Even 30 seconds. So I could have said I actually played in United's European Cup-winning side. I didn't want to wish Alex any harm but I would have loved to have been on the pitch, especially as it was at Wembley. When it got to 4–1 it was all over. I could have gone on then. Just for a bit, to be part of it. But that sort of thing didn't happen then and I had to just sit there.

Rimmer had been cast as the 'forgotten man' and somehow he could never quite break free of the part. He played for the first team in 20 League matches during 1970–71, yet made only a handful of appearances in the three seasons before and after. And then another young goalkeeper came into the picture. Rimmer was no longer in the frame.

Sir Matt thought I should have stayed at the club and told Tommy Docherty he shouldn't sell me. Harry Gregg always recommended me and reckoned I was the biggest goalkeeping talent at the club. But Tommy Doc thought otherwise. Paddy Roche was coming through and I had to go. No disrespect to Paddy, but look what happened afterwards. Even Tommy Doc admitted later that he got that wrong. I know I made one or two mistakes as well, but you have to allow for that with a young keeper. Sir Matt thought I was reaching the right age to be given a chance and a run in the first team. At a club like United there are always going to be young players who don't get a chance and have to move on. It can be hard, but that's the way it is.

In a way I should thank Tommy Doc for selling me to Arsenal. I'd moved from one massive club to another and got regular first-team football. Then I moved to another great club in Villa, and there we went all the way to the European Cup. So I had a tremendous career, at different clubs, in different parts of the country, and enjoyed a lot of success. I also played for my country, so I could hardly have done more. It's just that I'll always wonder what might have happened if I'd stayed at United. It's only natural. You don't want to look back and you always say there's no point, but even so . . .

Setting the second part of the trivia question did nothing to assuage him.

> We'd had a great run through to the final at Villa and I'd played in the other games, but then I got injured in the last League game. It was on the Friday night, funnily enough against Swansea. I went up for a ball with Bob Latchford, fell over backwards and hurt my neck. Tony Barton, the manager, wanted me to play and I had injections, as we did then, and it was decided we should give it a go. It didn't work. After 11 minutes I had to come off and on went Nigel Spink. It seems I was just fated as far as European Cup finals were concerned, but it makes a good trivia question. I suppose it's a claim to fame.

If Rimmer left the grand stage bearing the scars of frustration, he was to eke out a lasting satisfaction from the fringe theatre of the European game. At Swansea he played his last matches in Britain and turned to coaching with the club.

> I had ten years with them, coaching the youth and reserve teams, and produced a lot of players for them. Eight or nine of them became first-team regulars and a number of others moved on to become first-team players with other clubs. I think I can feel proud of what we achieved over those years, and it's a good feeling knowing you've put something back into the game by bringing through these young lads. And then I got the sack. When football is all you've done and all you've known from 15 to 50 and you are suddenly told you're no longer wanted, it comes as a terrible blow. I was out of the game for six months, apart from doing a bit of scouting.

It is the Tony Dunne scenario all over again: wandering the grounds and boardrooms under the dubious cover of 'scouting' duties, with half an eye on somebody else's job. Like Dunne, Rimmer wanted to feel better about himself. A solution was offered by Ted Buxton, long-time friend, aide and confidant of Terry Venables.

> I had realised after talking to friends that there was no point feeling sorry for myself, moping around and waiting for the phone to ring. I'd got to start ringing around to let people know I was eager and available for work. You can be

forgotten all too quickly in this game and I didn't intend to let that happen to me. So I put out some feelers. Then Ted rang me and said there was a job in China. He's the technical advisor and they wanted a coach. So I became their first English coach.

His brief, ostensibly, was to work on the goalkeepers – two of them giants at 6ft 4in and 6ft 5in – but he has gradually extended his sphere of influence, to the apparent approval of his employers and charges.

I love it. One or two of the players and members of staff speak English, so communication is not proving a problem, and I've never come across anyone so disciplined and dedicated. The squad were together, away from their homes and families, for four and a half months earlier this year. We've got this stint in England, and then we're back to the World Cup qualifiers for another couple of months. They're more than happy to work and train long hours – ten till twelve, four till six and then another hour in the evening. They desperately want to do well and they are technically brilliant – different class. On top of it all the money is good. I've made more in the last year than in five years with Swansea.

Much as he has warmed to the challenge and his new work colleagues, this spell back in the old country has rekindled a desire to make an impact here.

It has been enjoyable for me and a good experience for the players. We've got games with teams at Nottingham Forest, Crystal Palace, Chelsea, Charlton and Arsenal, behind closed doors. The Chinese don't like to play friendlies in public. All these clubs have been co-operative, as have Charlton and Greenwich University, allowing us to use their training facilities. I've got to admit I'd like another chance to show what I can do over here. We're happy living in Swansea but I'll move for the work. Maybe if I get China to the World Cup finals for the first time in their history, I'll get noticed and be offered a job.

And no longer be the forgotten man? China, alas, did not qualify.

174

THE ONE MISSING: DENIS LAW

Born: Aberdeen, 24-2-40
Debut: v West Bromwich Albion (h), 18-8-62
United career: Football League – 305 (4) appearances, 171 goals;
FA Cup – 44 (2), 34; Football League Cup – 11, 3; Europe – 33, 28.
Total – 393 (6), 236.

They crowned him King and the statistics above should provide sufficient explanation. But they do not. They reveal nothing of his charisma, his aura, his sheer presence. They give no inkling of the lightning reflexes, his phenomenal aerial ability, his agility and powers of improvisation, or the posturing of the supreme showman. The goals were despatched with a flourish and audacity as well as astonishing regularity. The moment he trotted on to the pitch, his blond mane flopping in time with his short, light steps, shirt out, the cuffs of his sleeves gripped in his fists, a sense of excited expectation seized his subjects. Denis Law generated enough electricity to light a small town.

He hit Old Trafford like a high-voltage bolt, that instant, dramatic impact jolting club and supporters into new life and a state of optimism. Bobby Charlton had carried the weight of the crusade since Munich and the burden had taken its toll. The arrival of George Best was still a year away. Law was the catalyst for the revival, even if his new team-mates required the best part of a season to effect the chemical reaction. Victory in the European Cup final completed the process, but Law was not at Wembley to share the glorious conclusion. As we have heard, he was there in 'spirit', laid up in hospital because of his lingering knee trouble.

He might well have reflected, in a trough of self-pity, that he never wanted to be a footballer in the first place. The son of an Aberdeen trawlerman, he had no intention of following in his father's wet footsteps,

175

either, a sample of life at sea convincing him he should stay on dry land. His boyhood ambition was to be a draughtsman, no meagre aspiration considering his background. He was brought up in a council tenement block, the youngest of seven children. A little money had to go a long way. He was 14 before he had his first pair of proper shoes. His first pair of new boots, like other luxuries such as socks, had to be hidden when his father was home from sea. However tough times may be, mothers will always spoil their sons.

Football was the escape, yet even when, at the age of 15, he was invited to Huddersfield Town for trials he harboured no serious thoughts of making a career in the game. One glance at the kid down from Scotland suggested he was wise not to dream. He was frail, pale, of modest height and wore corrective glasses because of a squint in his right eye. All of which goes to prove first impressions can be deceptive.

An operation cured the squint, rendered the glasses redundant and gave the young Aberdonian a different perspective on his life. The new-found confidence was reflected in his football and others recognised an uncommon talent. He was only 16 and playing in Huddersfield's youth team when the club were offered £10,000 for his services. The bid, which was rejected, had been made by Manchester United's Matt Busby. Law was still 16 when he made his League debut, so establishing a club record. Two years later he had his first full international cap – a post-war record – and scored, albeit fortuitously, in the 3–0 win against Wales. Scotland's manager at the time was Matt Busby.

Law went on to score 30 goals in 55 appearances for his country and was acknowledged as one of the great exponents of the global game. He played, and scored, for the Rest of the World side against England at Wembley in 1963, a match which celebrated the centenary of the FA. The following year he became only the second British player, after Sir Stanley Matthews, to be voted European Footballer of the Year.

His domestic career did eventually take him from Huddersfield to Manchester, though not directly to United. In 1960 he was transferred to City for £55,000. His new team proved a letdown, but he confirmed an extraordinary instinct for scoring goals and became the subject of another trivia classic. He scored seven goals in an FA Cup tie and ended up on the losing side. He had scored all City's goals as they led 6–2 at Luton when the match was abandoned because of a waterlogged pitch. He scored again in the rearranged tie, which City lost 3–1.

In the summer of 1961 he joined the bounty-hunters headed for Italy and became the first Briton to be involved in a £100,000 transfer. He signed for Torino, whose entire side had perished in a plane crash in 1949.

Even with Joe Baker, another Scot, for company, Law could not come to terms with the suppressed version of the game accepted as the norm in Italy, or the constant attention of the media. He had occasion to confide in an old admirer that he yearned to return to England. On 12 July 1962, and after lengthy and tedious negotiations, Matt Busby had his man. Law became a Manchester United player for a British record fee of £116,000.

He scored his first League goal for the club within seven minutes against West Bromwich Albion – and the making of a King had begun. His goals kept a floundering United out of the Second Division and a characteristic piece of opportunism to beat Gordon Banks put the team on course for their 1963 FA Cup final victory against Leicester City. His influence and appeal reached a peak in the mid-'60s, coinciding with United's Championship successes.

Harnessing this dynamic force, however, came at a price. The overspill of energy regularly landed the Scot in trouble with referees – so regularly, in fact, it became a slightly embarrassing joke that he timed his annual explosion of temper and subsequent suspension conveniently for the Christmas holiday footballers were not supposed to have. He explained candidly that when kicked or punched, he kicked and punched back. Recurring knee problems blighted his later years and deprived him of what would have been his biggest match, the European Cup final.

He survived two transfer listings by United – the first in a famous stand-off with Busby over wages, the second when everyone seemingly ignored it – before he was finally released in 1973. He returned to City for his encore season and, with his final act in League football, back-heeled the goal which effectively consigned United to the Second Division. He ended his playing days in more joyous circumstances, with Scotland at the World Cup finals in Germany. He came back to Maine Road to be told they could offer him only reserve-team football. This was not the way to go. Strutting the game's grandest stage was. He'd done that; he'd done just about everything. This was the time to quit.

The father of five was never drawn to the idea of adopting his own football family as a manager and drifted instead into the TV and radio punditary business. Considering his aversion to the media throughout his playing career, this development was viewed with contempt by some of his new colleagues, but the name and the personality represented an undeniably attractive proposition. Although his broadcasting work has diminished in recent years, he has a vibrant after-dinner routine and loyal subjects who will forever regard him as the King.

* * *

A light drizzle speckles the panoramic window of the clubhouse and Denis Law grimaces. He checks his watch and paces the lounge again. Still no sign of his playing partner but then, given the conditions out there, he is not unduly concerned about waiting in here, especially if he can organise a warm drink. The beverage ordered, he nestles into an easy chair.

Shay Brennan was surprised to hear Law was playing golf again, and the Scot nods. 'Yes, after 20 years, and I'm enjoying it. I love the game and played quite a lot when I was younger. I had to give it up because of the old knee trouble. But, touch wood,' he says, leaning forward to tap the table, 'I've had no problems. I'm playing off 18. Mind you, I'm a bit of a fair-weather player. Can't say I'm too enthusiastic about playing when it's cold and wet.'

He glances over his shoulder towards the window. The rain appears to have all but ceased, clearing the view across a gentle, green Cheshire landscape. Law is encouraged to stand and take a closer look. The stance is eerily familiar. At the age of 57 he could still be the King. Still lean, straight. Sharp features beneath a full thatch of hair. The face is lined but the expressions are alert. The electrical supply is still switched on. Here, however, he has uncovered a quiet haven and can play golf in relative anonymity. Providing, that is, his playing partner turns up.

'Typical Crerand,' he says with exaggerated dismay. 'Late as usual.'

Almost before the words have tumbled, a phone rings. Guess who?

'Aye, it's Pat. He's at the hospital. His daughter's just had a baby. He'll probably be an hour or so yet.'

Outside, a pale sun is reflecting from the damp practice green and one or two more members are dragging trollies from their cars.

'That's better. I think I'll go and hit a few balls till grandad gets here.'

Law and Crerand are and always were kindred spirits. They joined United within seven months of each other. More specifically, they joined Matt Busby and his new family. They responded to the Scottish bond and, although they were more volatile than their boss, he valued their fervour. He convinced Law, as he would convince Crerand, they were coming in at ground level of something big. Law had played under Bill Shankly at Huddersfield and although he, too, was a very different character from Busby, their roots and football principles were the same. Both managers hailed from the Scottish coalfields; both believed in a beautifully simple game played by committed men, as Law recalls.

> I think it was always said that people from Scotland, like
> people from the North-East, would battle for you. Managers
> looked for that in players. Busby had lost half his team at

Munich and I was happy to come back from Italy to play
with the likes of Bobby Charlton. It was a dream come true
for me. Then, a year later, George Best came into the team
and the next five years or so were great years at the club.

Although I didn't enjoy the football in Italy – it was very
defensive, very negative – there's no doubt I came back a
better player. After a season of being really tightly marked I
had a much sharper awareness and learned how to find space
for myself. So when I came back to England, where forwards
had more time and space anyway, I found it much easier to
score goals. It's a much better game in Italy now and I loved
everything away from the football: the food, the people,
everything. Today I'd probably enjoy playing over there. But
not then. It was awful.

Such was Law's determination to leave Italy he refused a lucrative move
to Torino's neighbours, Juventus. He was encouraged by Busby's reciprocal
resolve and inspired by the ethos the manager – and his assistant, Jimmy
Murphy – imbued at Old Trafford. Law had stood on the Scoreboard End
the night United played their first match after the crash, the FA Cup tie
against Sheffield Wednesday, and was moved by the emotion of the
occasion. With Busby still seriously ill in Munich, Murphy was in
temporary charge. Law would discover that Busby 'treated his players like
human beings' and that Murphy would have no truck with cheats.

Playing with Charlton (interestingly, Law felt the England hero was more
effective as a winger than a midfield player), then Crerand and then Best,
he was able to exploit the sharper awaresness he had added to his game. The
direct supply or the rebounds ensured rich and often easy pickings for a
player capable of flying, jack-knife headers and acrobatic scissor kicks.

We had so many great players and the way we played, always
going forward, there were always plenty of chances. Bobby
could knock in those 30-yard goals with that terrific shot of
his, but I used to get a lot of my goals from the shots the
goalkeeper saved but couldn't hold. When Bobby lined up to
shoot I'd move in on the keeper because I knew there was a
good chance he'd drop it, and often he did. I picked up the
scraps. I couldn't shoot like Bobby. The six-yard box was my
area. Anything further than the penalty spot was a bit too far
for me.

179

Self-deprecating? Of course. A hint of old rivalry? Very likely. Law, like Charlton, maintains they are embraced in genuine camaraderie, but the Scot must have pondered, as he lay in his hospital bed, that he should have been raising aloft the European Cup. He had been the captain. Now the honour was Charlton's. Law would also express the view that Best sometimes held on to the ball too long and would reveal that some players resented the publicity the Irishman attracted. They were all human. Including the King.

But Law knew his value to the team. Busby effectively confirmed it when he insisted Law had to play in the decisive League match at home to Arsenal on Monday, 26 April 1965, despite having half a dozen stitches in his knee. He scored twice in the 3–1 win while Leeds drew 3–3 at Birmingham, a combination of results which ensured the Championship was United's.

The following year Law decided it was time his value was appropriately recognised and 'tried it on' with Busby. He asked for more money and threatened to leave if the club did not comply. Busby put him on the transfer list and summoned him from Aberdeen to Old Trafford. Law, who had no desire to join another club, was forced to make a public climb-down and read out a prepared statement of apology. Behind the scenes, however, Busby had given him a rise, although not the signing-on fee Law had also requested. A compromise had been struck and, in the eyes of the outside world and the other players, the pay structure had not been broken to accommodate the wishes of one individual. Busby and Law were happy.

Law continued to repay United with his goals – celebrated with his trademark salute, a ramrod right arm thrust into the air – but at increasing cost to himself. The stitches, strappings and painkilling injections could not keep him going indefinitely and, after United's Championship victory in 1967, 'the old knee trouble' proved more difficult to patch up. He made only 23 League appearances in the 1967–68 season and mustered a mere seven goals. He scored twice in his three European Cup games before bowing to the inevitable. He failed a fitness test on the morning of the return leg against Real Madrid. He sat in the dug-out as his team-mates eked out an improbable passage to the final and solemnly accepted he could have no part at Wembley.

He elected to forego a trip to the final as a spectator and instead sought to cure his knee problem. Three days before the biggest match in United's history, Law was admitted to St Joseph's Hospital, Whalley Range, Manchester, for an operation. The surgeon removed a one-and-a-half piece of cartilage and with it a load off the player's mind. Law had arranged for friends to join him at his bedside to watch the match, but had not bargained for the enthusiasm of the nuns.

One of the sisters came in that morning – I couldn't believe it – at six o'clock in the morning and she had this huge rosette. I wanted to see that at six o'clock in the morning like I wanted a hole in the head! So the celebrations started well, well before the game.

I was dying for the lads to do it for Matt. That was what mattered. It was very nerve-racking, particularly when Eusebio broke through a few minutes from time. I thought, 'That's it, we're never going to win this thing,' but somehow either Alex Stepney saved his shot or it hit him. I think Eusebio saw the headlines because he tried to blast it. If he could have his day again I'm sure he would side-foot it. If Jimmy Greaves had been on the end of that chance we would have lost. But we deserved to win because we went at them throughout.

After the game the lads phoned me up in a drunken haze while I was having a few beers in the ward with some pals. I think I was the only one in bed that night! At one stage the TV cameras came in but they wouldn't take any shots of me because, as they put it, I was too 'emotionally disturbed'. The next day Sir Matt and the players came by the hospital with the Cup. A lovely gesture.

Law's version of the aborted television interview corresponds roughly with David Coleman's. His assessment of United's, and more specifically Busby's, achievement is unequivocal.

When you think that Matt nearly died at Munich and then, ten years later, had created another great side and won the European Cup, it is incredible. He had taken English football into Europe, way back in the '50s, and it was fitting Manchester United should become the first English team to win the European Cup. The Cup-Winners' Cup and UEFA Cup are good trophies, but the main one is the European Cup.

Law was able to play a more regular part in United's 1968–69 campaign and scored 30 goals from 43 games, but when the match officials refused to rule he had turned the ball over Milan's line in the Old Trafford leg of their semi-final, his hopes of a European Cup final appearance had gone. His hopes of playing on with United into the 1973–74 season were dashed by

Docherty, and he went back to Maine Road. And then came *that* goal.

> The ball came into the box, a few minutes to go, and I just
> back-heeled it in. I hadn't got a clue where the goal was, but it
> went in. It was a fluke, really.

Fluke or not, United were on their way to the Second Division and even a
pitch invasion could not save the former champions of Europe from their
wretched fate. Law's countenance was as glum as any Stretford Ender's. There
was no ramrod salute of the right arm, no self-satisfied grin, no celebratory
jig. Just a funereal march away from the scene of the treachery, his head
bowed in sorrow. 'I have seldom been as depressed as I was that weekend,' he
admits.

Making the Scotland World Cup squad revived his spirits and playing in
the match against Zaire provided an appropriate finale. He had realised a
lifetime's ambition. A season in City's reserves was highly unlikely to top that
and so, on August Bank Holiday, 1974, Law announced his retirement.
Management did not appeal to him and it was only when his playing days
became memories that he began to appreciate fully the life he had left behind.

> Management is a different ball game. You need a hard streak
> in you to do the job. You've got to be good and cruel, and if
> you've not got it you'll be out. If you had your time as a player
> again you'd probably enjoy it a bit more. When you retire you
> miss the lads more than anything. It took me three years to get
> over it. Mind you, it wasn't so much of a family when someone
> had to get a round in!

The radio work has also dwindled and again Law is self-deprecating. 'Past
my sell-by date,' he says. His enduring popularity with dinner audiences and
fast-food supporters would indicate this is not so. His enthusiasm for United
past and present bridges the generation gap.

> It would be apt for United to win the European Cup again 30
> years after the first win and 40 years after the Munich tragedy.
> The old players would be delighted for the club and the fans.
> I was fortunate to play under two great Scottish managers in
> Bill Shankly and Sir Matt, and I'm sure that if Alex Ferguson
> wins the European Cup he will be regarded in the same
> mould. Like Matt's team in the '60s, Fergie's team plays
> exciting, entertaining football.

PART IV

REALITY . . . AND NEW DREAMS

Sir Matt Busby's European champions returned to domestic football an even more prestigious scalp. Their achievement had earned the respect and admiration of the English game but now it was back to the day job and they were put through the mill. The injured Aston was replaced by Willie Morgan, signed from Burnley, and although some of the old swagger was occasionally evident – they annihilated Queens Park Rangers 8–1 – their League form was ominously erratic. They finished the First Division campaign 11th, their lowest position for six years.

This season, however, offered a new challenge, even beyond the boundaries of the European game. United's success at Wembley had booked them a meeting with their South American counterparts, Estudiantes of Argentina, over two legs for the World Club Championship and, despite the savagery that had marred Celtic's encounter with Racing Club the year before, Busby and his adventurers embarked on this journey into the unknown.

Any foreboding was totally justified. Hostility on and off the field soured the entire experience. On arrival in Buenos Aires for the first leg, United were soon made aware Argentina were not amused at being called 'animals' by Sir Alf Ramsey during the 1966 World Cup. The Argentine media and public, in turn, denounced Stiles as the 'Assassin'. The United party were given armed guards, even at Mass. On the field of play they were afforded no such protection. Charlton had to have stitches in a gashed shin and Stiles had a cut and swollen eye after being butted and punched. To add almost inevitable insult to injury, he was sent off for a characteristic gesture.

In the circumstances, United were content to be returning home trailing only 1–0. That confidence was shaken when Estudiantes plundered a goal just five minutes into the night at Old Trafford. They were in command and knew it, stifling, containing and frustrating United's every manoeuvre. The cynicism was less overt, but eventually it caused Best to snap, the Irishman's retaliatory punch resulting in his dismissal. Morgan turned in Crerand's free-kick three minutes from the end, but a play-off, and intercontinental supremacy, proved beyond them.

Consolation might have been retrieved on the more familiar fields of Europe, in defence of their trophy. They loosened up with a 10–2 aggregate defeat of Waterford, Law announcing his recovery from surgery with seven of the goals. Another two from the Scot and one by Kidd appeared to have seen off Anderlecht but United required a goal from Carlo Sartori in the away leg to squeeze through 4–3 on aggregate. Progress against Rapid Vienna was more comfortable, United following up another 3–0 home win (two for Best, one for Morgan) with a goalless draw in Austria.

United had sustained their remarkable record of consistency in the competition, reaching their fifth semi-final in five attempts. A second consecutive final loomed larger in their sights as they came through the first half-hour of their match against Milan at the San Siro unscathed. More encouraging still was the withdrawal, through injury, of the sublime Gianni Rivera. But goals either side of half-time, by Sormani and Hamrin, swung the balance of power. It might have been worse, especially after the dismissal of the tempestuous young full-back John Fitzpatrick.

Back at Old Trafford the faithful remained convinced the cause was not hopeless. A lone voice from the 63,000 called out, 'Andiamo vincere, Rocco.' Whether or not Milan's coach heard that vote of confidence, the Italians did indeed go on to win the tie on aggregate. Charlton's goal, fashioned by Best 20 minutes from the end, was all United could eke from Milan's stubborn resistance. They claimed another, insisting Law had put the ball over the line, but the officials were unmoved. United were out, their exasperation compounded by the knowledge Ajax would be no match for the winners of this semi-final. Their judgement was sound, Milan winning the final 4–1. They also won the World Club Championship – against Estudiantes.

It was a sad and poignant night for another reason. Sir Matt Busby, creator and inspiration of all that Manchester United stood for, was stepping down. To be more precise, he was stepping up, to general manager, and from 1 June 1969 Wilf McGuinness, one of the family, a man who understood the dream and felt for the crusade, would take over team affairs with the title of chief coach. Being called manager at this stage might have been too much pressure for a 31-year-old promoted from youth-team coach, Busby reasoned. He was told he had the job for three years and Sir Matt would be there to help, counsel and generally take the administrative and political weight off his shoulders.

McGuinness, his promising international and club playing career truncated by injury, had no problem with the general arrangement. He was a bouncy, bumptious Mancunian. He had worked with the England squad during the 1966 World Cup. He was brimming with enthusiasm and ideas. New ideas. Tactics. Strategies. He believed United had to adapt to an evolving game by harnessing their traditional flair rather than giving it free rein. And if he didn't get what he wanted from established players, he would replace them. Even if their names were Charlton and Law. The senior players were his contemporaries, his friends. But if he had to be tough and bruise a few egos, then so be it.

McGuinness improved United's League position that 1969–70 season to eighth and they reached the semi-finals of the League Cup and FA Cup. It was, to use more recent football parlance, 'something to build on', and McGuinness was rewarded with the title of manager. Shay Brennan, McGuinness's best man, was released as part of the restructuring. He saw Rimmer as the long-term goalkeeper. Fresh faces were introduced, and he still had Best shredding defences and capable of rescuing the team single-handedly. Best could not, alas, rescue McGuinness. Two days after Christmas, the manager was sacked.

United had again reached the semi-final of the League Cup under McGuinness and again lost, but it was their indifferent showing in the League which concerned Busby and the board. That and the stories of discontent among the senior players. For all that cocky exterior, McGuinness had a fragile soul, and to be shunned this way by his club, and by Busby, shattered him. Busby took temporary charge, and the team stabilised and finished the season eighth. Again. The club would resume the search for his successor, this time outside the family.

McGuinness was offered his old job but found Bill Foulkes in the way and instead accepted an invitation from Aris Salonica, in Greece. His hair went white, then went altogether. Coming to terms with baldness was the easy part. Over the years, however, he learned to live with the emotional scars. He had a short spell with a second Greek club, Panachaiki Patras, before returning to England. He worked with York, Hull and Bury, ultimately as physiotherapist.

Today McGuinness deploys his ready chatter and regenerated enthusiasm on the after-dinner circuit and local radio. He lives with his wife, Beryl, in a large Victorian house in a quiet neighbourhood where Altrincham becomes Timperley. At the age of 60, he is as jovial, friendly and candid as the image he has always projected. 'I've not changed – I'm still bald.'

He was another Collyhurst Catholic, although his family moved up Rochdale Road to Blackley and he went to Mount Carmel School. 'Bernard Manning went there as well.' A school for comedians, presumably. Like

Manning, he had roots in the other camp. His father was a City fan. But McGuinness maintains, 'In those days we wanted all our teams to do well. I was a Manchester lad and supported all the teams in the area. I still do.'

He jumped at the chance of playing for United.

I joined in the same week, Coronation Week, 1953, as Bobby. I was in the team before Bobby. As a 17-year-old I was understudy to Duncan Edwards and got a Championship medal in 1956. I shot up very quickly after the accident. Within six months of being a reserve at United I was playing for England, at the age of 20. I played twice for the national team. I felt that even if Duncan Edwards had still been around I could have got in the side because he was that great he could play anywhere.

I had a great belief in myself. I think everybody does, but I was noisier than others. Cockier. Roger Byrne clipped me more than once for standing my ground. I missed only one of the European trips before Belgrade and was on the list for that match, but I twisted my knee and was carried off in the reserve game on the Saturday before. It was diagnosed as a torn cartilage and my name was crossed off the list.

I was in Manchester city centre that Thursday with a friend from the *News Chronicle*. There was a placard and this guy was shouting, 'United plane crashes on runway.' We thought they'd bumped something, never for a minute that it was serious. We went round to the *News Chron* offices and somebody said, 'There's been fatalities.' I couldn't believe it. We were in a state of shock. At first we just heard the names of survivors – Bobby, Dennis Viollet, Bill Foulkes, Harry Gregg. And we're saying, 'What about all the others?' It was late at night when that news came through.

When I got home that evening my mum and dad knew about it and my mum said, 'Come on, we're going to church.' They were having a novena at Mount Carmel and I'll always remember praying there, in tears, hoping all the names would come through, that they'd survived. I was praying and promising I'll never do this or that again if my friends can be alive. But then when we got back home, late at night, I knew my friends had died.

The next morning I went down and into the dressing room. One or two reserve players were there and Jimmy came in and just said, 'See you Monday.' There were private tears. We were just stunned. Gordon Clayton and I went to see Eddie Colman's parents and girlfriend. We didn't know what to say. I think Gordon and I went to every funeral. We were the representatives because we were injured.

McGuinness recovered from that injury but suffered a more serious setback the following year. 'I broke my leg and there were complications.' He rolls up his trouser leg to reveal what looks like the surface of the moon.

I had a bone graft and Matt Busby said there was a job for me here. I could train, keep fit and if ever I felt I could make it back, go for it. That's what I did. The lads used to laugh at me, limping round the ground. It was pretty awful, really. But I was only 22 when I broke my leg. Nowadays I probably would have got back.

I was a coach with England Youth from 1964 and in 1966 worked with Alf Ramsey's World Cup squad. I felt good in training and matched some of them, so I thought if I could do that I could get in United's team. So the next season I made a comeback and played 30-odd Central League games, but was never quite there. I was sub at Leicester and Paddy had a bad match, and I was saying, 'Come on, Paddy, get off.' But he didn't. I never got a game but I told them I made them play that well they won the Championship in 1967. I decided it was time to concentrate on the coaching, where I had something to offer.

I thought Matt would go on a lot longer, and I was hoping he would. Then I thought I'd be in with a chance of working beneath him. But not when he announced it, not really. The odd flash and dream that you might be in with a chance goes across your mind, I must admit. If you're the type of person I am you believe anything's possible. I thought they might get a big name from outside, and usually they bring in their own staff. But, in fairness to Matt Busby, he was very loyal to his staff. Everybody had been there a long time – maybe too long, some people say.

Then I had a little whisper, from the Irish scout, Billy Behan, who'd been talking to Matt, that I was in with a shout, and I told a few people to get a bet on. And I think the day before, the word was, 'You'd better come in with a tie on tomorrow, there's an announcement.' I thought, bloody hell, I could be in here. Whether it was over-confidence I don't know, but I wasn't a bit nervous, because he'd still be here, which I was glad about. As for the rest of the staff, like Johnny Aston and Jack Crompton, I didn't think it was for them. So I thought, that'll do.

He called me in before the press conference and said all the team duties were mine, the coaching and the training, and that he'd act as general manager. But the team was mine; I'd pick it. There were a few grey areas but I thought we'd sort them out later. This was great. Really it would have been better if we'd dotted the i's and crossed the t's. There were certain players I mentioned I'd have liked – such as Mick Mills, Colin Todd and Malcolm Macdonald – and if we had got them it might have helped. I went to watch Macdonald playing for Luton at Mansfield and stood on the popular side. Sir Matt and Jimmy Murphy went in disguise to watch him somewhere and said, 'Yes, you're right.' He did all the negotiating but said Macdonald had an option with Liverpool. Then, blow me, he went to Newcastle. If I'd been more experienced and really at it I might have done something about it. I mean, we let them have four of our players in that period, including Don Givens and Jimmy Ryan, good players, and we should have forced the issue.

But did he try to force the issue too vehemently with his players, his old pals?

Not really. I wanted to be fair. I tried to do it the Matt Busby way, in many ways. Tactically I might have tried to bring in things they may have thought weren't for them. But Matt Busby did tactics. He was the first with the tactical board, no matter what they say about playing off the cuff. His final words were always, 'Go out and play and enjoy yourselves.' But on a Friday he'd have a team talk. He went round every player of the opposition. I followed those sort of lines.

But I also learned from Alf. I remember a goal Denis Law scored from a free-kick played behind the wall after he ran over the ball. Well, I got that from England Youth and told the lads, before I became manager. I told them to try things. I came with ideas. Sometimes when you're at one club you get blinkers on. Yes, I know you can over-coach and that wasn't Manchester United's way, but dealing with young players and the World Cup-winning team you pick up other ideas which are good ideas. They could have helped.

Another was what we called 'restart'. Some of the players said 'restart?' and I explained it was when the referee blew his whistle for a throw-in, corner, whatever, and you work on it to retain the ball or work a goalscoring position from it. We could have enhanced ourselves, I felt, with some of those ideas but based on the United way of playing. I think some of the lads appreciated that. Where it went wrong was through misunderstandings, and stories that were presented or interpreted the wrong way. I look back and say, yes, that happened, but it didn't happen anything like the story that has come out.

There were stories that Bobby resented me. He didn't resent me one bit. I was a bit annoyed at Alex Stepney for putting it out that I made Bobby do press-ups in the rain. That was a light-hearted thing and it wasn't in the rain. Look, I'd grown up with lads like Bobby and Shay Brennan. Then little Nobby came on the scene. 'Happy', we called him. Well, we called him a lot of things, but he was a great lad, a Collyhurst lad. And Brian Kidd. I thought I was friends with them all. I fell out, sure I did, with certain people. You do that. But the club's the main thing and personalities mean very little when it comes down to it. We were United.

Anyway, Nobby and Shay were fun-loving lads and the other lads joined in. If they lost at cards they'd carry people's bags, call people 'sir'. Little fun things. I grew up with that. Another rule was that anyone caught with his hands in his tracksuit pockets during training does ten press-ups. This particular day Bobby had something on in town and got changed into his suit before the usual team talk. So he joined us on the pitch at the Cliff for that and Shay and Nobby went behind him, pointing. He'd got his hands in his pockets. I said, 'Bobby, I'm sorry, they've caught you. Ten press-ups.' Well, Bobby wasn't going to laugh at it, but he bent down, in his suit, did his ten press-ups and that was it. Do you think he would have been standing out there if it had been raining? That annoyed me. It was rubbish.

The day I got the sack Kiddo blasted off at the others –
'You've done this, you've done that.' He told them they'd let
me down. Young Kiddo, Collyhurst lad. He was one of my
favourites for the future. He felt there was a reason to do
that. I don't know if anybody was talking behind my back. I
knew some of the lads played golf with Sir Matt and
discussed things. Why not? He was the general manager. He
had so much faith in me to give me the job and I had so
much faith in him because I thought the world of him. We
all did. So I could see no problem. I didn't see it as going
behind my back. I honestly believed he would see it in the
right way.

I never really found out why it happened. Perhaps it was
those grey areas, too many of them, and me being
inexperienced. Of course, I was learning, and of course I
made mistakes. Even the most experienced do. It's part of the
learning process. So these things didn't worry me and that's
why I was hurt when it finally happened. Because I felt we
were going through together, and that hurt. And I was bitter.
I felt that if I'd had my three years, not just 18 months, I
would have been that much better. I spent two hours trying
to make him change his mind.

In hindsight, it did come too soon for me. It would have
been far better if he'd brought me on a lot slower, rather than
letting me pick the team. But he wanted out, really. I didn't
realise how much it had taken out of him. Especially
Munich, of course. And yet coming back showed how strong
he was. And, don't forget, he was in his sixties.

At the time I didn't think the job was that big. People say
the pressure of managing caused my hair to fall out. It wasn't
that at all. I went white and then lost my hair after I left
United and went to Greece. I put it down to leaving United,
not worrying. I was very hurt and wanted to hurt back. I felt
badly let down. I never hated Matt. I just wanted him to feel
like I felt. That's why I wanted them to think I was going to
tell my story to the papers. You do things like that. To me it
was the end of the world.

I went for the whisky in the boardroom and there was
none in. There usually was. On Sundays we had meetings of
the staff – Jack, Johnny, myself. Like they did before Munich
– Matt, Jimmy, Bert and Ted. That was another blow. Ted

died before I got the job. You need people like that. We'd have a chat, a couple of whiskies, then off home. So that day I was drinking sherry and Jack came in. I'd rung him and said it was all over. Jack was kind. I banged my head against a pillar, I was that hurt. When they went down I thought, 'Serves you right.' They'd had two others after me and still hadn't put it right, so it wasn't only me.

Matt was a hard act to follow. It wasn't that he interfered. I felt I was nearly there. We did well in the cups. But they couldn't keep it up in the League and the youth policy had stopped. Some players were getting old, some had injuries. They were creaking. When I dropped Bobby and Denis you'd have thought I'd dropped the atom bomb. But Matt Busby had done it. I learned the lesson, though, that you don't drop people unless you've got somebody better to replace them. Bestie was brilliant for me, most of the time. People say Matt should have done this or that with him, but he played a lot of games for the club and I'll never knock him.

The reason I still love United is because of all the enjoyment I've had, especially in my playing days. I loved those people. I loved the Busby Babes. We were all together. And I wouldn't have been anything without Jimmy Murphy. He made us believe. It was the combination of Matt and Jimmy that made it work. And all the unknown people at United, behind the scenes, who helped. I owed them all so much, not only Matt Busby and Jimmy Murphy.

But that night at Wembley, in '68, we all knew what we were doing it for. Because he *was* Manchester United. To me, anyway. It wasn't the directors or whatever else. It was Matt Busby. I knew he was thinking of the lads who died at Munich, and the ones who were injured. I thought, this great man, he's thinking it's for them, and I'm thinking it's for him. He's Manchester United. And this really is Matt Busby. I was very emotional that evening. I never stopped shouting during the match. It's all right thinking it's your destiny, but you've still got to win it. And it was magnificent.

It's better to remember the good things first. Forget the bad things. My son, Paul, runs the School of Excellence there but I would have the same feelings now if he didn't. It was my life. Alex Ferguson brought the 1990 FA Cup-winning side over to Bury for my testimonial, at no charge. I was at

Bury for 11 years as coach, trainer, physio and cat-feeder. I was limping away and couldn't carry on. We got 8,000. It was great.

And now it's great for me to see the present team, like it is for Bobby, because we went through it all from 1953. It's tremendous to watch these kids today put together the kind of moves that bring back all the memories. Bobby says the same. I have tears in my eyes because we are back to the Babes.

I believe Alex Ferguson's side will win the European Cup in the near future. Alex is different in many ways from Matt Busby. You can see when Alex is angry; you couldn't be sure with Matt. He could smile warmly, then rip you apart. But the end product is the same, and now, for me, Alex is Manchester United, as Matt was. Alex has proved himself as time has gone on. Perhaps if I'd had time to develop . . .

* * *

While Busby steadied the ship in the second half of the 1970–71 season, completing his record stint as manager of one club, the search was on to find his next successor. Don Revie and Dave Sexton were among those mooted, but the concerted move was for Jock Stein, the man who had made Celtic champions of Europe a year before Busby's triumph. Crerand, a common confidant, approached Stein, who then met Busby, and the deal seemed done. Until Stein turned down the job, explaining his wife did not wish to leave Glasgow.

When Sexton also dropped out of the running and nothing developed on the Revie front, United turned to Frank O'Farrell. The Irishman's astute stewardship of Leicester had impressed Old Trafford. He also carried himself with dignity. And he was a Catholic. Busby assured him there would be no interference from him, that he was bound for the boardroom. O'Farrell, with his No. 2 Malcolm Musgrove in tow, accepted.

O'Farrell's United blazed into the 1971–72 season. By the turn of the year they were five points clear at the top of the First Division. Best was superb. But if three consecutive draws hadn't provided evidence the flame was flickering, seven successive defeats were conclusive. Now the true sentiments came out. O'Farrell believed the old guard were past it; they regarded him as a distant, introverted stranger, tucked away in his eyrie. Best, disillusioned by it all, was into disappearing mode. United finished yet another Championship eighth best.

The club responded to O'Farrell's demands for new players. Martin Buchan was a good investment and injury cut down the luckless Ian Moore. Wyn Davies was an inexpensive flutter, but Ted MacDougall, signed from Bournemouth for £200,000, was a more damning gamble. He was simply out of his depth. Many inside and outside the club reached the same verdict on the manager. A humiliating 5–0 defeat at Crystal Palace on 16 December 1972 left United second bottom of the First Division. Behind the scenes at Selhurst Park, O'Farrell's successor was being primed. Three days later O'Farrell, along with Musgrove and Aston senior, were sacked. United announced that Best was out also.

Tommy Docherty had been a particularly interested spectator at the Palace match and his presence was remarkably convenient for United. Busby had been taken by his management of Chelsea and Scotland. He appeared to have the strength of character and purpose deemed necessary at Old Trafford. He was bumptious and outspoken, a rogue even, the antithesis of O'Farrell. But look where nice, quiet men get you! Law and Morgan, who worked with the Doc on the international scene, backed Busby's judgement. Docherty, duly released by the Scottish FA, was walking through the door at Old Trafford almost before it had slammed behind O'Farrell.

That door would rarely be closed over the ensuing months, such was the frenzy of comings and goings. With Paddy Crerand as his assistant, Docherty feverishly went about the task of resuscitating the ailing giant. George Graham, Alex Forsyth, Jim Holton, Mick Martin and Lou Macari came in. In a less conspicuous deal, he lined up a young Irishman called Gerry Daly. MacDougall went to West Ham.

Docherty now had to consider what roles Charlton and Law might play in his plans. Charlton took the matter out of his hands and retired at the end of the season, making his final appearance for United at Chelsea. Law was dismayed by a statement he would be given a free transfer. He claimed Docherty reneged on an agreement there would be no announcement until the player's testimonial, scheduled for early the following season. But Docherty was restless to pursue his renaissance. He had steered the club away from relegation – they finished 18th – and now he believed the only way was up.

Best made a last, ill-fated attempt at a comeback to reinforce the new crusade, and Law and Dunne appreciated his contribution to their testimonials. But perhaps symptomatic of United's state of health was their resorting to Stepney as penalty-taker. At one stage of the season his two successful conversions made him joint top-scorer. Docherty signed Stewart Houston and Jim McCalliog, and introduced Brian Greenhoff, yet could not resist the spectre of relegation this time. The reality of United's ignominy was numbing, the irony of Law's part in the last act Shakespearean. They finished the season 21st, the position they had occupied when Docherty was appointed.

The club could not countenance further managerial upheaval and gleaned some consolation from a restoration of traditional footballing values in the closing matches. That optimism and trust were not misplaced. Docherty's dervishes rampaged through the Second Division. He had a new centre-forward, Stuart Pearson, and then bought a right-winger from Tranmere called Steve Coppell. The tempo and enthusiasm of the team were set by the midfield men, Daly and Sammy McIlroy, the player cast as the last Busby Babe. They returned to the First Division as champions.

That momentum, sustained with the recruitment of a left-winger, Gordon Hill, and picked up again after Stepney reclaimed his place from the hapless Paddy Roche, carried them to third place in the League and to the FA Cup final. Defeat at the hands of Second Division Southampton at Wembley tarnished the recovery, but did not inhibit it or the ebullient manager. The club were back in Europe for the first time since 1969.

United overcame Ajax in the first round of the UEFA Cup, only to be eclipsed by Juventus. They were also more vulnerable in the League and tailed off in sixth place. In the FA Cup, however, they were not to be denied, defeating champions Liverpool 2–1 in the final with goals by Pearson and Jimmy Greenhoff, brother of Brian, who added guile to Docherty's vivacious team. Jimmy Nicholl and Arthur Albiston had emerged as the full-backs, and Stepney had garnished his career with another Wembley success. Docherty now recalls,

> When I took the job they were obviously in decline, otherwise they wouldn't have come for a new manager. I saw that game at Palace and could see the state of the thing. The '68 team had grown old together and the team now needed not one or two players but seven or eight. There was very little youth policy and I felt a lot of players weren't interested in how they were playing as much as how long they were playing. I could see what Frank O'Farrell was trying to do but was unable to do. So when I got the job I thought, if I don't get rid of some of them, they'll get rid of me – the way they got rid of Frank O'Farrell.
>
> I always felt it was my destiny to manage Manchester United. I don't know why, it was just in my bones. I knew Matt very well. He was manager when I played for Scotland.

After the Munich crash Jimmy Murphy tried to sign me for Old Trafford, but Preston wouldn't let me go to Manchester United. In fact, I'd been invited for trials at United after finishing my National Service. Had I accepted I might have been in the crash. With all these things, I just felt I was destined to go there some day, in some capacity.

The players I got rid of had been great players. Bobby helped me by saying he was thinking of retiring. Eventually I would have had to tell him his days had gone, and I'm grateful he spared me that. It's difficult to tell the supporters their favourite is leaving. Same with Denis Law. They idolised him. But I knew Denis had gone. I'd known him a long time. I captained Scotland when he got his first cap. I took him under my wing. He and Dave Mackay and I were great pals, which made it much harder. But I wasn't running the club for Tommy Docherty or Denis Law, I was running it for Manchester United, and I told Denis to his face he was cheating. Matt was against it. He was very fond of his old players, which was understandable. But they had to go.

I agreed to have Paddy as my assistant because I thought it would please Matt. Worst decision I've ever made in my life! I should have got the sack for that. Socially, first-class, but the most disorganised person you've ever met in your life! About a year later I told the board I'd made a mistake. Matt was obviously in favour of Paddy but Big Louis and the rest never really were, and they decided for him to step down. Paddy had daggers drawn for me after that. There are stories saying I stitched him up, but I didn't have to – he stitched himself up.

It was Matt and Paddy who brought George back. Matt asked me what I thought and I said the way we were going we'd be glad for anything. Crerand said he could get in touch with him and I thought, 'There's a surprise.' I had a chat with George and he looked all right. Paddy arranged a place for him to train in the afternoons. Fair dos, he worked hard, and he was still only 27. He should have been at his peak – and that's what annoyed me about him. He deprived so many kids of seeing arguably the best in the world.

Anyway, he got himself in decent condition and played a few games, the last one at QPR. But you could see the fear in his eyes before games. He could beat people, piece of cake, but couldn't leave them for dead. The pace had gone. Whether the blood clot was bothering him I don't know, but he was moaning and groaning, and, of course, people were out to make a name for themselves against him. They'd say, 'Bestie's back, I'll show him.'

He was picked to play in the Cup tie against Plymouth. Pre-match meal was 11.30 for 12. No sign of George. I was told at 2.30 he'd arrived. He was stoned. I said, 'George, come back on Monday and I'll talk to you. You're in no condition to play today.' We had to change the team-sheet to hand in to the referee. He didn't come in on the Monday and I never saw him for a long time after that.

I fell out with Stepney and Morgan after leaving them out. They thought it was personal. It wasn't. I had to make these decisions for the good of the club. Wilf didn't have a chance. He was a player with them all and a lot of players undermined him. I felt sorry for Frank because he tried to make the break. We were players together at Preston and he was godfather to my son. Lovely man. But we fell out when I took the job and I said if I hadn't, somebody else would have. When Frank left, John Aston got the sack as well, and there was a deal done to keep his mouth shut. I assumed Jimmy Murphy was still there, and Jack Crompton. I brought them back to bring back all that experience.

Matt wasn't too pleased about Jimmy coming back. Something went wrong there. I believe when Frank arrived, Jimmy left with a payment that was meagre and Jimmy was disappointed Matt didn't look after him the way he felt Matt should have. When I got Jimmy back he was very emotional. I brought him back for scouting. And decisions. He found Coppell and Hill. He'd say sign him or don't sign him. I didn't see Coppell before he came here – £30,000, plus £15,000 after 50 matches. After two games we sent Tranmere the extra money.

Jimmy Murphy was different class. He didn't get half the credit he deserved. What upsets me about Manchester United is how little is spoken about the man. In my opinion he was as great as Busby. Matt was wonderful, but he wouldn't have been half the man without Jimmy, and vice versa.

Jimmy Murphy died on 14 November 1989, aged 79. Docherty continues,

> I never felt under pressure to follow Matt. I just wanted to improve the team. One of the mistakes I made the year we went down was going too defensive. Matt said, 'Tom, it's none of my business, but if we're going down let's go down with a bit of style.' He was right, and we had a bit of a flurry.
>
> I don't agree with those who think it was a good thing we went down. I'd like to have struggled a couple of years and stayed in the division. It's a blemish on your personal reputation. When we got back up and did well I didn't really think we were heading for the Championship. We didn't have the steel. We weren't strong enough at the back. We were more of a Cup side. Great to watch, but not quite there for the Championship.
>
> They were always careful with money at United. Lots of times we should have gone into the market and they wouldn't, which was disappointing. They are the biggest club in the world and everyone wants to play for them. I would have got the players. Peter Shilton would have come but they wouldn't pay the wages. Our players were on £300 a week. Shilton wanted £400.
>
> To this day I don't really know the reason for my sacking. I've heard lots of stories. Heard it was the directors' wives, heard it was some of the players' wives. I personally think if Matt had said 'he stays', I'd have stayed. I didn't socialise with Matt so much and consequently I think I cut myself off. I heard that Laurie knew about other things that had gone on at the club and said that if I didn't get the sack he'd spill the beans.
>
> I'd like to think I could have got United to where they are with Fergie's resources. Dave Sexton got more money to spend than I got, Ron got more and Fergie has had more again. I think the present team is potentially better than the '68 team. They've got class players. Schmeichel is the best in the world. Keane is outstanding. You don't need some of his antics off the pitch. But you need a dirty bugger in the middle of the park, yes. I would have made Keane captain. My favourite is Scholes. Great player. But Law, Best, Charlton – now you're talking about a different breed

197

altogether. There's nothing like that in the side today. If Law played today they'd definitely win the European Cup. If Denis had played against Dortmund he would have had a hat-trick. Maybe four, maybe five.

* * *

After the roller-coaster ride with Docherty, United opted for the boating lake. They entrusted Dave Sexton with the oars. A good man, widely respected in the game. And quiet. And wary. And discreet. And a Catholic of the kind O'Farrell was. As Docherty ruefully observes, the club did support Sexton with a substantially bigger budget. He had earned recognition at Chelsea and Queens Park Rangers with more modest means, but now exercised his financial muscle to bring in Gordon McQueen, Joe Jordan, Ray Wilkins and Garry Birtles for £2.75m. And still United could not find their panacea.

They were knocked out of the Cup-Winners' Cup in the second round by Porto and finished tenth in the League in 1977–78. They improved by only one position the following season but reached the FA Cup final and lost 3–2 to Arsenal in a thrilling climax. Gary Bailey had become the regular goalkeeper and in 1979–80 Sexton had the foundation for a Championship challenge. They were runners-up. A year on, however, they were back in an ominously familiar spot, eighth, having failed to clear the first hurdle in the UEFA Cup. A run of seven wins from the last seven matches was a mite unfortunate from the board's point of view. They had already decided Sexton must go.

The directors – and many critics and supporters – felt United had lost their sparkle, that they had become downbeat in the image and likeness of their boss. They needed a lift, a fresh vitality. So they went back to the other end of the managerial spectrum, to an expansive personality. Big in every sense. Ron Atkinson was the man they believed would fit the bill. He revelled in the role of the flamboyant manager-star. Anonymity was not in his vocabulary, although he was no less a football man than any of his predecessors. He was not, however, a Catholic, but suggested, 'I could be converted!' Witty, too.

Fun was back on the agenda at Old Trafford, yet not at the expense of business. Atkinson paid £1m for Frank Stapleton and a British record transfer fee of £1.5m to sign Bryan Robson from his former club, West Bromwich Albion. Few shared Atkinson's conviction it was money well spent, but soon Robson would be captain of club and country and acknowledged as the most influential player of his generation. The

Dutchman Arnold Muhren complemented Robson's midfield power with his subtlety. Paul McGrath combined both qualities at the heart of the defence, the emergence of a young striker called Mark Hughes persuaded Atkinson he should not shell out more cash for Peter Beardsley, Norman Whiteside was a first-team substitute at 16, and Jesper Olsen and Gordon Strachan relit the torch for wingers. These were some of the key figures in Atkinson's evolving team.

They delivered results with style. United won the FA Cup in 1983 and 1985 and were regular contenders in Europe again, defeating Barcelona before losing to Juventus in the Cup-Winners' Cup semi-finals in 1984. They opened the 1985–86 First Division campaign with ten consecutive wins. Their first title in 19 years beckoned. And then the style and the results waned. Injuries to Robson palpably weakened the side but other reasons were sought, and by the end of the season sections of the gallery were calling for Atkinson's head.

Extrovert though he was, he could not bring himself to court the fans, and they never warmed to him the way they had to Docherty. He complained the crowd had to be stoked up by the team, that they lacked passion. Like Docherty, he left home for another woman, and although Maggie Harrison – now Mrs Atkinson – was unrelated to anyone at the club, the inevitable publicity was not well received in some quarters. Perhaps more relevant were stories of indiscipline and excessive drinking among the players. Whatever their cumulative effect, a dismal start to 1986–87 sucked him into the abyss. The Championship – and a return to the European Cup – had disappeared from United's view and Atkinson paid with his job. He now says,

> When I went there the first statement I made was that I
> wanted to make them a major European club again, which
> we did. We got into Europe every year, and I think that from
> 1969 to when I joined them they had got there only three
> times. It was a hell of a night when we beat Barcelona 3–0 at
> Old Trafford to go through on aggregate, but I have to say we
> were a bit fortunate in that match. The one I look back on
> was the semi, which we lost 3–2 on aggregate against possibly
> the greatest Juventus side ever, with seven or eight of the
> Italian team that went on to win the World Cup in 1986.
> The following year we were the first team to win at Dundee
> United in a European game.
>
> We had quality players, no question about that, and I
> thought the Championship was within our capabilities.

People used to go on about the fact that United had not won the League for 15 years or whatever it was, but I'd say don't blame me for that. I've been here only two. I think the present team are very good and must have a chance of the European Cup.

Atkinson looked on from a variety of posts, in England and the Continent, as his successor survived inauspicious early years of tenure to create a team with such prospects. He had the satisfaction of denying United the League Cup in two finals, with Sheffield Wednesday and then with Aston Villa, but wryly digested the irony that the club's faith and patience in Alex Ferguson were eventually rewarded.

Many observers believed the man who made Aberdeen dare to take on and conquer the Old Firm had been the object of United's attention for some time before Atkinson was removed. Ferguson was renowned as tough, as a disciplinarian, and as a winner. He had taken the Cup-Winners' Cup to that far-flung corner of Britain. Here was the man to get the Old Trafford house in order. He in turn considered himself the man to shift the English seat of power from Merseyside. New players arrived in waves: Brian McClair, Steve Bruce, Mark Hughes (retrieved from Barcelona); then Mike Phelan, Neil Webb, Gary Pallister (for a record £2.3m fee), Paul Ince and Danny Wallace. Paul McGrath and Norman Whiteside departed. But more than three years into the job, Ferguson had made scant impression on the game south of the border.

'You maybe analyse more when you are in that situation, and deep down you worry,' he says. 'I'm no different from anyone else. I felt we were going the right way, but what I needed was a bit of luck. I had that with Mark Robins's goal and the FA Cup win against Forest. Eventually winning the Cup against Palace helped the players overcome a lot of doubts about whether they were good enough to play for Manchester United.'

United followed up that success by winning the Cup-Winners' Cup in 1991, their first European triumph since 1968, defeating Barcelona 2–1 in the final at Rotterdam. They mopped up the obscure 'Super Cup' but now the clamour was for the Championship, and Ferguson, aided by his new assistant Brian Kidd, steered United to the brink of the title after winning the 1992 League Cup. Ferguson blamed a fixture congestion in the final week for their capitulation; critics contended the manager's anxieties had been transmitted to the players. Either way, Leeds United, whose players included Gordon Strachan and a Frenchman, Eric Cantona, edged in front to become champions.

The jury is similarly split on Ferguson's signing of a new striker in

November 1992: inspiration or desperation? Beyond dispute is that Cantona, at £1.2m, proved one of the club's greatest investments. United won their first title – in the shape of the inaugural Premier League Championship – for 26 years at a canter. Among those who acclaimed the champions at Old Trafford was the president, Sir Matt Busby. Smiling, applauding and doubtless reminiscing.

As Ferguson says, 'Winning the League for the first time with United was definitely the high point, because that was the catalyst. That settled everyone down. The supporters lost their anxiety.'

So, too, perhaps did Ferguson. He might also say Cantona was the catalyst. Here was a man apart (who else would have contrived that kung-fu assault or the subsequent philosophical drivel?) and yet adored within the team and in the stands as a cult-figure-cum-messiah. He was the most venerated player at Old Trafford since the Holy Trinity. His football was almost spiritual, his goals as crucial as they were divine. And around him Ferguson assembled worthy disciples: Peter Schmeichel, Denis Irwin, Roy Keane (the natural successor to Robson) and Andrei Kanchelskis. Equally important was the influx from the junior ranks: Ryan Giggs and then Gary and Phil Neville, Nicky Butt, David Beckham and Paul Scholes, enabling Ferguson to maintain his domination of the domestic game.

Sir Matt Busby was not among those who acclaimed United's League and FA Cup double-winners of 1994. He died, at the age of 84, on 20 January 1994. The outpouring of grief, the carpet of flowers and red and white favours, and the tributes from around the world testified to his legacy and stature. Although some, as we have heard, would defer, most subscribe to the view that this was also fitting recognition of his humanity. And most suspected he was smiling and applauding approvingly from his celestial vantage point as his club embraced their maiden double.

His momentous European Cup achievement, however, had not been emulated and, much as Ferguson was conscious of a potential 'albatross', he could not camouflage his ultimate ambition. A new generation of players and supporters had hooked on to the old dream. United made an uneasy return to the grand stage, nudging past Kispest-Honved of Hungary but losing to Galatasaray on the away-goals rule. They beat the same Turks 4–0 a year later but that was not enough to keep them in the Champions League. A 4–0 defeat in Barcelona effectively put paid to that. United were still out of their depth in this company. English football's five-year exile following the Heysel tragedy was a factor, as was the three-foreigner rule, restricting the manager's options and disrupting the team pattern.

Ferguson's side, deprived of Cantona's brilliance as a consequence of events at Selhurst Park and frustrated at the last by the profligacy of Andy

Cole, their record £7m signing, yielded their Championship to Blackburn Rovers and the FA Cup to Everton. Although Schmeichel's heroic late goal saved United's unbeaten home record in Europe, it could not spare them a first-round exit to Rotor Volgograd in the UEFA Cup. Salvation to the greater good was at hand. Cantona was restored to active duty and his propensity for conjuring vital goals brought the title back to Old Trafford. Against Liverpool, it also reclaimed the FA Cup and completed an historic second double.

The remaining challenge for Cantona, as well as United, was the European Cup. Neither he nor Schmeichel could prolong that proud, 40-year run at home. That it should be ended by a fluke goal and a modest Fenerbahce team rendered it all the more galling. United were beaten 1–0 on five occasions, twice by Juventus, twice by their semi-final conquerors, Borussia Dortmund (yes, that team again). Despite their 4–0 obliteration of Porto in the home leg of their quarter-final, a deficiency in front of goal proved their undoing against Dortmund. Had they been able to sign Alan Shearer . . . Hypothetical now. Another Championship, United's fourth in five seasons, revived most hearts, but not Cantona's. His influence had diminished and he decided his remarkable four and a half years at Old Trafford were over. The thespian manqué was off to find a new *Théâtre des Rêves*.

Ferguson was accompanied for the formal announcement of Cantona's retirement from football not by the player but by Martin Edwards, the club chairman and chief executive. Edwards appears for signings and other such public rituals yet rarely looks comfortable in the glare of the media. Unlike some of his counterparts, he prefers to cede publicity to his manager and players, stay indoors and keep his own counsel. Adverse reports in the past regarding club and private matters have made him retreat still further into his lair. But then he has always advocated the right of the manager to manage. He has pledged his managers moral and financial support, and got on with the next stage of building United's business empire.

Edwards became chairman at the age of 34 in succession to his father, Louis, who died in February 1980 after television allegations about his business affairs. Edwards junior's reputation took a buffeting over the aborted sell-out deals with Robert Maxwell and Michael Knighton before he floated United on the stock exchange. He has been perceived as a money man rather than a football man. He rejects that notion, insisting his motivation has always been the prosperity, on and off the field, of the club, just as his father's was. Big Louis was sometimes portrayed as a comic figure, as Busby's stooge, but his son believes he played a defining role in the development of the Manchester United we see today.

Edwards, sitting in his unextravagant office, says,

> The European Cup was the highlight of my father's involvement with United. He was made a director the day after the crash and he'd seen it through to '68. Although he didn't become chairman till 1965, when Harold Hardman died, he had effectively been the leading light for some time because Harold Hardman had been ill. He was a great friend of Matt's, so he would have got a lot of pleasure out of Matt's winning it. Together they had driven the club after Munich, culminating in that great win at Wembley. I was with the party that night and I think in his own way it meant as much to father as it did to Matt.
>
> It's very difficult for a son to talk about his father, but I have no illusion as to how he did build the club up after Munich. It needed a strong personality and he put the club on a very sound financial footing. He was very instrumental in building the old North Stand for the World Cup in 1966 and that stand was a model for everybody else. We were the first club to introduce boxes, and all that helped fund the side of the '60s. Before Munich, United weren't big buyers, but a lot of the players who helped build up the club were bought in the early '60s.
>
> There are differences between my father and me in terms of personality, but we are very alike in that we have both allowed the manager to manage. i think the job of chairman, and chief executive, is one of support. You have to balance the development of the stadium with the development of the team. There's no point having a magnificent stadium if you can't fill it. And I think if we moved from here it would be over my dead body.

Ferguson's declared ambition is for Old Trafford, which now has a three-tier North Stand and an all-seated capacity of 55,300, eventually to house 80,000. Planning and financial considerations present problems, although Edwards has stoked up the debate on the reintroduction of standing areas both to accommodate more customers and enhance the atmosphere. It was an uncharacteristic venture into the media spotlight.

> Some chairmen like publicity. It's down to the individual. I don't seek publicity. I'm happy if I'm not in print, but also

because it tends to mean everything is going reasonably well. If the board decides something's wrong with the business and that the manager has to go, then clearly it's the chairman who has to do the dirty work. I've had to do it twice. The first time, with Dave, was probably harder because I'd been chairman for only a year and we'd finished the season with seven wins on the trot. But I felt we'd gone backwards, and we needed a change. People were voting with their feet.

With Ron it was slightly easier. Although we'd finished the previous season fourth, our form in the second half of the season was actually relegation form. That continued into the start of the next season and I think we were in 19th place or something. It was nothing to do with personal matters.

It took Alex time but the circumstances were different. We took into consideration that he was new to the English game. Coming down from Scotland it was difficult. I don't think Alex knew the players quite as well as he thought he knew them. He inherited a team he wanted to change. He brought in a lot of new players and we knew it was going to take time to bed them in. Plus we knew how hard he was working behind the scenes on youth development and the structure of the club. Not many clubs would have been as patient, but that 'non-decision', if you like, was as important as any decision we've made. I take pride in that.

We know we made the right decision because of the success we've had since. Now we're having those great European nights again and I'd love us to win the European Cup again, but you've got to be careful you don't get too hung up on it, otherwise it becomes a millstone. A bit like the League became. The European Cup will be a bonus. Now that we're not restricted by that ridiculous three-foreigner rule which forced us to drop key players, we have no excuses and can be judged for the team we are. Our youngsters have gained experience in Europe and with England, and if we're going to achieve the big one that's all going to help.

The '60s team was great, and I don't think we had anything in the '70s and '80s to compare with it, but the '90s team does, and in a very big way. I think the double-winning side of '94, in every way, was as good as the '60s team. For me the '94 side was better than the '96 side, although that side is still growing. But I've been watching United regularly since 1958 and I think, man for man, the '94 side was the best I've ever seen. Charlton, Law and Best were absolutely exceptional, but the quality, in depth, of the '94 side was even greater. Think about it. Schmeichel, Parker and Irwin at full-back, Bruce and Pallister together, Keane and Ince, Kanchelskis and Giggs wide, Hughes and Cantona at their peaks up front. And remember, that team nearly did the treble.

The success of the team and the company, now valued at more than £400m, is indisputable. But what about the image of United as a gargantuan manifestation of greed? An image he has possibly perpetuated through his negotiations to sell control of the club? And by cold-shouldering old players?

The Robert Maxwell thing never got off the ground. He rang me up and said he wanted to make an offer and we fixed a date. We agreed it should be kept quiet, then he announced it to the world and in the end it was all about nothing. Michael Knighton said he would buy my share, make a general offer to other shareholders, but also provide £10m to fund the redevelopment of the Stretford End. We hadn't got the cash to do that, which is why I don't regret agreeing the sale. Unfortunately his backers withdrew and it got very messy.

I don't accept that we don't make former players welcome. Does Shay Brennan have a problem? Does Pat Crerand have a problem? Does Denis Law have a problem? They don't. But having said that, you can't make allowances for every old player at every game. If they want to come on a selective basis, fine. We welcome them. But these are the difficulties we have.

Of course I am concerned about our image. But a lot of things about Manchester United get blown up out of all proportion. At one time United was everybody's second favourite team, and when we became successful and probably commercial, that changed. Now you either love United or you hate them, and I don't think we're everybody's second favourite team any more. It's the nature of this country. In America if you are successful you are a hero. We get a lot more stick for doing exactly the same thing that everybody else does. Every club would like to be as commercially successful as United.

There will come a time when I know it's right for me to step aside. I'm not one of those who believes you can go on forever, and in business things change, attitudes change, systems change. You need new ideas coming in. If I step aside as chief executive and the club want to retain me in some capacity, perhaps as chairman or a role with a watching brief, then I would be delighted to stay. I've given too much of my life to United to outstay my welcome. The club is more important than me.

Ferguson also stressed the club was more important than any individual as he resumed the European Cup campaign in 1997–98 without Cantona, the soul of his team. A self-inflicted knee-ligament injury to Keane tore the heart out of the team as well. But Ferguson had bought Teddy Sheringham to play in Cantona's role, and Henning Berg to reinforce the defence. He looked to Ole Gunnar Solskjaer and Ronny Johnsen to confirm the promise of their first year, Karel Poborsky and Jordi Cruyff to improve, and Cole to rediscover a semblance of the form that made him a goalscoring sensation at Newcastle. And, of course, he had his kids, growing, developing, oozing the self-belief of their forebears.

The lesson of Best, an entirely new phenomenon in the game of the '60s, had forewarned and forearmed Ferguson. He had not been caught unawares and would not allow his young players to be exposed to the temptations and pitfalls of the outside world. In a sense Cantona, too, protected and nurtured them. His departure released them like doves to glorious flight. And now United looked an even stronger team, neither dependent on nor in awe of any individual.

Goals from Irwin, Berg and Cole away to the Slovakians FC Kosice instantly smoothed United's European path. Next up, at Old Trafford, were Juventus, who had beaten them twice in the previous Champions League but had lost in the final to Dortmund. United were reliving the nightmare when Alessandro del Piero floated beyond the grasp of their defence to score after just 23 seconds. Deep into that first half Ferguson's side could still not get to grips with the Italians. But gradually Sheringham imposed himself and when he leapt to head the equaliser the course of the contest changed. Didier Deschamps's dismissal left United important extra space, but by then their football was irresistible. Scholes's composed finish and Giggs's rocket, launched from a narrow angle, had the stadium in a state of frenzied exultation.

This was the kind of emotion-charged night Ferguson and Schmeichel implored of their fans, the kind of night Atkinson yearned for, the kind of night that hypnotised Charlton and Stiles. The people stood *en masse* behind the goals in defiance and in timeless honour of the cause. This is no bonus. This is everything.

Zinedine Zidane's converted late free-kick irritated rather than threatened United and Juventus did not misinterpret the message already delivered.

Another delightful execution by Scholes and Irwin's emphatic penalty emphasised the ascendancy in a 2–1 win against Feyenoord at Old Trafford. Cole became the club's first player to score a hat-trick in the European Cup since Denis Law against Waterford in 1968 as United defeated the Dutch again, in Rotterdam, 3–1. They were the only team in the competition with maximum points from four matches and had virtually guaranteed passage to the quarter-finals. A 3–0 home win against Kosice confirmed the booking, and although a 1–0 away defeat to Juventus allowed the Italians on board as one of the two best runner-up teams, United anticipated a springtime trip to Monaco with justified optimism

The dream was alive again.

Do You Believe in Miracles?

By

Rick Fortunato

Published in 2012 by FeedARead.com Publishing – Arts Council
funded
Copyright © Rick Fortunato 2012

First Edition

A CIP catalogue record for this title is available from the British
Library.

This book is dedicated to my Mum, Agnes Boswell Seraphina (Nancy), who was, and always will be, "Simply the Best."

ACKNOWLEDGEMENTS

I would like to thank Emma, Duncan, Angus, Ian, and Louise for keeping me constantly busy, but still allowing me at least thirty minutes a month to do some writing. I would also like to thank Nancy, Lorraine, and Sara for correcting the many grammatical errors in my earliest drafts. And Emma and Sara again, for helping with the photos for the front and back covers. I would also like to thank everyone who has read one draft or another of the story; and Freddie and Seve for their inspiration and genius.

Hardly a second or a minute goes by, when I don't stop and ask myself why?

But then I see your smiling face, and I remember you're in a far better place.

Through all the hard times, the struggle and the pain.

Don't wait till the clouds pass, just dance in the rain.

Summer, 1965.

All the other mourners had left, but he was still standing at the graveside, with his head bowed, when his old neighbour, and friend, Sam walked up to him and patted him on the shoulder. No words were exchanged. Both men simply stood there. One man didn't want to speak, while the other didn't know what to say. What could you say after something so tragic? Sam had no idea, but he felt he had to at least try and say something, just to let him know that everyone was thinking of him. Things like this aren't meant to happen. Not to people you know. You might read about it in the newspapers, but that doesn't seem real, because it happened to other people. The whole town was still in shock, and Sam had no idea how his old friend was going to cope. You wake up one morning, and it seems just like any other. Little do you realise, that your life will never be the same ever again. One tiny moment in the vast scheme of things, can have such a devastating effect. One second there is life. The next there is none.

"It was a very good turn out today," Sam finally mumbled after he couldn't really think of anything else to say. He originally thought of mentioning the weather, as it was a warm, sunny day, but decided against it. "At the church it was standing room only," he continued. "I've never seen it so packed. And the minister was good. I always think it spoils a service when they get too religious and preachy."

His old friend remained silent, but nodded in agreement.

"How's the back? Do the doctor's think you'll have to use the walking stick permanently?" Sam realised, as soon as he said it, that he maybe should have mentioned the weather instead of mentioning his old friend's back, which he happened to hurt in an accident where his wife and two children died, and, at first, the doctor's thought it would be touch and go whether he would even walk again. Perhaps Sam should have just left with the other mourners? He decided it would be best to stop talking.

"I've told the doctor that the walking stick will only be temporary," his old friend replied, not seeming to mind discussing the subject. He held the stick up briefly and gave it a look of disgust, "I'm far too young to be walking about with one of these things."

"Good for you," Sam patted his old friend on the shoulder again. "And what about your back?"

"My back, like a lot of things, probably won't heal properly."

"You know if you need anything. Me and Marie are there for you. Even if you want to move in with us indefinitely. It would be a tight squeeze, but it would be no problem," Sam said.

Sam's old friend clumsily moved the walking stick from his right to his left hand, and gave a slight wince at the effort. Now it was his turn to pat Sam on the shoulder. "I know you are. But that won't be necessary."

"Are you sure? How are you going to cope on your own?"

"Who said I'm on my own?" He pointed his walking stick at the grave. "You don't actually think Georgina, Henry, and Emily are in there, do you?"

"Well...I", Sam stuttered. "Where are they?"

His old friend pointed to his head, "They are here." Pointed to his heart, "Here." And then waved his stick about him, "They are everywhere. In the grass, the trees, and the clouds. They are pure infinite energy which cannot die. Nothing has ended. It's just that they have reached the next destination before I have."

"I see," Sam said. But he didn't. Sam believed that once you were dead you were dead. But if it made his old friend feel better then that was fine with Sam. "So what are you going to do then?" Sam asked.

"Live," he replied.

"What?" Sam asked.

His old friend, for the first time today, smiled. He then looked Sam in the eye, and the old twinkle that Sam remembered appeared to be there. "I am going to live," he said.

CHAPTER ONE

Summer, 2007.

Eddie staggered out of the pub oblivious to the world around him. This was an occurrence that had gradually become more frequent over the past seven years, until now it was more or less a daily one. To the occasional passer by, Eddie looked a sorry sight as he made his way along the High Street. Beneath the orange neon glow of the street lights, Eddie mumbled incoherently to himself as he stumbled over a kerb, thumped against a shop window, or stood in someone's discarded half-eaten kebab lying on the pavement; food that would either be a meal for the rats during night-time, or the seagulls come daylight. As Eddie continued to make his not so merry way home, keeping a short distance behind him, someone was taking an interest in Eddie's journey.

Eventually, Eddie made it home. After a struggle, and the odd swear word, he slid his key into the lock and opened the door. Eddie stumbled over the front step as he entered his house; while the figure who had followed him home stood and watched, hiding in the shadows of a shop doorway across the road, as Eddie shut the door, making enough noise to wake the neighbourhood, and as a light in the house went on and off again. Then, as the High Street Steeple struck midnight, they were gone.

The sharp, piercing sound of the alarm went off. From underneath the duvet, Eddie groaned as he listened to Joan switch it off, before she got out of bed humming the same tune she did every morning. Eddie gave another groan. With some effort, he managed to stick his head out from under the warm duvet and open his eyes enough to glance at the clock on the bedside table; it was 7:33 a.m. Eddie wasn't surprised. With his eyes half closed he shouted out, "Why do you always set that bloody alarm for seven thirty? You don't even start work till ten."

Joan continued to hum the tune. "I think we've discussed this before, Eddie" she finally replied as he watched her put on her white fluffy dressing gown. She was right. Although, technically, it wasn't usually a discussion, more like an early morning moan from a hungover Eddie. "I like to get up and get things done," Joan continued with the discussion. "We can't all stay lying in our pit all day, can we?" Joan had a quick glimpse in the mirror on the fitted wardrobe as she went past it. Her long brown hair, to Eddie's tired and half closed eyes, appeared as immaculate as ever despite just getting up.

Eddie couldn't be bothered to reply. He gave his third groan in a minute before pulling the hideous, in his opinion, red flowery duvet back over himself.

As Eddie lay there in the darkness under the duvet, which, despite hating, he seemed to spend a lot of time under, his head was throbbing, he was nauseous, and his throat was parched. The sound of the rain battering against the bedroom window didn't exactly make him want to get up, either. Eddie thought it always seemed to rain these days, as he listened to Joan move about the room still humming that tune. A tune he thought he knew, but didn't. "Why do you keep humming that tune?" A muffled voice cried out from under the duvet, "I'm trying to get back to sleep."

He could have sworn Joan began humming it louder before she replied, "This is something else we've discussed before. I like to hum the tune, even though I don't know the name of it. Because it somehow cheers me up. And I certainly need cheering up listening to you first thing."

Eddie groaned again.

"But you can't lie in bed till noon or beyond today, can you, Eddie?" Joan cheerfully reminded him. "Today's the day you make your fortnightly visit to the Job Centre to sign on. At ten o clock I believe?"

"Don't remind me," Eddie struggled to say.

"Too late. I already have." Eddie was sure he could hear sadistic pleasure in Joan's voice as she spoke. "What was it you said that afternoon, when you staggered into my work drunk?" she asked. Her voice sounded like it had gone beyond the sadistic pleasure stage. It was now at the almost euphoric one.

Here we bloody go again! Eddie thought."I don't remember," he said. But he did remember. How could he possibly forget? When a week doesn't go by that Joan somehow manages to subtly sledgehammer it into the conversation.

"Wasn't it something about having to get up at ten o clock on a Monday morning being an infringement of your Human Rights?"

Eddie remained silent as his head throbbed. *Of course it is. You last mentioned it about five days ago.*

"I'm sure it was." She laughed. "Just as well I managed to stop you from marching up to the Job Centre and making an idiot of yourself that day."

"Are you finished?" Eddie moaned.

"I'll leave you in peace," Joan said.

"Good," Eddie said, but he doubted Joan meant it.

The dulcet tones of Sir Terry Wogan now filled the room.

"Not the radio!" Eddie cried. He was sure Joan done this every morning just to wind him up.

"You know I like to wake up with Wogan," Joan said.

"You don't just wake up with him, though, do you? There's also the *Eurovision Song Contest, Children in need,* or anything else he's in."

"We all know who you would like to wake up with, don't we?" Joan said.

"Who?" Eddie began to stir again beneath the duvet.

"Shania Twain."

"How do you-"

"It's a bit obvious. Your eyes practically pop out every time you see her."

Eddie pulled the duvet down. With a struggle, he managed to fully peel open his crusty, bloodshot eyes. He could just make out Joan standing by the bedroom door with what looked like her make-up bag in one hand and hair-dryer in the other.

"What's wrong with liking her? At least she's not an OAP like Terry." Eddie sat up.

"Sir Terry," Joan corrected him.

"Whatever he is. I could easily see me waking up with Shania beside me in bed. All she's wearing is the white shirt from the video 'Man I Feel Like A Woman', as she snuggles up and serenades me with a heartfelt rendition of 'You're Still The One'." Eddie took a deep breath and closed his eyes. Thinking about Shania made him feel better.

"'You're Still The One'? I think you should make your fantasy a bit more realistic."

"How?" Eddie opened his eyes again.

"Let's face it. You're not exactly Don Juan, nowadays, when it comes to the love making department. I think poor Shania would probably sing 'That Don't Impress Me Much' as she runs for dear life from the bedroom." Joan burst out laughing.

Eddie collapsed back on the bed and hauled the duvet up over his head. Despite being under the duvet, and with the radio on, he could still hear Joan laughing as she made her way down the hallway. The laughter stopped and Joan shouted out, "Will I need to lock the

11

bathroom door? I would hate for you to pounce on me in the shower if you were feeling frisky? Anyway, when's the last time you were actually frisky? New Year, was it?" Joan answered her own question. "The year didn't exactly start off with a bang. Talk about 'Forty-Five Seconds Of Ecstasy'." Joan laughed again. Eddie heard the bathroom door close. He wasn't sure if Joan locked it or not?

Yes, after the New Year's Eve party at the Golf Club may well have been the last time Eddie could be classed as being anywhere near amorous with Joan, and he wasn't all that close then. He could vaguely remember fumbling about with Joan's bra like it was some sort of fiendish challenge from *The Crystal Maze* as he tried to undo the strap, Eddie was sure he heard Richard O' Brien shouting in the background 'Come on team!' Yet, despite these imaginary shouts of encouragement, Eddie's attempt to take Joan's bra off ended up as successful as the Sinclair C5. Forty-five seconds of ecstasy may be a bit harsh. It was, at least, a good two minutes before the exertion became too much for Eddie, and he collapsed on the bed as Richard O'Brien walked away in disgust shaking his head and mumbling about going home to tell 'Mumsy.'

Eddie tried to turn his attention away from the subject of his flagging libido, which seemed to have lost all its power, like Superman at the first sight of Kryptonite. The song "Bad Moon Rising", by Creedance Clearwater Revival, just came on the radio. It was a good one. Good enough to take Eddie's mind off certain things. He also remembered the song was from a film Jenny used to love that she and Eddie would watch together. Joan used to say Jenny was too young to watch those types of films, but Eddie thought it was all right as long as he was watching it with her. After some mental effort for this time in the morning, the name of the film came to him: *An American Werewolf in London.* Eddie snuggled under the duvet. *Not a bad film,* he thought, *very good times. Brilliant times. But times firmly in the past, that will never return, no matter how much I want them to.*

Eddie felt sleepy again. As he began to doze off, Creedance Clearwater Revival sang about rivers that were overflowing.

No longer in bed, Eddie was lying on wet grass underneath a large oak tree, wearing only a pair of red, baggy shorts, with a newspaper on top of his bare chest. Eddie sat up and glanced at the date on the newspaper, 16th August 2000. He put the paper down on the wet grass, stood up, and reluctantly walked out from underneath the shelter of the tree into the driving rain; making his way towards the river he knew was behind the trees at the bottom of the slope. The rain was heavy and the dark, grey clouds were becoming more ominous as Eddie reached the top of thirty three wooden steps. He glanced through a gap in the trees at the white, raging river below before making his way down the steps, gripping on to an old, wooden, rickety rail for support. Eddie remembered to duck below a large overreaching branch when he arrived at the bottom.

Eddie walked along a narrow, muddy path that led him onto the red, brown, and green covered rocks at the side of the river. He knew where he was going; a larger rock jutting out from the others that resembled a finger pointing to a spot in the river. When he reached it, after negotiating the wet and slippery smaller rocks, Eddie stood close to the river's edge and stared into the furious, ghostly abyss that rushed noisily, almost mockingly by. Minutes passed as Eddie stood there in his shorts, motionless, as the rain continued to fall, and the river tried to tempt and tease him to join it. Why stay in a banal, meaningless world when you can be free? Eddie would like to be free. Who wouldn't? Why stay in the Darkness when you can enter the Light? And Eddie had been in the Darkness for a long time. Eddie took a small step towards the edge. He was about to take another final step, a step that would change everything, when he was distracted as something dripped onto the rock by his feet that he knew wasn't rain. Eddie touched his forehead with his right hand. When he brought the hand down again, his fingers were covered in blood.

Eddie went back into the Darkness.

When Eddie awoke and sat up in bed, as well as his usual hangover symptoms, his heart was racing and he was short of breath. The time was 9:13 a.m. Eddie didn't want to get up, and he didn't want to stay in bed. Eddie stepped out of bed once his heart slowed down and he got his breath back. He stood at the bedroom window shivering, in his blue and white striped boxer shorts, as he gazed out at the grey, miserable wet weather, watching the people rushing about aimlessly on the road to nowhere. Eddie rubbed his forehead. He then made his way across the lush, red bedroom carpet which felt cosy on his feet. After a couple of steps, he stood on something sharp. Eddie stopped and looked down thinking it would be a drawing pin. What caught his eye was the expanse of stomach overhanging his boxers. Eddie would be the first to admit he was no longer at his fighting weight, but he was

13

still shocked at the sight of fat and loose skin he was witnessing. The chip shop being conveniently situated next door to the bookies didn't really help Eddie's Battle of the Bulge. His favourite delicacy, which is a real artery clogging and calorie laden meal, is a black pudding supper. A meal he consumes on most days squeezed in between, such healthy pursuits as, betting and drinking.

Eddie breathed in; his stomach almost resembled its appearance of a few years ago, but not quite. He lifted his foot to see it was only a hair clasp he'd stood on. With great relief, Eddie breathed out again. His rotund stomach was back in all its glory. Eddie couldn't be bothered picking up the clasp, so it was left on the floor as he made his way to the radio. Billy Joel was singing about "The River Of Dreams". Eddie usually loved the song. This morning, ridiculous as it seemed, the song was making him feel uncomfortable. Eddie switched the radio off before leaving the bedroom.

"Your breakfast's ready," Joan shouted from downstairs just as Eddie entered the hallway.

Eddie paid no attention as he ambled to the bathroom.

"Hurry up. Your breakfast will get cold," Joan shouted louder this time. "Jeremy Kyle's about to come on the telly," she added.

Eddie still never answered as he reached the bathroom door.

"I think you should come and watch this episode, Eddie," Joan shouted up a third time. "It may be of some interest to you." Then, after a slight pause, she continued, "It's called-*Why won't you get off your backside and find a job?"*

Eddie sighed as he entered the bathroom.

14

CHAPTER TWO

When Eddie entered the Job Centre he saw Edith Strachan, his nemesis for the last four years or so, waiting for him. She was ready for battle in the next round of the epic *Rumble in the Job Centre*. With wild, black, frizzy hair that seemed to have a life of its own like the snakes on Medusa's head; complimented by large thick spectacles which were probably so strong that on a clear night she could spot Uranus through them.

"Take a seat, please, Mr Ryan," Edith said as Eddie hovered by her desk, "I'll be with you in a moment."

Eddie followed orders and sat down. As he waited impatiently, and rubbed his forehead, his mind wandered to how old Edith actually was. To Eddie she appeared in her fifties, but could be younger as she doesn't do herself many favours. Eddie's never seen her wear make up. Plus, a polar neck jumper for every occasion wasn't exactly the sexiest of clothing; she had on her red one today.

"Sorry for the delay, Mr Ryan," Edith said without bothering to look up.

"That's okay," Eddie said. Right now time was of no concern to him, for it was still a while before the bookies and pubs opened.

"Now then, Mr Ryan," Edith said as she finally put her paperwork to one side and lifted her head up. "Have you actively been looking for work over the last two weeks?"

It was the same question she opened with every time. As always, hangover or no hangover, Eddie was more than ready for it. "Well, I bought newspapers for the job vacancies," he said. "And I also searched the internet, at the library, for jobs. Unfortunately, I couldn't find anything suitable." This little story may not resemble the truth in any way, but poor Edith doesn't know that.

To give credit where credit's due, Eddie did try to find a job for six months after he was made redundant, but after receiving two rejections, when he went to all the trouble of filling in an application and attending the interview, he asked himself the question "Was It All Worth It?" The answer he came to was a resounding "No." He then decided the only way to avoid the hassle and the rejection was to not bother applying in the first place. That became his new Protestant Work Ethic. It was an ethic he's managed to stick to ever since.

"Mmm. I see," Edith answered. "We'll have a look on the computer system. Hopefully, we might have more luck." She battered away ferociously on the keyboard like a concert pianist attempting a Rachmaninoff concerto.

One thing Eddie's noticed about Edith's desk, which was different from all the others in this office, was a lack of photos. Every other desk had at least one photo on it; while the young blonde's desk, over in the corner, appeared to have nothing but photos on it, accompanied by a small selection of cuddly toys. Mind you, Eddie wouldn't mind having to come and see her, every two weeks, as she was more pleasing on the eye than Edith. Why didn't Edith have any photos on her desk? Was it because she has no partner or family to have photos of? Eddie had noticed there was no ring on her finger, so she didn't appear to be married; this could explain a lot.

By now Eddie's mind had gone into overdrive, as he pictured the sad existence Edith had away from work; sitting alone in her empty house with nothing but two cats and the odd soap opera for company; constantly watching the clock, while stroking the two cats on her lonely lap, hoping for time to hurry round to 9 a.m. as quickly as possible, so she could get back to work and be in the company of other human beings again.

Just as Eddie was starting to feel the tiniest crumb of sympathy for Edith, the battle resumed when she fired a jab in his direction.

"There appears to be a vacancy for a taxi driver," she asked, unsmiling.

"Sorry, I can't drive. So I don't think I would be any good at that." Eddie avoided that jab easily.

Edith must be getting a bit sloppy? She knows by now I can't drive. Doesn't look like her mind is on the job today. Something could be bothering her. Maybe one of her cats is ill? Eddie sat back in his seat. He felt at ease for the first time since he had walked in the office today. It appeared this particular battle was going to be quick and painless.

"Okay, Mr Ryan. I'll just have a quick look for something else on the system," Edith said as she battered away again at her keyboard.

That's my girl. You don't give up easily, do you? Eddie thought with some smugness.

"There's a vacancy for a handyman at a local farm. Are you any good with your hands?" Edith asked

"My wife tells me I am," Eddie said, and laughed. He was now almost enjoying himself.

Edith didn't seem to appreciate Eddie's wit as much as he did.

16

She merely stared at him, through her thick lenses, seemingly awaiting a proper reply.

"When you say a farm? It must be out in the country? And because I can't drive, then I won't have any transport to get there," Eddie said.

"Yes, it's in the country. Oh well." She sighed in apparent defeat. "I'll have one more look, but there doesn't appear to be very many jobs on the system today."

You can look all you want. Then again, if that handyman job had been at Hugh Hefner's Playboy_Mansion, then we may have been talking.

This fight was almost over. While he waited for the ref to stop the fight and put Edith out of her misery, Eddie was floating like a butterfly round the ring.

"There doesn't appear to be any more jobs suitable for you," Edith said, in a tone of voice that sounded totally defeated. Just as she said that, something on the screen appeared to catch her eye, "No, wait...there may be one," Edith hadn't given up yet. "There's a vacancy for a night porter at a hotel in the town centre, which would only be a five minute walk from your home to get there. So transport, obviously, wouldn't be a problem." Edith looked up from her computer screen, for a brief second, before continuing. "It's only minimum wage at the moment, but after a six month trial period your pay would go up. The hours are eleven p.m. till seven-thirty a.m., Sunday to Friday, with a half hour break. That's a forty hour week. How does that sound, Mr Ryan?"

Eddie didn't answer. His mind was a Tabula rasa.

Edith smiled for the first time today. Although manic grin might be a more apt description; like Jack Nicholson, in the famous bathroom door scene, from *The Shining*. Eddie was half expecting the chilling words "Heeeeeres Edith!" to echo round the building, as an axe is produced from under the, photo and cuddly toy free, desk. Thankfully, there was no shouting, no axe, and the manic grinning Edith had quickly been replaced by the normal straight-faced one. Despite Edith appearing the same; however, things had changed. Eddie knew it, and Edith knew it. It had only been a matter of seconds, yet in that time the balance of power had shifted. Just when Eddie thought the fight was more or less done and dusted, she's hit him with an uppercut. Now he's on the ropes battered, bruised, and reeling badly.

"Well, Mr Ryan, what do you think?" Edith enquired again.

She could now smell blood… and fear.

"It sound's em…it sounds not too bad," Eddie struggled to say.

It sounds not too bad? What on earth are you playing at? She's got you on the ropes and this is the fight you're putting up? What's happened to the fancy footwork of Pretty-Boy-Ryan?

It appeared Pretty-Boy-Ryan's four and a half year undefeated run was about to come to a painful end.

Eddie sat, slumped in the chair at Edith's mercy, waiting to be finished off.

A frown appeared on Edith's face. "Oh dear, that's a pity," she said.

Eddie's heart lifted at those five lovely words.

"I'm sorry, but it appears this vacancy has already been filled."

The Pretty-Boy was back. At that moment, Eddie felt like grabbing Edith and giving her a great big kiss; then he wanted to get everyone else in the office up on their feet to join him in a celebratory conga.

"That's a shame," Eddie said. "It seemed like a good job." He nodded.

"It did seem a good one, Mr Ryan," Edith agreed as she searched in her drawer for the form Eddie has to sign. "I can only apologise for getting your hopes up. We'll just have to keep on trying."

"That's okay," Eddie said. Trying with great difficulty to hide the sheer joy he was feeling right now.

He signed the form, which was a declaration of actively seeking employment, and then he was free to go. It had been close this week, far too close, yet he had gotten away with it and that was the important thing. After Eddie said "goodbye" to Edith, for another couple of weeks, what mattered now was picking a couple of winners at the bookies and then either celebrating or drowning his sorrows in the pub afterwards.

"Right then, let's pick a couple of winners," Eddie uttered to himself as he entered the bookies rubbing his hands together. There might be a smoking ban in the bookies, along with every other public place, but no matter how many times they redecorated here you were still hit by a stale aroma every time you came in. Inside were the usual suspects who frequented the establishment day in day out; mainly, the unemployed and the unemployable. At the weekends it was different, a lot more unfamiliar faces would appear, but on a Monday morning it was just the hardcore crowd.

Eddie glanced at the bank of ten screens, situated to his right, which took up the majority of the wall. Screens which showed horse racing, grey hound racing, virtual racing, the latest bookmaker's odds, *Sky Sports News*, and a host of other things. It was all different now. Eddie could remember when all they had here was a radio and one TV. The TV was stuck away in the corner, and it rarely showed live coverage of any races. Most of the time there would be a crowd of people huddled round the screen wishing, praying, and awaiting in great anticipation for the result to come up on Teletext or Ceefax. Today it's big business. All computers and technology. You can watch every race, and bet on almost anything you can think of-twenty four hours a day. Technology is great. It has given the punter a thousand more ways to lose their money than they had before.

As Eddie watched *Sky Sports News* on one of the screens, Clive Easterhouse strode up to him.

"Good morning, Eddie," he said in a cheerful tone.

"Morning," Eddie said and turned to face him. Clive was wearing his usual attire of a tight pair of jeans and even tighter t-shirt. The t-shirt always had some sort of character (usually comedy) on the front; today's was blue with a faded picture of Leonard de Tompkinson on it and "Boxing for God!" written below.

Clive is under the impression he's the spitting image of a well known movie star. It's not Brad "the beefcake" Pitt. As Eddie had joked if Clive starred in the film *Fight Club,* instead of Brad, and went topless on screen, they would've had to rename the film *Fright Club,* instead. No, Clive, for some inexplicable reason, believes he is the double of Clint Eastwood. And because they also share the same initials, this makes Clive believe even more, not only that is he Clint's Doppelganger, but that there must also be a special bond between the two of them.

Eddie thought that Clive with his red hair, patchy beard, short stature, and chubby physique actually resembled Clyde, the orang-utan, who starred in the *Every Which Way But Loose* films with Clint, more than he actually resembled the man himself. He hadn't mentioned this to Clive yet. But one of these days Clive was bound to annoy him so much that it was sure to slip out by mistake. Eddie was actually looking forward to that day.

19

"Did you hear the BBC's decided to spice up their Sunday evening TV viewing?" Clive said.

"Have I what?" Eddie said, showing little interest.

Clive repeated what he had said. This time the penny dropped for Eddie. Not only did Clive believe he is a Clint Eastwood look alike, he also believed he was a bit of a comedian. Every time they met, Clive had a new joke for Eddie that he claimed he'd made up the night before. Eddie still isn't entirely sure if Clive makes up the jokes or not, yet he thinks Clive probably does because the jokes are usually awful.

Eddie sighed and said, "No, I haven't heard that."

Clive smiled. "The BBC has decided to spice up their Sunday night TV viewing. A sexy new show will be starting soon. This will include a mixture of hymns and scantily clad women. The sure-fire ratings winner is going to be called *Thongs of Praise.*" Clive stuck out his pigeon chest with apparent pride at his latest Meisterwerk.

"Very good," Eddie said.

"If you liked that one, wait till you hear this other joke I thought of," Clive said with incredible enthusiasm. "Did you hear about the policeman who couldn't get out of his bed?"

"No," Eddie grunted.

"He was an undercover cop."

Eddie thought, for a moment, about mentioning Clyde the orang-utan, but decided against it. Even though it would've cheered Eddie up, he didn't think the joke deserved any kind of a response. Without saying a thing, Eddie headed over to look at a poster with today's race meetings on it.

"What hot tips have you got for me today?" Eddie asked as Clive caught up with him. They both stood analysing the poster on the wall.

"*Staying Power* running in the one p.m. at Doncaster is definitely a sure fire bet. I never heard it from the horse's mouth, but I did hear it from the next best thing." Clive chuckled.

Eddie didn't. "What exactly was the next best thing?" he asked.

"Brody Mcdowell told me about it."

"Brody Mcdowell! I haven't seen him here in ages. What would he know about picking a winner? The last win he had at the bookies wasn't a horse. It was when he backed Michelle Mcmanus to win *Pop Idol*. How many years ago was that? I also heard he only put the bet on because his wife told him to."

20

"Brody hasn't bet in a while, but he got this tip from a reliable source. He also told me he's due a win."

"Due a win? I think we've more chance of seeing Haley's Comet again, before we see him pick another winner at the bookies." Eddie picked out a slip and started to write on it. "How is Brody so sure this horse is going to win?" he asked.

"He claims to know some guy who is part of a syndicate down South. They are betting heavily on this horse."

"Where's this syndicate been while Brody's been picking all these losers?" Eddie asked. He was then distracted when someone walked in that he'd never seen before; very unusual for a Monday morning.

Eddie couldn't help but stare. It wasn't the stranger's pencil moustache, or his black greased back hair that was grabbing Eddie's attention. It was his attire. He was actually wearing a white suit complimented with, what appeared to be, a maroon paisley pattern cravat around his neck. Not only had Eddie never seen anyone wear anything remotely similar in the bookies before, he had never seen anyone wear an outfit remotely similar anywhere else.

Eddie continued to watch as the stranger, in the white suit and paisley pattern cravat, strode across to one of the many TV screens on the far wall. He looked so out of place.

"Brody told me he only got in touch with them, over the weekend, through a friend of a friend. This is the first tip they've given him," Clive finally answered.

"You what?"

"You asked me where this syndicates been for the last three years, and why Brody's never had a tip from them before."

"Oh! Yeah-right." Eddie was silent, for a second or two, before pointing across to the stranger who'd come in. "Have you ever seen that bloke before? The one standing in front of the screens?" he asked.

Clive glanced across. "No," he replied.

"Are you sure?"

"I'm positive. I've got a memory for faces, and I can honestly say I've never seen him before, anywhere." Clive screwed up his face, "He looks about retiring age. So maybe he's just retired and moved here? That's why we haven't seen him before?" he added.

Eddie nodded. "You could be right." *He'll just come here one day a week to start with, like I did. Eventually, as time drags on, whether he wants to or not, he'll be here every day with the rest of the*

Riff Raff and it won't be long till he can't be bothered to dress up like that. The suit and cravat will soon be replaced by a scruffy pair of jeans and a t- shirt or jumper.

Eddie had a final glance over his shoulder at the funnily dressed stranger who seemed to be in the process of filling out a betting slip. "The first of many, mate...the first of many," Eddie whispered. *"Now, let's get down to Brass Tacks.* What odds is the horse?" he asked.

"At the moment, it's seven to one," Clive replied.

Eddie tore up his slip and threw it in the grey bin beside him. "I must be going slightly mad?" he said as he took out another slip. "Right, it's the one pm at Doncaster? Name of the horse is *Staying Power?* And its odds are seven to one?"

"Affirmative-Eddie-affirmative," Clive said and gave a salute.

Eddie took a deep breath and wrote on the new slip. He stopped before filling it out and again stared at the poster in front of him. "No, *Dragon Attack,* the two to one favourite looks tempting. I think I'll stick with that one," he said, and began to chew on one of the bookmaker's small red pens.

"But, Eddie," Clive pleaded, "Brody said this is a certainty. I think you'd be a fool to pass it up. I can feel it in my waterworks that *Staying Power* is the one we should go for."

"You go for what you want," Eddie said as he took the pen out of his mouth. He threw another slip in the bin. "Brody doesn't have a clue about picking a winner at anything. And if you believe his cock n bull story about a mysterious betting syndicate, then you also deserve to lose." Eddie took out another slip and wrote on it: *Dragon Attack to win. Fifteen pound stake@ two to one.* "I'm backing *Dragon Attack,*" he said. "If you want to go for *Staying Power,* that's entirely up to you." He picked up his slip and showed it to Clive.

Clive looked in horror at it, "Eddie! You're betting fifteen quid. I thought we agreed to have a ten pound maximum for bets?"

"I'm so confident my horse will come in, I'm prepared to put a bit more on it. Let's face it, Clive. If Brody's track record is anything to go by, I'd be very surprised if the horse has enough *Staying Power* to get over the first fence, let alone win the actual race." Eddie strutted to the counter and placed his bet.

Today was definitely the day his luck was finally going to change.

"You can't win them all," Clive said as he patted Eddie on the back. If it was an attempt to console him, it was a futile one. Clive jumped off his seat and went to collect his winnings of seventy pounds.

Eddie held his head in his hands. Nothing ever seemed to go right for him anymore. *How could a horse Brody tipped ever win? And how could it beat the favourite who was in the hottest form of its career after winning four races in a row?* Eddie asked himself. "Why do I even bother?" he mumbled, before tearing up his betting slip and throwing it in the bin. He glanced up at the poster with today's race meetings on it and sighed, "What's the point? There's no way I'll ever win," he moaned, before taking out another betting slip and writing on it: *Bijou to win. Five pound stake@ Evens.*

"Well then, was it a good day at the office?"

Eddie felt yet another pat on his back. It was about the fifth of the day, for Clive had given him a consoling pat each time one of Eddie's horses had failed to win. Eddie reluctantly raised his head. Looming over him was Brody McDowell. Or, Scruffy McDowell as Eddie called him whenever Brody wasn't around. With his skinny frame, long unkempt hair, and scraggly brown beard with the odd fleck of grey in it. Brody doesn't come here that often now because he has to look after his wife, but he's been a regular at the bookies as far back as Eddie's dad can remember. Eddie hadn't seen him in a while, but Brody probably had the same clothes on as last time; the stained white t-shirt with the rather snazzy pair of, half-mast, brown corduroy trousers. Not forgetting the bright yellow socks that complimented his brown Jesus boots perfectly.

"No, it hasn't been a good day at the office," Eddie said.

"That's too bad." Brody shook his head. "Didn't Clive give you that tip I told him about? That little beauty came in at seven to one. I normally don't bet much anymore, as you know?"

Eddie wished Brody would just bugger off. He couldn't be bothered speaking to him at the best of times, but today was even more painful than usual. Eddie knew the climax of this conversation would be Brody telling him how much he had won today. In all honesty, Eddie couldn't give a monkey's. "That's right, Brody. You don't," he replied.

"No, I don't," Brody appeared serious. "When I got that tip, which I was told was a certainty. Well, I still had some doubts, as you do, don't you?"

Eddie didn't get a chance to reply.

Brody continued his story. He was in full flow now.

I bet the next horse you back will be called The Twelfth of Never. Because, Brody, my old mucka, that's exactly when you'll have your next winner. They say every dog has his day and you've just had yours. Make the most of it because you won't get another one, mate. This thought cheered Eddie up.

"So I told my wife, Mary, about it," Brody continued, "and I thought she'd tell me I'd be a mug to put a bet on the horse." Brody was getting more animated by the second as his arms flailed about wildly. "So, I told her, and do you know what she asked me?" Brody stopped waving his hands about and bent down till his face was only a matter of inches from Eddie's.

Eddie could now smell Brody's breath and quickly jerked his head away. *I know what she asked. If you do win at the bookies, is the first thing you buy with your winnings going to be a bottle of mouthwash? Because your breath stinks.*

"She asked me," Brody's voice now a whisper, "if I really thought the horse would win? I told her I didn't know, but those people told me it will. Then she said to me again, 'Do-you-think-this-horse-will-win?' I have no idea why I said this to her? Without thinking about it, I replied, 'I don't think it will win, my love. I know it will'." Brody moved his face closer to Eddie's treating him to another whiff of the sweet aroma of his breath. "Do you know what?" Brody said. With each word Eddie was being hit by a horrific wall of smell. "At that moment, that very second when I told her the horse will win. I really did believe it would. I don't think I have ever been more certain about anything before in my life. God knows why? I swear, on my 'dear Mary's life', that I haven't." Brody stopped talking and scratched his head. "Mind you, there was that other time, a couple of years ago, when I really believed 'Boom Boom It's Christmas', by Basil Brush, would be the Christmas number one. I don't even think the song made it into the Top Twenty?" Brody stood up straight again and laughed so loudly that a couple of punters turned to see what all the hilarity was about. They quickly turned to watch the TV screens again when they realised it was nothing too exciting.

Eddie also gave a laugh, of sorts, but it was one that contained little, if no, humour.

"Mary told me to put money on it if I really believed it would win," Brody said. "She gave me fifty quid out of her purse. Fifty quid!

24

I told her if we win we're going away on holiday abroad. We've never been abroad before." Brody stopped talking and gave out a sigh. "She's not well enough to travel. But there's no harm in dreaming. You have to believe in miracles, I suppose?"

Eddie nodded half heartedly.

"With her fifty and my thirty quid," Brody seemed to perk up again. "We've just won an incredible five-hundred-and-sixty quid. Plus, the eighty quid, can't forget that. This means we now have over six hundred quid burning a hole in our pockets." Brody stopped talking. There was a distant look in his eyes and a smile etched upon his face. It almost seemed as if he was picturing himself on holiday. "Six hundred quid," Brody repeated in what sounded like total disbelief. Then, in a flash, the distant look was gone. Brody was back with Eddie in the bookies. "We're off to the pub for a couple of celebratory drinks. If you would like to join us?" he asked.

"No thanks," Eddie immediately replied.

"Okay. We're only going for a couple as I have to get back to Mary. If you do change your mind, you know where we'll be." Brody gave a thumbs up and then practically skipped out the door in his Jesus boots.

Eddie was left alone to ponder where it had all gone wrong?
Eddie did go to the pub after he'd bet on two more horses. The first horse fell at the third fence; the second horse was more successful because at least it finished eighth out of a field of nine. Clive gave Eddie a loan of twenty pounds. This was part of his winnings from the now legendary *Staying Power*. After Eddie almost snatched the money out of Clive's hand, they went across to their local pub, *The Queen's Head*. Eddie was pleased to see Brody had gone. Clive only stayed for two pints before heading home for tea and to think up his new joke for tomorrow, while Eddie stayed on to drown his many sorrows.

Despite his favourite barmaid, Stacy, working tonight, Eddie's mood did not improve. Like normal, she attempted to have a bit of a laugh with him, but Eddie was having none of it. The only time he acknowledged her was when he would order another drink. The rest of the time he spent in his own miserable, little world. Sitting by himself at the end of the bar, with his head down, staring into his pint glass while rarely attempting to make eye contact or conversation with anyone. It wasn't just that he had lost a lot of money today that was getting to Eddie; he had lost more than this before. It was more about

25

the incredible injustice in how someone like Brody McDowell could win six hundred quid? How on earth does he deserve to win and Eddie doesn't? It just wasn't fair. The more Eddie thought about it, the more frustrated and angrier he got. At closing time Eddie staggered out of the pub, without saying goodbye to anyone, while muttering under his alcohol smelling breath.

As he followed his normal route along the High street, Eddie stopped, leaned against a lamp post for support, and turned round. Did he hear someone behind him? The street appeared deserted. Eddie shrugged his shoulders and made his way home.

When he reached his house, Eddie dropped his key as he went through the usual routine of attempting to open the door. When he bent down to pick it up, Eddie thought he noticed a silhouette move in the shadows of the shop doorway across the road. With Eddie's drunken vision, it was hard to tell if someone was there. The more he tried to focus and concentrate, the more blurry his vision became. After many attempts, Eddie grabbed his key. He stood up, as straight as possible, and peered across the road. Just as the decision was made to go and see if there was someone watching him, Eddie lurched backwards and clattered against his door with a thud.

"Bugger off!" he shouted out. Now Eddie couldn't be bothered having to stagger across the road. The only thing that mattered was opening the door then getting to bed.

Eddie managed to open the door first time, but he wasn't as successful in negotiating the front step. He tripped over it as he entered the house and luckily avoided going head first into the set of golf clubs, gathering dust, in the front hallway. Instead of head first into the clubs, he bounced off the wall. Eddie kicked the set of clubs for having the audacity to almost be in his way. Then he shut the door with as much drunken force as possible.

Had there been a person watching outside, or had it only been his drunken imagination? Eddie now no longer cared. By morning he wouldn't even remember. And, anyway, why would someone want to follow him home?

CHAPTER THREE

"Good afternoon, Eddie. How are you?" Clive asked in his usual cheerful tone. Today's t-shirt was orange with a picture of Max and Paddy and "What time do they open?" written on it.

"I've felt better," Eddie, pale, unshaven, and with bloodshot eyes answered.

"I thought it may be a boozy one last night. That's why I left you to it. Did you have a good time and a nice chat with Stacy?" Clive winked.

"No to both questions," Eddie answered. He yawned and rubbed his right shoulder; it was mysteriously sore today.

"That's too bad. Never mind, I've got some exciting news for you," Clive said.

"What's that?" Eddie answered, and then yawned.

"They're looking for auditions for a new reality TV show."

"So?"

"So, I think you would be perfect for it."

"Why?"

"Because it's a new show, by Simon Cowell, that's going to have Britain's laziest people in it. Can you guess what it's going to be called?"

"I've no idea."

"It's going to be called-*Bone Idol.*" Clive laughed and held his hand up almost in apology, "Sorry about that, Eddie," he said. "I was only joking."

"Oh!" Eddie said. "That was a joke, was it?" He yawned again.

"It maybe wasn't my best," Clive said.

Eddie glared at Clive.

"I have another joke. I thought about it when I saw a report on the news about a flu epidemic. I'm sure you'll like this one."

Eddie had his doubts.

"A man goes away to the Far East on business. On his return he doesn't feel very well. He has a temperature and he keeps getting cold sweats. But most worrying of all, is that he keeps getting a strange urge to put on a pair of red pyjamas and start doing karate kicks while up the High Street." Clive stopped and watched as Eddie filled out a betting slip. "Are you following this, Eddie?" he asked.

Eddie did not bother to reply.

Clive sighed, but he continued to tell his joke despite Eddie showing no interest in it. "The man goes to the doctor and tells him he's just back from the Far East. He mentions all the symptoms, such as, the temperature, the cold sweats, and the strange urge to put on a pair of red pyjamas and do karate kicks. The doctor listens intently, gives a smile, then replies, 'You have nothing to worry about, sir,' he says. 'It's quite rare, but not life threatening in any way. What you are suffering from, is actually a bad case of Hong Kong Fluey. " Yet again, Clive laughed at his own joke.

Yet again, there was no response from Eddie

"Do you get it, Eddie?" Clive asked. "Hong Kong Fluey. Remember the cartoon that starts off as Henry the mild mannered janitor, who then goes into a set of drawers and comes out as the crime fighting pooch-Hong Kong Phooey?"

Eddie stopped filling out the betting slip, put the pen down, and turned to face Clive. "Look! Just because I didn't laugh, doesn't mean I didn't get it. I got it, but the reason I didn't laugh is because it wasn't funny. Do you understand, Clive? That's why people don't laugh at your jokes. Not because the jokes are too clever, but because they just-aren't-funny. Now, if that's the jokes of the day over? I would like a bit of peace. My head is splitting and I want to pick my first horse. Okay?" *But if you do want to hear something funny. How about the fact that you resemble an orang-utan!*

"Okay, Eddie," Clive said, with his head bowed like a naughty schoolboy who had just gotten into trouble with his teacher. "I'll nip to the toilet and leave you to pick your horse."

"Good," Eddie muttered as Clive left him in peace.

By 4:36 p.m. Eddie's head was better, but his mood wasn't. He'd bet on three races and again had a perfect failure rate. One horse he'd backed, *Dancer,* had at one point looked like winning. The horse was well clear coming into the home stretch. Then, out of nowhere, the horse was caught right on the finishing line by *Mustapha.* In a photo finish, the inevitable happened, *Dancer* was awarded second place.

Eddie didn't think his mood could have gotten any worse until he heard the rumour spreading round the bookies. Clive had been told by a cashier that the man in the white suit, James, they think his name was, had now won six races in a row since he started coming here. They weren't entirely sure how much money he had won, but some people claimed it was at least well into the hundreds, or could even be over a thousand.

"Bloody marvellous!" Eddie said as he threw his hands up in the air when first hearing the news. "First it was Brody. Now some Johnny-come-lately dressed in a white suit and cravat. What next?" he cried. "You'll probably win the ruddy lottery this Saturday, Clive. That'll be just what I need to finally push myself over the edge."

"Cheers, Eddie," Clive said. Eddie may have had a miserable afternoon, but Clive had managed to pick himself two winners. This, funnily enough, hadn't helped Eddie's foul mood.

"Well. You know what I mean?" Eddie said. "It's nothing personal. It just seems everyone's having a bit of luck, except me. I think because of everything I've been through, I deserve something good to happen once in a while, don't you?"

"Of course. But getting in a tizzy like this isn't going to help," Clive said.

Eddie had stopped listening to Clive. He was now focusing all his attention and anger on the man in the white suit who was sitting beside the gaming machines and the toilets. It appeared to Eddie that he had a smug grin upon his face.

"Look at you," Eddie said, thinking out loud. "You waltz in here dressed like a Dandy. Then you go and win six in a row, you jammy sod. You don't even belong here. Just bugger off! And while you're at it, take that ridiculous suit and even more ridiculous cravat with you."

For the next ten minutes, Eddie continued with his own personal tirade towards a man whom he had never spoken to in his life and whom he knew nothing about, except that he may or may not have won six races in a row at the bookies.

Once Eddie had tired himself out venting his spleen about the man in the white suit, Clive managed to persuade him to head over to the pub. When they walked in, the place was practically empty, apart from a couple of pensioners, nursing a half pint each, sitting at a table playing dominoes. *The Queen's Head* wasn't the most modern or popular pub in town; the reason Eddie liked it was because it wasn't the most modern or popular pub in town. It had a pool table and a dart board through the back. In the front there were a variety of tables, chairs with ripped upholstery, and very unfashionable wood panelling on the walls. The once white ceiling had long become brown with cigarette smoke, so, just like the bookies, the stale aroma of cigarettes still hit you as you walked in the door. There was a jukebox on the far wall which was currently playing "I Want To Break Free". Right beside the entrance was the most important part of any pub, as far as Eddie was concerned, and that's the actual bar where the glorious amber nectar gets served. *The Queen's Head* also had something else going for it. Namely, a very attractive barmaid called Stacy.

According to Eddie, Stacy was almost up there with Shania Twain. She was the barmaid Eddie ignored last night, but he was sure she wouldn't take it too personally. Eddie ignored everyone so she was bound to understand he'd just had a bad day at the office. Most of the time they had a bit of a laugh together, although, on occasion, he also got the impression there may be a bit more between them than the normal customer and barmaid relationship.

A lot of the punters who came in here probably think the barmaids have a thing for them, but Eddie's sure he's seen a certain glint in Stacy's eye when she's chatting to him he doesn't see when she's chatting to anyone else. While some of her conversations are laden with enough innuendos and double entendres, they manage to make Eddie blush even after he's consumed ten pints of inhibition lowering lager. Eddie knows how unlikely it seemed that a good looking twenty five year old blonde barmaid, who, incidentally, also lived with her boyfriend, would be interested in him; yet, the odd glance and comment was more than enough evidence, in his eyes, to prove it possible. Obviously, nothing would ever happen between the two of them, but just the merest glimmer of hope that something could actually happen was enough. Not many things gave Eddie much pleasure anymore. The thought of Stacy walking up to him at the end of her shift and whispering in his ear, "Would you like to take me home, Big-Boy?" most certainly did.

Eddie had a look to see who was working. It was Brenda. Eddie was disappointed. No offence to Brenda, as she was nice enough, but she wasn't in Stacy's league, and Eddie thought the sooner he apologised to Stacy for last night the better. He and Clive stood at the bar. "Pint of lager," Eddie said to him.

Clive didn't reply. He shouted on Brenda. When she came across Clive ordered two pints of lager.

Brenda was a lively, friendly woman who got on with all the customers. She had short, brown, curly hair, and always wore a gold cross on a chain around her neck. Brenda appeared about Eddie's age, but he found it hard to tell exactly how old she was because of the layers of make up she always had slapped on. Eddie found this a bit off putting. It made him wonder what was actually hidden under all those layers. He watched as she poured out the drinks, quickly and efficiently without any wastage, and then carried them back to where Eddie and Clive were standing.

"You know how much that'll be, gentlemen," Brenda said, "Four pounds and sixty pence, please." She placed the two pints down on the bar beside Eddie and Clive.

After a bit of fumbling about, Clive took a fiver out of his wallet. Just as he was about to hand his money over a clipped English voice from behind him said, "I shall purchase those two drinks."

Eddie and Clive both turned to see who had offered to buy them a drink. Standing before them was the man in the white suit and cravat.

The man smiled, and asked, "I hope you two gentlemen don't mind if I buy you both a drink?"

"No," Clive said.

Eddie, meanwhile, just stared at the man in the white suit.

"Well, Eddie, will you let this gentleman buy you a drink?" Brenda asked.

Eddie faced her, "Yes," he finally answered.

"Splendid!" the man in the white suit said as he handed over a new, crisp ten pound note to Brenda. "May I also get a whisky and water for myself, please? Oh! Of course," he added theatrically, "plus one for yourself," and proceeded to give Brenda the most dazzling of smiles.

"Why, thank you very much, sir," she said, and giggled like a schoolgirl.

"My pleasure, my dear," he said, showing off his gleaming white teeth. The man in the white suit then turned his attention back to Eddie and Clive, "My name's James." He held his hand out to Clive who shook it without any hesitation.

Clive introduced himself.

James, as it seems his name is, then had a puzzled expression on his face. "If you don't mind me asking," he said. "But you happen to look very familiar, like a celebrity I know. I'm sure it's an actor or someone? I just can't put my finger on his name." He put a finger up to his lips; after some thought he nodded. "I know. It's Clint Eastwood, isn't it? I hope you're not annoyed at me mentioning that, as I bet you get people coming up and saying it to you all the time?"

"Well, it does happen every now and then," Clive said, his face beaming with delight. "But no, it doesn't annoy me at all."

31

"The resemblance is uncanny," James added.

Eddie was about to comment that in all the years he's known Clive, that until today, not one single person has remarked on Clive's uncanny resemblance to Clint Eastwood, except Clive himself. Before Eddie could say anything, James held his hand out to Eddie.

"My name's James," he said, "I'm pleased to meet you." He smiled and looked Eddie straight in the eye.

Eddie returned the gaze, but he didn't shake his hand. An uncomfortable second or two passed before Eddie finally relented. With a limp grip, which couldn't crush a grape, he shook James's hand. "My name's Eddie," he said.

"Clive and Eddie? Wasn't that the name of a group, in the nineties, who had about one hit?" James asked.

Clive answered straight away. "No, that was Charles and Eddie. They had a hit in nineteen ninety two called 'Would I Lie To You?' Do you want to know an interesting fact about them?"

"I certainly do, "James said.

Eddie tutted. *I've heard this a few times*, he thought as he prepared for his crucial first pint of the day. A lot depended on the first pint. It had to be at just the right temperature, if not, then the aftertaste and memory of that poor first one could put a dampener on the rest of the day's drinking experience. Eddie picked up the glass. It seemed cool to the touch. That was a good sign, and Eddie wasn't disappointed as the lager slipped easily down his throat. He put the glass back down on the bar and wiped his mouth with the back of his hand. That was an excellent start. Eddie's mini-euphoria was, unfortunately, short lived as he came back to reality and remembered what Clive was talking about. Eddie knew the story word for word, so he wasn't going to listen to it again. Instead, he watched James who appeared engrossed in Clive's boring little anecdote about a bunch of one-hit wonders most people hadn't even heard of. James had to be pretending he was interested in Clive's story. That was Eddie's sudden conclusion. There had to be an ulterior motive? No one ever showed this much interest in what Clive says; not even Clive's own wife. Eddie shook his head and took another sip of his pint. He didn't know what was going on here; it was like he'd walked into the *Twilight Zone*.

"That's how they met because they were both fans of Marvin Gaye? You are, indeed, a fountain of knowledge," James shouted out. He then immediately spun around and turned his attention to Brenda. "And you, my dear. What is your name?" he asked.

"It's Brenda," she said. Multiple layers of make up or not, it still wasn't enough to cover up her now scarlet face.

"A very lovely name for a very lovely lady," James said. "Now, I hope I'm not being too forward?" James leant across the bar and took her hand. "I know we have only just this moment met, but I have something to ask you. I dearly hope you will answer."

"Certainly." Brenda appeared out of breath.

"I was wondering," James paused, gazed into Brenda's starstruck eyes, and said, "Could you tell me where the gentlemen's toilets are?"

"Yes, yes I would," Brenda said. As it slowly seemed to register what James had actually said, she snatched her hand away from him and took a step back, "You what?" she cried.

James, in one swift move, had hold of both her hands again. "Once you have answered that question," he said, quietly and calmly. "I was wondering if you could answer another one." James moved closer, "Which is…would you be free to join me for dinner some time?"

It seemed to take another second or two for this question to sink in, but once it had, Brenda said, "Yes, yes I would." She laughed a nervous high pitched sort of laugh.

"Excellent, my dear," James said. "But regarding my first query? Because if I have an accident in my white suit, I feel it may be slightly noticeable."

Brenda let go of one of James's hands and pointed, "You go through the back there. Then it's straight ahead past the pool table."

"Thank you very much. I shall see you shortly," James said, and kissed Brenda on the hand he was still holding. He faced Eddie and Clive and said, "Gentlemen," before heading to the toilet, stopping briefly to study the jukebox on his way.

"What was that all about?" Eddie asked Brenda.

"What was all what about?" Brenda said as she cleaned a glass, acting as though nothing out of the ordinary had happened. It was just your typical afternoon in the bustling Queen's Head pub.

"You-know-what. That performance just now between you and him." Eddie thumbed towards the toilet.

"I wouldn't say it was a performance," Brenda said, still cleaning the glass. "There's just something about him. As soon as he walked into the bar, for some unknown reason, I just felt attracted to him. I know he's not your typical pin up type," Brenda admitted as she checked how clean the glass was in the light.

"Unless you go for the nineteen twenties look," Eddie butted in.

Brenda ignored him. "There have certainly been far younger and far better looking men who have walked through these doors, with far better dress sense." Brenda put the glass away behind the bar. "You'll think this is stupid and probably won't believe me." She now began wiping the top of the bar with the towel. "I'm not even sure it happened myself? When he spoke to me at the bar. Just for the briefest second, I was no longer simply a barmaid struggling to make ends meet. Working for minimum wage, with two cheating husbands and two failed marriages behind me. I actually felt like I was someone special. That my future was actually going to be something to look forward to. And, another thing," Brenda said as she put the bar towel over her shoulder and played with the cross around her neck, "When he held my hand, I could have sworn I felt a tingle. Like a small electric shock. I know it sounds crazy, but that's what happened. Or that's what I think happened."

"For once I agree with you," Eddie said. "It does sound crazy."

"I believe you, Brenda," Clive chipped in, "I think he's great as well."

"Listen to the two of you?" Eddie said, slamming his empty pint glass down on the bar. "Just because he's bought us a drink and made Brenda go weak at the knees, in the space of about five minutes, doesn't mean I'm going to be buddies for life with him. Any member of the male species who even breathes in Brenda's direction can have that affect on her."

"A little jealous are we, Edward?" Brenda politely said as she glanced across at the front door. "I think it's been a long time since you made anyone feel weak at the knees. He seems a gentleman. Something you have forgotten how to be. That is, if you knew how to be one in the first place? Now, if you will excuse me, two customers have just come in." Brenda sauntered away.

"I know we've just met James," Clive said. "And it's not just because he bought us a drink. I can tell almost straight away if I like someone, and I do like him."

"Hmmph," Eddie grunted. He took his wallet out of his pocket to see how much money he had. "You like him because he found your Charles and Eddie anecdote so riveting," he said while opening his wallet. "I wouldn't be at all surprised if he wasn't on your Christmas card list already? Give it a few weeks. He'll quickly grow fed up of your stories and jokes. Just like everyone else does. You won't think he's so wonderful then." Eddie counted the money in his wallet. When he saw how much (or how little) there was, he gave a quiet groan to himself. Eddie quickly put the wallet back in his pocket, "I think we've discussed him more than enough," he said. "Get the drinks in. I'm sure it's your round. Where's Brenda got to?" Eddie looked round to see if she had finished serving the two customers. "Bloody great!" he said.

"What is it?" Clive asked.

"Look who came in."

Clive had a look, "Oh no!" he said. The colour in his normally red, chubby cheeks seemed to immediately drain away at the sight of the two customers who'd just entered the pub.

CHAPTER FOUR

Eddie turned away quickly before making any eye contact with the two men who'd entered the pub. "Great," he whispered to Clive. "They've noticed us. Here they come."

One of the men was tall, with scraggly and dirty blonde hair. He also had a weasly face and beady untrusting eyes, which always seemed to dart from side to side. He was called Mike Bailey. Although Eddie wouldn't trust him an inch, he didn't particularly dislike Mike that much because he rarely caused any bother. Basically, he was just the other man's stooge. The other man being Douglas Kennedy, and he was a completely different proposition altogether. Douglas was shorter than Mike, but a lot stockier, with a shaven head, and what always appeared to be a number of day's stubble on his face. Not enough stubble; however, to cover the scar running along his left jaw line. A scar Douglas got during one of his many bar room brawls he's been involved in over the years. Brawls which, the majority of times, he's started. Douglas was a loudmouthed bully, who had very few, if any, redeeming features which Eddie knew of.

"LOOK WHO IT IS!" a voice with a Glaswegian twang to it boomed out. A twang, which Eddie remembers, suddenly appeared after Douglas spent a whole weekend in Glasgow to watch an Old Firm derby.

"I said to Mike," the voice continued to boom out, "we should come in here for a change of scenery. Maybe meet some good friends we don't see as often as we should. Look who's here? Why, it's Eddie the ringmaster and his trained chimp Clive." As he passed, Douglas gave Eddie a pat on the back and Clive a pat on the head.

Mike also gave Clive a pat on the head. They were apparently enjoying themselves already. Eddie believed these two were intending having a lot more fun; with most of it likely to be at Clive's expense.

"Two pints of lager again?" Brenda asked Clive and Eddie as she picked up Eddie's empty glass.

"I'm not too sure," Eddie said. "I don't have all that much money on me today. I don't think Clive has any money on him either. Do you?" he asked, hoping Clive would say "No".

Clive just shook his head.

"That's a shame, Eddie. You haven't trained your chimp very well, have you? He can't even speak yet," Douglas shouted out, hoping the whole bar would hear him, yet forgetting they were the

36

whole bar, except for the two old fossils playing dominoes in the corner. Never mind, any audience to someone like Douglas is better than no audience.

"The trained chimp can't even speak yet," Mike repeated. Laughing as his eyes darted from side to side.

"Well then, Eddie. Do you want another pint?" Brenda asked again.

Before Eddie could answer, someone else answered for him.

"Of course he does, my dear. Same drinks again, please," James said on his return from the toilet.

Eddie had forgotten all about James since the other two had appeared. As first impressions had gone, Eddie, admittedly, hadn't fallen in love with James like Brenda and Clive had. Yet, he didn't think James deserved to be thrown to the lions like this. Douglas was going to have a field day with James and his white suit and cravat. Eddie feared the worst.

"You have gone awfully quiet," James said to Clive as he took his wallet out. "I'm sure you would like another pint?"

"I…I'm not too sure," Clive barely managed to mumble.

"Nonsense. Same again, please, Brenda," James said. "And two for these gentleman, who must have come in while I was unavoidably detained elsewhere." James held out his hand to Douglas, "My name is James, I'm very pleased to meet you," he said. His dazzling smile returned with a vengeance.

Eddie didn't want to watch. It was going to be painful. A smile appeared on Douglas's face. Predictably, he didn't shake James's hand. He just laughed and said, "Who the hell are you? It shouldn't be a drink you're offering us. It should be some Kentucky fried chicken, because you look like Colonel Saunders in that outfit."

Mike almost spat his lager out.

"Look at you? What is that outfit all about?" Douglas continued his tirade. "Why don't you bugger off back to the eighteen hundreds, or wherever it is you came from? You white- suited-weirdo."

Eddie looked across at Mike. There was now a smug grin permanently fixed on his weasly face. He appeared, unsurprisingly, to be loving every second of this. For once in his life, Eddie would rather be anywhere else than here in the pub right now.

"My name's Douglas," he said. A smug grin was also firmly etched on his face. "Not that it's any of your business what my name is. And no, I don't want a drink, you finger-licking-freak."

Before Douglas could say anymore, Clive shouted out, "Why don't you leave him alone!"

For at least a second, Douglas appeared speechless. He pushed James out of the way. As he marched over to Clive, Eddie could have sworn he saw a vein bulging on Douglas's forehead.

"What did you say, you little chimp?" Douglas began ranting "If it isn't the monkey that roared. So he can speak, can he? He's going to wish he couldn't when I've finished with him." When Douglas got to Clive, Eddie stood in his way.

"What exactly are you going to do?" Douglas said and stared at Eddie.

Eddie couldn't answer, because he had no idea why he'd just done what he did. Eddie may have slight height advantage, but he didn't have the weight advantage (despite his ever increasing waistline), and he wasn't much of a fighter (nor a lover anymore). Eddie instantly regretted his action as his hands began to tremble.

"It's after five p.m. and you're still sober. That must be a record?" Douglas said, still staring Eddie in the eye.

Eddie lowered his gaze. A large brown stain on the blue worn carpet caught his attention. If this situation got any worse, Eddie worried there might be a brown stain somewhere else, namely in his boxer shorts.

"What's wrong? Have you run out of people to scrounge drinks off?" Douglas almost spat the words out. "Or, maybe you're just cutting down on drink to save money for Christmas, so you can afford to buy the wife and kids some Christmas presents?" Douglas slapped himself on the wrist. "My mistake," he said. "I completely forgot. I should've said wife-and-kid, shouldn't I? It's singular, not plural. Isn't it, Eddie?"

As Douglas stood there with the smuggest grin Eddie had ever seen in his life, all fear suddenly evaporated. It was now replaced by anger. Right at this very second in time, the thing that would give Eddie the greatest pleasure in life wasn't a night of passion with a young blonde barmaid, or a big win at the bookies. It was the chance to pummel that smug face till there wasn't a trace of a grin left. Eddie would probably end up with the biggest hiding of his life, yet it would still be worth it just to land one clean punch.

Before a punch was thrown, Brenda yelled, "That's enough, Douglas. If you don't have your drink quietly, you'll be barred."

A look of child-like innocence came across Douglas's face. "Brenda!" he pleaded. "The chimp told me to shut up. That wasn't very nice?"

Brenda had seen his antics too many times before. "I've told you, Douglas," she said, "Drink quietly. Or, you'll be barred."

Douglas put his right hand into a fist. He pointed at it with his left hand, "This is for you, chimp," he said. "You'll get it very soon. Don't you worry." Then Douglas made his way back beside his partner in crime, who was now practically wide-eyed with excitement.

"Brenda, my dear. Four drinks, please, as I think we need them," James said when things appeared to have settled.

"No, I've had enough," Eddie said before Brenda could pour the pints.

"Yeah. Me too, James. But thank you," added Clive.

James took no notice as he produced another ten pound note out of his expensive looking black leather wallet. He handed the money to Brenda. "I insist," he said. "There's no point in having a bit of a windfall if you can't share your winnings."

Brenda poured two more pints for Eddie and Clive despite their lack of enthusiasm. James had a whisky and water. Brenda got herself a Diet Coke. As she handed over the drinks, James chatted as though nothing had just happened.

"Now, Clive. Tell me? This knowledge of yours, have you ever thought of appearing on a game show on TV?" James took a sniff of his whisky, "mmm...excellent aroma," he said as he closed his eyes for a second or two. "Yes, I think you would do rather well," he said as he opened his eyes.

"I thought about applying to appear on *The Weakest Link*," Clive said, appearing perkier again. "You know, the quiz with Anne Robinson?"

James nodded

"I like that programme," Clive said, "but I probably wouldn't do very well. So I've never bothered."

"I think you would do very well on it, my friend," James said. "You should give it a go. You may surprise yourself."

Douglas was apparently listening to this conversation with great interest. He butted in before Clive got a chance to reply. "The chimp wanting to be on TV?" he shouted out. "You on *The Weakest Link*? You've got to be joking? If you appeared on TV it would have to be after the nine p.m. watershed in case any children were watching. Listen to this one, Mike." Not that Mike was doing anything else except hang on Douglas's every word. "If the chimp did appear on a game show, they would have to change the name from *The Weakest Link* to *The Missing Link.*"

Mike almost doubled over with laughter. There were now actual tears in his eyes.

Appearing very pleased with himself, Douglas took a long sip of his pint. When Douglas finished, much to Eddie's surprise, and horror, James was standing right beside him.

Oh my God! What the hell are you doing? He's going to murder you, you idiot.

Brenda seemed to be having the same thought as Eddie. A look of panic could be seen on her heavily made-up face. Sensing, perhaps, that the first person who's asked her out on a date in over six months was now on the verge of getting put in hospital? "Forget it, James, he's just a bully," Brenda said in a high pitched squeal, as she groped her gold cross for assurance, or perhaps hoping for some Divine intervention.

James ignored her. "Have you ever heard the song 'Walk A Mile In My Shoes'*?"* he asked Douglas, whilst standing toe to toe with him. "It's a song written by Joe South. Elvis has sung it. So has Bryan Ferry. I feel it's a song you should maybe listen to. It's about the subject of empathy. A subject, I get the impression, you don't really know a lot about? It's an ability to understand someone else's feelings as if they were one's own. There's also a song, by Roger Watters, called 'Myself in every stranger's eyes'. This could be about the same thing, but you've probably not heard that one, either.*"*

"I don't know what you're talking about?" Douglas said. Sounding to Eddie a bit confused, as though James may have caught him off guard.

"You think you don't," James said. "But maybe you do?" James stepped away from Douglas and faced Mike. "Are you and your friend...I'm sorry, we haven't been introduced."

"His name is Mike," Douglas answered for him, still sounding confused.

"I'm pleased to meet you, Mike," James said and held his hand out.

Mike shook James's hand quickly. Then he scurried away and stood behind Douglas with a smile no longer on his face, either. Mike also seemed surprised at how events were unfolding as the permanent grin had disappeared from his rodent-like face.

"Now we have all been formally introduced," James said, "I was wondering what you both do for a living? I thought that because you were intelligent, but also, by the looks of things, physically strong. Maybe you're a builder?"

Douglas didn't answer. Even from a distance, Eddie thought he could see Douglas's long, untrimmed nose hair start to flutter as he started to breathe louder and louder. The initial look of confusion had quickly gone. Douglas now had an expression on his face like he'd just checked his shoes to find he'd stood on something nice, warm, and smelly which a kindly dog had left on the ground for him. Things were going to get ugly.

"Because you're one step ahead of the rest," James added, oblivious to, or not caring about, Douglas's face-of-fury. "Then, you're now a gaffer. Instead of getting told what to do, you do the telling. Am I correct?"

Douglas's breathing got louder, and he clenched both fists as he stepped towards James. Eddie was sure he could see the vein throbbing again, almost synchronised in time with the nasal hair. "Yes, I used to be a builder," Douglas said, "and so did Mike. But we both haven't worked for a long time now. And I'll tell you why, even though it's none of your business. Because telling you is a lot easier than putting up with all the hassle I'll get if I punch your lights out." Douglas unclenched his fists and the nasal hair stopped moving. "This pub's a dump, but I could do without getting banned from this one as well, " he said as he picked up his pint from the bar. "The reason we don't work is simple. We don't want to. Life is too short to spend it doing something you don't want to do. So, we do whatever we want, whenever we want. Some poor sap spends all his time working, busting a gut. Then, on his last day of work, what happens? After forty years of service he gets knocked down by a bus. Well-mate, that won't happen to us, because we're living life to the full. That is my philosophy." Douglas turned away from James. "Now bugger off," he said with his back turned, "As I'm growing to dislike you very quickly." Douglas gulped down the remains of his pint, "Get me another pint, Brenda," he demanded.

Brenda, without any hesitation, took Douglas's pint glass.

"Your philosophy is living life to the full," James said, still standing in the same spot and obviously not deciding to "bugger off".

41

"Excellent! I could not agree with you more, my friend. Your motto is Carpe Diem. A Latin phrase which became particularly popular during the Baroque period of history. One which I'm sure you know means seize the day."

Douglas turned to see James, standing beside him, with a carefree smile upon his face. The vein on Douglas's forehead appeared to throb even more.

Look out captain-it's going to blow!

"Crappy-what? Look, I don't have a clue what you're talking about," Douglas said. "And I don't want to have a clue. I told you to bugger off. If you don't in the next five seconds, then, I swear, I will flatten you. I don't care if I get barred or not. But I will smash your face in. I don't think you want to get blood all over that white suit of yours, do you?"

James did not budge an inch.

"I think you better do as he says, James," Brenda pleaded whilst handing over Douglas's pint. 'A Whiter Shade Of Pale' had appropriately come on the jukebox, because that's the colour Brenda's face now was. "I think you've made your point. Just leave it-please." Brenda turned her attention to Douglas. With one hand still grasping her gold cross so tightly that it was a wonder the chain didn't snap. "The pint's on the house, if you drink it without any trouble," she said, obviously hoping the offer of free alcohol might work, as it didn't appear Douglas was about to be struck by lightning any time soon.

"Thank you, Brenda." Douglas, unsmiling, rubbed the scar on his face. "I'm being provoked. I've asked him to leave me in peace, but he hasn't. If he continues to invade my personal space, then I will have to do something about it."

The bar went silent as Douglas drank his pint. It was soon broken when James said to him, "I have a little proposal for you. Don't worry. It's not an indecent one." James laughed.

Douglas glowered over his pint glass.

"All I ask is five minutes of your time to have a small debate with you," James continued. "That's all. In that time I hope to help you see, that, maybe, you could change your philosophy on life a little for the better. You are free to voice your opinion at any time. But, if you could listen. And, more importantly, refrain from any sort of violence in the five minutes. At the end, if you have not changed your philosophy on life in any way, I have a crispy fifty pound note in my wallet that is yours. Do we have a deal?"

42

"Fifty quid!" Douglas almost dropped his pint glass. "Just to stand here, have a pint, and listen to you prattle on for five minutes? You're a bigger idiot than I thought. Which is some achievement. Hold on, where's the catch? What's in it for you?"

"If I can change your view on life, then that's what's in it for me," James said. "You have my word, there is no catch."

Douglas seemed suspicious, but said, "Right. You better get on with it." He glanced at the watch strapped round his large, hairy wrist. "That's about ten seconds gone already."

"You see, my friend," James said. "In reality, life is very simple. Here is another Latin phrase-'Memento Mori'. This can be translated as 'Remember-you-will-die'. It applies to every single one of us, young or old, weak or strong, rich or poor. No matter who we are, from Plato to Presley, the grim reaper stands patiently by our side from the day we are born. Waiting for the inevitable time when we're the next name on the list to be taken into the great unknown."

Eddie thought if James was going to waffle on for a while, he may as well have a seat. He pulled out one of the barstools and made himself more comfortable.

"We could be living 'La Dolce Vita' one moment," James said. "The next, we're no more than dust. Each day that passes is one day we've moved closer to our grave. Your philosophy is in one way correct. We must celebrate and make the most of every single moment of life we can. Because, as far as any one of us knows, there is no guarantee we will get another one. Life is for living. It's not for going through the motions. At the end of the day, if we can follow Kipling's advice and 'fill the unforgiving minute with sixty seconds worth of distance run.' What more can we do?"

"Ha… is that it?" Douglas sneered. "I thought you would come out with something more exciting than that? What are you, a minister or something? No, I know what you are," Douglas corrected himself. "You're a boring old-fart. That's what." Douglas had another look at his watch, "That's a minute of your time gone."

"My, this is a challenge, isn't it?" James said as he took a white handkerchief out of his pocket. It wasn't to wave in the air to admit defeat. The handkerchief was to wipe his brow with. "Another whisky, my dear. I think I'm going to need it," James said as he folded the handkerchief neatly, before putting it back in his pocket.

Brenda poured James a whisky while he continued.

"What I'm trying to say, is the idea of Carpe Diem is wonderful. It is without doubt something each and every one of us would do well to live by. But, do you honestly think that spending almost every day of your existence drinking in the pub and belittling your fellow man. Do you honestly think that is seizing the day and living life to the full?"

"To me it is," Douglas said as he got some change out of his pocket and began to count it at the bar.

"It seems to me," James said, "that the only day you are seizing is *Groundhog Day*. There's a whole world out there to see, a whole life to be lived. You could do so much, but, so far, you seem to be doing so little. You drink as though there's no tomorrow. Then, when you wake up next morning and realize there is a tomorrow. That you have been granted the gift of another day. What do you do? Do you wake up and be thankful? Or, do you bemoan your hangover caused by the indulgence of the day before. Then go on and do the same thing all over again?"

"Here's your drink, James," Brenda said. "Sorry! I should have waited till you had stopped speaking," she immediately tried to apologise.

"Nonsense," James said. "My throat was getting dry. The whisky has arrived at just the right time." He took the glass and said, "Down the hatch," before proceeding to drink his whisky in one go. James put the glass back on the bar then directed his attention back to Douglas. "Right," he said, "I hope you can stay awake for the final three minutes."

This comment drew a loud yawn from Douglas; the loud yawn drew a quiet snigger from Mike.

James cleared his throat before continuing, "We shall move away from boring old Latin phrases. Let's talk about something a bit more up to date. Something you may actually know about. Have you ever seen the *Saw* films?" he asked

"Yes, I've seen all of them," Douglas said with something almost resembling interest in his voice. "That's what you call my sort of film. Lots of blood and gore. I must've watched the first one at least five times."

"That's good," James said. "I can't say they're exactly my cup of tea. But there are a couple of reasons I've mentioned the films. The first reason is because I had a sneaky suspicion you may like them. The second reason is because the main character, Jigsaw, who I don't

44

think actually kills anyone in the films? Well, strange as it may seem, his view on life was much the same as the one I'm talking about."

"You don't go around trying to kill people, do you?" Douglas asked. For a brief moment, at least, James definitely seemed to have his full attention.

James laughed. "No, I don't," he said. "Jigsaw may be more extreme in trying to get his message across than me."

Douglas had already lost interest as he went back to counting his change at the bar.

"Remember this is just my interpretation of the film," James said. "I could easily be wrong. I have been many times before, and I'm sure I will be many times again. The great Socrates once said, not the Socrates who played football for Brazil, in the eighties, but the famous philosopher, 'Wisest is he who knows he does not know'."

The mention of a Brazilian footballer, from the eighties, wasn't enough to regain Douglas's attention. Douglas was now firmly focused on a shiny one pound coin as he held it up and observed it closely in the afternoon light, which had fought its way through the grimy pub window.

James watched Douglas and his lack of interest. "In the film, Jigsaw has been diagnosed with incurable cancer," he said. "I also seem to remember that he attempts to kill himself, but survives. It's when he survives that he realises just how precious life is. Yet, around him, he sees so many people who don't appreciate life and are wasting it. That's what he's trying to do by putting them in these situations. Because if they, somehow, survive the game he's set for them, they will see life in a different light. A sort of awakening-"

"I don't know about awakening," Douglas interrupted as he put his shiny pound coin back on the bar with the rest of his change. "But I do know you're almost putting me to sleep. You really are a bore."

"Thank you for your honesty," James said. "You will be pleased to hear I am almost finished."

"Very," Douglas said as he finally took his change off the bar and put it back in his pocket. "What's the point in this?" he asked. "You've less than a minute left, and there's no way you're going to have any effect on me. You might have the other four interested with your tiresome tales, but not me." Douglas turned his attention to Mike. "And as for you, you're like a bloody groupie. You'll be throwing your knickers at him next."

Mike, with a sheepish look on his face, tried to defend himself,

45

"Douglas-I-was just-" he stuttered.

Douglas waved his hand at him with disgust. "How any of you can find him interesting is beyond me?" he said. "The only entertainment I get from him is a good laugh at his ridiculous suit and cravat. I think your time's up, mate." Douglas held out his hand, "Let's see the colour of your money."

James took out his wallet, "My point is, your philosophy on life is flawed," he said. "You are not seizing any day, but are merely living a hedonistic life based purely around the pursuit of pleasure. Plato, for one, found the pursuit of pleasure foolish." James opened his wallet and took out a fifty pound note. He didn't immediately hand it over. "Then again," he said, "maybe I'm mistaken on the hedonistic part? Because I can't see what pleasure you must get out of life?"

"Don't worry, mate," Douglas said. "I get plenty of pleasure out of life. NOW GIVE US YOUR MONEY!" he shouted, sounding a lot like Bob Geldof with his famous rant during *Live Aid.*

"The true meaning of Carpe Diem," James said, "is not spending every day in the pub getting drunk and criticising who you meet. Whilst, at the same time, not caring about whom you hurt with your words or actions. It is about ensuring you make every day count. 'Think', said Dante, 'that this day will never dawn again'."

"That's a pity," Douglas said. "Because it's not everyday I fleece a mug like you out of fifty quid." Douglas held his hand out again.

"You foolishly believe you are living life to the full," James said, still not handing over the money. "Unfortunately, you are sadly mistaken. The sooner you realise this, the sooner your own life along with the life of those around you will become so much better."

Douglas pointed at his watch. "About bloody time," he cried out. "That's your five minutes up. This is the last time I am going to ask you. Hand-over-the-money."

"I will," James said. "But, could I possibly finish with a small ditty I've just thought of?"

Douglas tutted, "Hurry up," he said, and shouted at Brenda, "Get me a pint, will you. I'll pay for it with a fifty pound note, once the white-suited-windbag finally gets off his soap box."

"Thank you," James said. "This is a little poem of a few lines. I hope you like it? There once was a man who thought of a plan, I'm going to be happy he said. Yet the more that he tried looking outside, he found it was all in his head."

46

Douglas was again far from impressed. He pretended to wipe an imaginary tear from his eye. "Very moving," he said, then held his hand out again.

"I enjoyed it," Clive butted in.

"Thank you, Clive," James said. "But I don't believe there's very much wrong with your philosophy on life."

"I must admit," Brenda said as she handed Douglas his pint, and with the colour back in her cheeks, "when I came to work today, I didn't expect to be asked out on a date by someone who made up poems in the bar."

"I'm delighted you agreed to go out with a boring-old-fart who recites poetry," James said.

"This is getting like the *Love Boat*," Douglas said, and thumped his fist on the bar. "I don't care if you two are going out on some hot date. What I care about is the fifty quid you owe me."

"I'm a man of my word," James said, "and you'll get the money you're entitled to." He appeared to be about to place the money in Douglas's palm when he stopped and said, "I've had a thought."

"No more thoughts," Douglas said as he shook his head. "I want that money in the next five seconds. Or, I'll flatten you and just take the money anyway."

"How about double or quits?" James asked. "How does that tickle your taste buds?"

"What did you say?" Douglas asked.

"I said double or quits," James repeated. "You have the chance to earn yourself, not fifty pounds, but one hundred pounds. Would you kindly take this note for one second, please, my dear?" James handed over the fifty pound note to Brenda. He then took his wallet out and produced another crisp fifty pound note from it. "Would you also take this as well, please," he said, handing over the other note. "I realise what I've said has had little affect. Well, that's maybe an over exaggeration? Let's face it. What I've said has had no affect on you. I am only asking for one more chance to try and get through to you. Five minutes again. If I'm just as unsuccessful, then one hundred pounds is yours. You have my word on that. What do you have to lose except five minutes of your time?"

Douglas stared long and hard at James, "You better not be trying to get out of paying this bet?" he said eventually. "Because, if you are, it won't be five minutes you lose. It'll be all your front teeth."

"I am not trying to get out of paying anything," James said.

"Five more minutes, that is all I ask. Tell you what. I shall buy you another pint so you can sip it while I bore you again…Do we have a deal?"

Douglas eyed James with some suspicion, as though he knew James was up to something, but couldn't put his finger on what it was. "Right, get on with it," he said. "But if you try any funny stuff," he clenched his hand into a fist. "This will be for you instead of the chimp."

"Don't worry. I wouldn't know how to try any funny stuff, even if I wanted to," James assured him.

Eddie, still sitting upon the barstool, watched as James bought another pint for Douglas as well as everyone else in the pub, including the two old age pensioners who appeared highly delighted. As he awaited his next pint, Eddie thought about what was going on. *I've no idea what James is playing at? If he wants to throw his money away, then he should throw it in* my *direction, and not just give it to that idiot. Unless he is some sort of maniac like in the Saw films, and has merely lulled Douglas into a false sense of security? Highly unlikely, but we can always hope.*

Eddie was interrupted in his thinking when Brenda handed him the pint James had bought. He took a sip of it and got ready for what James had up his sleeve next. Hopefully a bit more than last time; if the rumours were true, and James had been on a winning streak recently, it now looked like the winning streak was about to come to a costly end.

"So then," James began. "You obviously haven't taken on board anything I've said, so far. Therefore, I've had to resort to Plan B." He shook his head, "I really didn't want to do this, but I feel I've no option," he said.

"I'm terrified-absolutely terrified," Douglas said and laughed. He put his hands out in front of him with palms facing down, "Look at my hands," he said, as they started to shake. "You've made me a bag of nerves with your threat-look." He showed Mike his shaky hands. The response was a forced smile; not the response Douglas was used to from his straight man.

James, meanwhile, paid no attention to Douglas's antics. He just carried on with his so-called Plan B. "One of the signs of good character and greatness in a man is how they treat other men," he said. "Particularly, those they believe are lesser men than themselves. You have shown me in the short space of time since we've met, just how

48

you treat what you consider to be 'lesser men'. I almost get the impression you believe everyone is a lesser man compared to yourself?"

"Yes," Douglas agreed. "I can't help it if I'm better than everyone else, can I? Like the name of that song, 'Oh-Lord It's Hard To Be Humble', or whatever it's called? "Hold on," Douglas added. An ominous looking grin appeared upon his face. "You gave us a boring made up poem earlier. So listen to what I just thought of. Oh-Lord it's hard to look like a chimp, who gets hairier every-day. I'm not able to look in the mirror, cause it'll probably just break anyway." Douglas seemed very impressed with his attempt at poetry.

"I think you do know how to empathise with people," James said with a sombre tone in his voice. "Particularly those who are abused and criticised."

"No," Douglas said, as chirpy as ever, while he got stuck into another pint.

"You don't? Well that is very interesting," James said. "You see. In this day and age, people do take offence at the slightest little thing, don't they? I mean, political correctness has gone mad, it really has. You can't say anything for fear of offending someone. But whose fault is it that we get offended over issues ranging from which football team we support, to which religion we follow? Even mentioning harmless Golliwogs from the *Noddy* stories can get some people hot and bothered."

Douglas burst out laughing. "You really have lost the plot," he said. "Talking about golliwogs? I think you should go home and lie down for a while. But only after you've given me my money first."

"Thank you for the advice," James said. "Maybe we're all too sensitive? It's our choice, and no-one else's, if we decide to take offence at something someone has said to us. Or, in the way they treat us. It's impossible to be offended without our own consent. We can't be offended by what anyone says or does if we don't allow ourselves to be. It is the offended who has the power over the situation, not the offender-"

"Well," Douglas interrupted, not for the first time. "Did you hear they named a song after me?" he asked; his grin was now wider than ever.

"A song?" James sounded bemused.

"Yes, a song. Freddie Mercury sang it, and some other group from ages ago. They call me 'The Great Offender'*!*" Douglas burst out laughing. It seemed like he really was having the time of his life.

Eddie had a look at the pub clock. Not long left now, and it will be over without any blood being spilt. So far, this plan B had been just as tame as Plan A, which was no surprise to Eddie, as *The Gentle Touch* was never going to work on Douglas. James may be many things but, by the look of it, he is no Jill Gascoine, who played Detective Inspector Maggie Forbes in the early eighties, that's for sure. Eddie used to have a soft spot for Jill, and always wondered how gentle her touch would be.

James downed the rest of his whisky, put the glass on the bar, and muttered under his breath, "Once more unto the breach, dear friends," before turning his attention back to Douglas. "Most of us mere mortals," he said, "find ourselves being controlled by other people's thoughts and comments about us. Someone criticises the clothes we wear, so we find ourselves getting all worked up-"

"No wonder people criticise the clothes you wear. Look at you?" Douglas interrupted once more.

James ignored him. "Likewise," he said, "someone praises the clothes we wear, and suddenly we feel good."

Douglas pointed at James, "I find it hard to believe anyone's ever praised the clothes *you* wear."

"Both times," James said without responding, "we find our mood and thoughts controlled by someone else. How we feel has depended on a few words uttered by another person. And those few little words can either make us happy, or they can make us miserable for the rest of the day. Often these words are uttered by someone we don't even like, someone who we think is merely a loudmouthed, ignorant idiot."

Douglas pointed at himself "I hope you're not meaning me?" he said, with a look of stupidity. He really was playing up to the crowd now.

"I'm not meaning anyone," James said.

"That's good. I will be able to sleep tonight," Douglas replied.

"Whether we like them or not, why should we care what anyone thinks of us? Praise or criticism, it shouldn't matter. If you accept one you must accept the other. Each time it is the ego which is affected, not the real I, the self which is hidden and drowned out by the constant chatter of the ego. It is our ego which thrives on praise, and it is our ego which gets all hot and bothered over criticism. For most unenlightened people, the ego controls all their thoughts and reactions

50

to events. Like in the old saying-wherever I go-ego." James chuckled.

"I've no idea what you're talking about," Douglas said. "But I know what I'm going to accept, and that's one hundred pounds."

"And it will be a hard earned one hundred pounds," James said. "I would like to add. Even though I'm sure you feel your opinion is incredibly important, unfortunately, to me, it isn't. I have learned not to take things people say personally. Whether compliment, or insult, they are one and the same. If you told me everything I say is so interesting and stimulating, it would have the exact same effect as telling me I am a Muppet."

Douglas slowly clapped his hands and said, "That's just as well because you are a Muppet. What you're saying is exactly what I want to hear. What a day this is turning out to be. Not only are you going to give me one hundred quid. You're also telling me I can say whatever I want, whenever I want, and it's not my fault if I offend anyone? If someone, like the chimp, happens to get upset I've hurt their feelings, I can simply shrug my shoulders because it's their fault for taking it personally."

"What I'm trying to say," James said. "Admittedly, I'm not doing a very good job of it. Is that, even though we should all try not to care what other people say about us, it doesn't mean we shouldn't try to care what we say about other people. Maybe practice a little empathy? When we belittle people and try to put them down, one of the reasons is because we have the absurd notion we are better than them. One of the most liberating thoughts we can ever have is to realise we are no better than anyone else. Likewise, no one is any better than we are. Think how wonderful that is?"

"I'm thinking how wonderful it will be when you finally shut up and hand over the money," Douglas said, and yawned. He looked again at his watch, "Great. That's your time almost up."

"Okay," James said, sounding downhearted. "Before I finish, I would like to mention Victor E Frankl. He was a prisoner of the Nazi concentration camps, where his parents, his brother, and his wife all died. The pain and suffering he must have gone through in that hell, is something none of us here can even attempt to comprehend. He knew the Nazis controlled his fate. From one day to the next he had no idea whether it would be his turn in the ovens. However, Frankl came to the decision that only he could decide how all of this horror was going to affect him. Only he had the power to choose his response to everything the Nazis did."

Just then, James was rudely interrupted when Douglas let out a loud fart. "Ooops!" he said, and started laughing. "Looks like you're not the only one in the pub who's full of wind."

James shook his head slowly. "We are humans," he said, "not Pavlov's dogs. Being human means we have the power to choose our response to anything that happens to us, no matter how trivial, or major, that thing is. It also means we can control, to some extent, our bodily functions."

Douglas waved his hand under his nose. "Looks like it's going to be a smelly one."

"If Victor E Frankl can manage it while in the Nazi concentration camps," James said, "surely we can manage it when someone comments on something as meaningless as our weight or our hairstyle? Between someone offending us and our response, we have the choice how it is going to affect us. So why not use that choice? Victor E Frankl did. So there is no reason why we can't?"

"Okay," Douglas said. "I'm going to make the choice that nothing you say is going to affect me in any way. So why are you still talking?"

"I've no idea," James admitted, "I may as well get my money's worth. So don't stop me now. When we realise we're all equals. That no one is better than us, and we are no better than anyone else. This is enough reason for us to never criticise or abuse another person. How can we possibly dare abuse another person when they are our equal?"

While James continued to speak, Eddie stopped listening, for the time being, and just watched Douglas. He was now constantly sighing and yawning, with a look of complete indifference on his face. It definitely looked like James had just lost one hundred quid. This was no great surprise to Eddie. Years of therapy wouldn't get through to that man, let alone a ten minute heart to heart in the middle of the pub. The best way of knocking any sense into Douglas's, coconut-shaped, cranium would be with Eddie's favourite 7-iron golf club. Eddie had known it was an impossible task what James had attempted to do. Yet, to be honest, Eddie still wasn't exactly sure what it was James had actually attempted to do? Whatever it was, he had about two minutes left to do it. He may be one hundred quid down, but at least James could take one positive from the last ten minutes-he still had his front teeth. Because, at one point, it looked odds on that James's gleaming smile was going to become a toothless grin.

"Are you finished yet?" Douglas asked, while attempting to

stuff a handful of peanuts into his mouth. Some nuts made it into his, large opinionated, mouth, while most ended up on the floor or the worktop of the bar.

"Not quite," James said

"Hurry up! The peanuts are almost finished. I want my hundred quid to take to another pub, where hopefully the company isn't so boring."

"You won't be bored for much longer," James said, and sighed. "I hoped I wouldn't have to resort to this, but, alas, it looks like I have no other choice." Then, before Douglas could get in his usual sarcastic retort, as his mouth was full of peanuts, James quickly asked him, "The big man we see before us isn't the same big man who exists behind closed doors, is he?"

"What did you just say?" Douglas asked, almost choking on the peanuts.

"You weren't the big man you are now back in Primary School, either. Were you?" James said

"What would you know about me back at Primary School?" Douglas shouted back at him, spraying more half chewed peanuts all over the bar. "I was the...the king of the playground, that's what I was." Douglas appeared startled.

"The king of the playground," James said, "Mmm. That is interesting, but not entirely accurate. You were a very late developer. Until you went to Secondary school, when you suddenly sprouted, I do believe you were actually the smallest boy in your class?"

"What are we getting? *This is Your Bloody Life?*" Douglas shouted. "Next you'll be telling me my old Primary teachers are hiding behind the bar?"

"Not your teachers. Your classmates," James said.

"My classmates?" Douglas glanced behind the bar.

"Of course there's no-one there," James assured him. "As you were 'the king of the playground', wouldn't it be wonderful to meet up with them again?"

"Yeah-wonderful," Douglas agreed as he had another glance behind the bar.

"Maybe another time," James said. "It couldn't have been easy for you, being not only the smallest boy in class, but also having the added handicap of being from the poorest family. Having to wear the same patched up clothes year after year. That must have been hard? Especially, when you're trying to fit in with your peers and not wanting to stand out. Children can be so cruel."

Douglas didn't answer. He stood open mouthed; treating everyone to a glimpse of the remains of his uneaten peanuts.

"They didn't care about your feelings back then, did they?" James said. "So why should you care about anyone's feelings now? Can you remember the taunts in the playground? That wasn't enough for them, by any means. At the end of the day they would follow you home mocking and sneering. Yes, it's all different now as you're the big man. You can get back at them by picking on the small man. Let someone else know what it's like to be made fun of."

Douglas still didn't utter a word, but he had, thankfully, for everyone else in the bar, managed to close his mouth.

"No matter what you say or do," James continued. "It can't erase those memories. The nights when you would cry yourself to sleep, dreading another day at school when the taunting would start all over again. They were hard times but, as you got older, you became the big man out in the street and in the pub. What about at home with your girlfriend?"

Douglas remained uncharacteristically quiet. Eddie had never known him to be this quiet for so long.

"Are you the big man there?" James asked. "You've made her so happy that, at the last count, she's had three affairs you know about. After the latest one you broke down and cried, like a baby, begging her not to leave. I also believe you told her that if she did leave, you would kill yourself? The big man's girlfriend is still with him, not out of love, but out of pity and emotional blackmail…Carpe Diem, Douglas. Carpe Diem."

The bar was quieter than a studio audience at the filming of an ITV comedy. The only sound to be heard was the ticking of the clock behind the bar, along with the occasional hum of the traffic outside. It seemed everyone in the *Queen's Head,* including the two old age pensioners, had their eyes firmly fixed on Douglas, expecting him to explode. Eddie could see the bulging vein was back, but wasn't sure if the whispering nasal hair had also reappeared. Surely, though, it was now only a matter of seconds before Douglas's hairy, caveman-like knuckles made contact with James's, pearly white, teeth?

But they didn't.

Instead, Douglas slammed his fist on the bar, scattering some peanuts, and shouted out, "Who do you think you are? You white suited…You white suited…" Douglas seemed lost for words, something Eddie didn't think he would ever witness in his lifetime. Douglas just stood at the bar shaking his head and staring, through half closed eyes, at James. A reaction Eddie wasn't expecting. Nor, apparently, were the pensioners as they resumed their game of dominoes, probably disappointed there hadn't been a bloodbath.

Douglas eventually stopped staring at James and, in turn, stared at Eddie, Clive, Mike, and Brenda, who, unlike the pensioners, were still engrossed in this un-Douglas-like reaction. "What are you all staring at?" he practically screamed. "Get me a pint, will you!" he said to Brenda as he wiped his sweaty forehead.

Mike walked up to Douglas, "Are you all right," he said, and then attempted to pat him on the back.

"Get your hands off me," Douglas shouted, and pushed Mike's hand away.

Mike did not need telling twice. He scurried off to stand behind James.

Brenda handed over the pint Douglas had asked for. "There you go," she said. "It's on the house." But Douglas didn't say a thing. He picked up his glass and drank most of it in one go; as he did this, James went across to him.

"No one deserved to go through what you did at school," James said. "Likewise, Victor E Frankl didn't deserve to be put in a concentration camp and have all his family killed. Many other people have things happen to them which they don't deserve, things they can't do anything about. Unfortunately, you cannot do anything about what happened to you. But you can do something about how it affects you. It's not too late."

Some of the lager dribbled down his chin as Douglas quickly downed the rest of his pint. "Why don't you just shut up?" he said, perspiring, appearing pale, and with lager on his chin and t-shirt.

James did not do as Douglas had asked. Instead, he walked right up to him and said, "The best way to prove you're stronger than those bullies were is not to become one, but to become the opposite of them. At the moment they have won. With the click of a finger, you can win. Show them that no matter how much pain and abuse they heaped upon you, you are a stronger person for what happened. From now on you will have a laugh with other people. You will no longer have a laugh at other people. When you walked in this pub today you still hated those children. Children, now adults, who have forgotten

55

what they did to you. You have to try and do the same. Not only forget, but also something more important…forgive."

"I asked you to shut up," Douglas said once more. But this did not sound like the cocky, smug, and full of bravado Douglas of earlier.

"It won't be easy," James said, again ignoring Douglas's request. "Yet, most things in life aren't easy. Not when they're important. I know you can't change your past and what happened. But if you try to forgive, then you can change your future. The bullying stopped a long time ago, but not here." James tapped the side of his head. "Those children are no longer responsible for how you feel today. You are."

"I'll feel a lot better once I get out of this dump and away from you," Douglas said.

"You have to become a different man from the one who walked in here today," James said. "The only way to do that is to forgive. Let go of the past and seize the day in the present. The first thing you have to do is speak to your girlfriend."

"Sod off," was Douglas's eloquent reply. He turned round and stomped towards the front door.

James shouted out, "You can forgive her for what she has done, but you cannot stop her from doing it again. Deep down you know she will. Neither of you are happy together. Hard as it will be, you have to let her leave. For you to move on, you have to allow her to move on. That is the only way. Thank her for the good times, and get on with the rest of your life."

Douglas opened the door and faced everyone at the bar.

"What about the money I owe you?" James asked

"You can stick it up your…." Douglas said, just as a lorry passed by outside drowning out the end of his sentence.

Then he was gone.

CHAPTER FIVE

A couple of hours had passed since Douglas left the pub. Mike had decided it was best if Douglas was left alone, so he had stayed for an hour and a half and five pints. The two domino playing pensioners had also headed off, and so had Clive. Brenda had finished her shift and was away for some pampering and a manicure before her date with James tomorrow. She had been replaced behind the bar by Stacy. So far Eddie hadn't even noticed her as he sat at a table engrossed in conversation with James.

Eddie leaned back on his chair, pint in hand, and laughed. "How did you know all that about Douglas? I mean… I've known him, haven't liked him, mind you. But I've known him for a good few years, and had no idea about those things. When he was at school. His girlfriend cheating on him. Who would have believed it?"

"Let's say, I have my sources," James said. He sipped an orange juice after having more than enough whiskies for one day. "Who knows? Maybe my sources have also told me things about you?"

Eddie gave an unconvincing laugh. "I don't think so."

"I don't know, Eddie. Everyone has a story. Why should you be any different?"

"Yes-but-" Eddie stuttered, now feeling uncomfortable. Of course he had a story. Who hasn't? If James has found out a lot about Douglas, what's to say he hasn't also found out a lot about Eddie? Hell, he could know about everyone in town for all Eddie knew?

"Relax," James said, before Eddie's mind could go into overdrive. "I don't know anything about you apart from what you've told me yourself. The reason I knew about Douglas, is because I know someone who went to school with him. Believe it or not, I also know one of the people his girlfriend had an affair with. I don't condone what happened, obviously, but I did know about it."

Eddie gave a sigh of relief, "That's all right, then," he said, feeling better after James's explanation, but still not entirely convinced about it. "Pity you didn't really get through to him. I admire what you tried to do, but it was never going to work."

James ran a hand through his almost jet black hair. "I don't know about that?" he said. "The mightiest oaks grow from the tiniest of seeds. Today I do think the tiniest of seeds may well have been planted in our good friend Douglas's mind."

57

"Whatever you say," Eddie said. "But I reckon the next time we see him again, our good friend Douglas will still be the same loud mouthed pain in the backside he usually is."

"We'll see about that." James had a sip of his orange juice. "I do believe the seed has been planted. Douglas may slowly, but surely, start moving in the right direction now."

Eddie shook his head in disbelief. "I doubt that very much. But if you're so convinced, can you do the same for me? You know? Plant a so-called little seed to help me move in the right direction?" The pints were now beginning to have some affect; Eddie was finding this conversation amusing.

"Mmm...Let me see," James pondered the question for a moment and replied. "It would certainly be a challenge. But, yes, I think I could."

Not the answer Eddie was expecting. "You're joking, right?" he asked, feeling uncomfortable again.

James just sat there and smiled.

"I mean. How can you lead me in your right direction if you don't know anything about me?"

James leaned forward, treating Eddie to a spicy whiff of his aftershave, "I may not know enough about you now," he said. "But I could learn."

Eddie leaned back in his chair away from James.

"What's wrong, Eddie? Don't you think you need a gentle push in the right direction?"

"What I need is a win at the bookies. That's what I need."

"I take it you haven't been doing too well on the betting front lately?"

"You could say that."

"Very well, let us discuss the bookies. Do you need another pint?" James asked and pointed at Eddie's glass.

Eddie looked at his pint, "It's half empty," he said, "but it'll do for now."

"You tell me you haven't had much luck at the bookies lately?"

"Hmmph...no. It's the worst run I've ever had," Eddie moaned.

"It's not fair when you see other people win and you don't?"

"No, it's not. I deserve to win just as much as anyone else does"

James nodded his head in agreement, "Yes, you're quite right."

Just as Eddie was about to moan some more, a female voice asked him, "Would you like a top up?"

Eddie looked up. It was Stacy. He immediately noticed she was wearing a very tight pink t-shirt.

"Oh! Em…I'm fine, thanks, Stacy," Eddie replied, feeling hot under the collar as he tried not to stare at her chest. "I didn't even know you were working today?"

"I took over from Brenda a while ago," Stacy said as she stroked her shoulder length blonde hair and put a hand on Eddie's shoulder. "But I'm beginning to get used to you ignoring me these days."

Eddie's face went red and he spluttered, "Yes-I'm-em-sorry about last night when I was in. I-I had a lot on my mind."

"And a lot of alcohol down your throat." Stacy laughed. She playfully ruffled Eddie's short, greying hair. "I'm only joking with you," she said.

"I knew you were," he said, lying.

"Who is your new friend?" Stacy asked.

Before Eddie could give an answer, James did it for him. "My name is James, my dear." He stood up and held out his hand. Stacy shook it, and then James sat down again. "I gather your name is Stacy?" he said.

"That's right," Stacy replied. "But I have to be honest as I did know your name. I only spoke to Brenda for about two minutes when I came in, but you were all she talked about."

"I hope it was all good things she was saying?" James asked.

"I'm afraid a lady can never disclose what she discusses with another lady. Particularly, when the subject is about a man."

James laughed. "Quite right, my dear. You keep your vow of silence."

"Don't worry, I will. Would you like a drink, James?"

"No. I'm fine as well. Thank you, Stacy."

"Okay then," Stacy said. "I better get back behind the bar and pretend to be busy. See you guys later."

"Bye, Stacy. It was a pleasure meeting you," James said, and treated her to the most dazzling of smiles.

"See you later," Eddie said. He then watched that lovely little wiggle of hers out of the corner of his eye as she strolled back to the bar.

Man on the boat overboard!

59

"Well, she is very attractive," James said.

"She's not too bad, I suppose," Eddie replied nonchalantly.

"Come now, Eddie. She's a bit better than not too bad. I think you know that?"

"What are you getting at?"

"I'm not getting at anything, just merely pointing out the obvious. She is a very attractive girl, who looks good, not only from the front, but also from behind. I mean, what about that sexy little wiggle? Ooh my goodness! If only I was a bit younger? I would sweep her right off her feet, that's what I would do."

"Well, you're not younger. And, anyway, she has a boyfriend," Eddie snapped.

"I see? And does the fact she has a boyfriend bother you, at all, by any chance?"

"No. I'm a married man. So why would I be bothered if she has a boyfriend or not?"

"I'm glad to hear that. Because in this day and age, being married or having a partner doesn't stop a lot of people jumping in to bed with whomever they like. You clearly have morals, and a sense of decency, which is a very rare commodity in society today. I thought I sensed a spark between yourself and Stacy, but I must have been mistaken? Maybe these whiskies have clouded my judgement?"

"I think they must have," Eddie agreed. "Can we get back to what we were discussing earlier?"

"Of course we can. I do ramble on a bit, don't I?" James looked across at the bar where Stacy was laughing and joking with a couple of male customers. "She's a siren that one," he said. "A siren, I tell you. And I've a funny feeling that being faithful isn't at the top of that little minxes list…"

The topic of conversation, thankfully for Eddie, moved away from Stacy and on to a topic that most males when in the pub together should always discuss-the topic of football.

"Do you support any football teams?" James asked.

"Yes I do," Eddie replied.

"And what about your football team, are they doing well?"

"No, they're not." Eddie's football team, much like himself, was in a bit of a slump.

"Life can be so cruel, it really can. You complain about your bad run at the bookies, and your football team not winning. You complain how God and the fates have conspired against you. Maybe you should actually ask yourself, why the team I support, or the horse I back should win?"

Eddie shrugged his shoulders.

"Is it because they somehow have a divine right to be victorious at all times? When your team wins, you're happy, while at the same time the supporters of the other team will be unhappy. That's okay, though, because you believe you deserve to be happy more than they do. Why? Likewise, when you back a horse that comes in first, there's always someone else who will back the horse that comes in second. Why did the horse you backed deserve to win more than the other horses?"

"I don't know," he muttered into his glass. "But what's the point in gambling at the bookies if you don't want to win? Or supporting a football team if they get beat every week?"

"You tell me. What is the point?"

"There's none."

"There's no harm in a flutter at the bookies or supporting a football team," James said. "But there is harm in having your happiness constantly relying on luck, or things that are entirely out of your control. You can't make your team win at football. You can support them, but whether they win or lose comes down to various factors. The referee, the opposition, how well your team played, and also an element of luck. At no point will the result depend on you. So why get too upset or too excited about the result? Because you had no hand in it whatsoever. So enjoy and appreciate it by all means, but do not have your happiness depend upon it."

Eddie had stopped listening; he was watching Stacy instead. She was now chatting and laughing with a young, macho-male. Eddie watched as Stacy played with her hair and appeared fascinated by the ponce in the purple shirts every word. Then again, she was laughing so much you would have thought it was Peter Kay she was speaking to. Although it didn't look like she was doing much speaking, she was far too busy fluttering her eye lashes.

Eddie diverted some of his attention back to James when the ponce left Stacy to go and put some tunes on the jukebox.

"Oh, are you listening again?" James asked.

"What? Yeah…yeah I am," Eddie said as he sneaked another glance across at the bar.

"I'm glad to hear it." James coughed. "When a football match or a horse race is over, it's over. There is nothing you can do to change the result no matter how much you may want to. You're relying pure and simply on lady luck to smile down on you, yet luck is indeed a fickle mistress and a double edged sword."

Eddie became distracted again as he watched Stacy's new friend strut back to the bar like the cock of the walk. His anger wasn't helped when he heard the first song that came on the jukebox-Rod Stewarts, 'Do You Think I'm Sexy?'

"I can see that winning at the bookies is important to you, so I'm going to give you a bit of advice before I go," James said.

"About how to win?" Eddie asked. That sentence seemed to magically grab his attention.

"Obviously we want our horse to be victorious. But remember what Plato said, 'The first and best victory is to conquer self'."

"Very helpful," Eddie replied as his attention quickly went back to Stacy behind the bar.

"I'm going to let you into a little secret, well, maybe it's not really a secret. But it's about the law of attraction. And I don't mean the type of attraction that constantly draws our gaze towards attractive barmaids."

Eddie glared at James.

"What you have in your life," James said, "and where you are today, is down to the thoughts and images you have in your mind. You attract things into your life by the way you think. This is an idea which an awful lot of people know about and believe in. While, on the other hand, a lot of people, like your good self, don't know anything about it or believe in it."

James was right. Eddie didn't know anything about it, nor did he think he wanted to know anything about it.

"There's an energy, or force, which we must tap into," James said, "if we really want to achieve something. An intelligence exists in every single thing in the universe, and everyone is linked into it. Carl Jung called it the 'Collective Unconscious'. But you can call it nature, or even God, if you like?"

"Hmmmph. I better not say what I would really like to call it," Eddie replied.

"No, you better not. But it's an energy that if we use and tap into correctly, then it can, over time, change our thoughts into a physical reality."

"I'm sorry, James. I can't take any of this seriously. You're honestly trying to tell me that it's like the Force in Star Wars, or nonsense like that?"

"I know it sounds a little unbelievable," James agreed. "But as I have said, an awful lot of people do actually believe in it. Not just Jedi Knights. What you must do is constantly feed your subconscious mind with strong and clear images. If they are jumbled and unclear, then they will not be of any use. Your subconscious mind works twenty four hours a day, even when you're sleeping. If it is constantly being fed thoughts of failure, then that is the physical equivalent you'll receive. It's even claimed your subconscious mind can't actually tell the difference between what is and isn't real."

"I think you should stick to the orange juice, as the whisky has made you delusional. Are you honestly trying to tell me if I picture in my mind myself as a millionaire, then I will become one?" Eddie shook his head, "I don't think so."

"In life, you usually get exactly what you focus and picture in your mind. Little more. You are not merely the slave of circumstances. You are the creator of your own destiny. And one way of changing your destiny, is to change the thoughts you pass into your subconscious."

"So, let me get this straight," Eddie said as he crossed his arms. "All I have to do is tell myself, 'I hope my horse will win', and picture it winning? Then, as if by magic, it wins? I say that to myself every time I bet on a horse, but it hasn't worked for ages."

"You may say to yourself 'I hope my horse will win', but do you really believe it will? Do you picture the race so clearly that you can tell me the colour of the horse, the colour of the jockey's silks and what the weather is like? Can you see the crowd cheering as your horse comes down the home straight? Then picture your horse striding majestically over the finishing line in first place?"

"Well...em."

"Well...em, exactly. You must picture it clearly. There's no point in merely hoping your horse will win, for a wish or a hope is no use. It must be a total belief that what you want to happen in your life, will happen. Your subconscious mind must be constantly fed this belief of success. If it's only fed a half hearted wish or hope, then it's no surprise you don't get what you want."

James stood up.

"Is that you going?" Eddie asked.

"Yes. I have a few things yet to do and I am running behind

schedule. But if you would like, I could meet you tomorrow at noon and we could continue our tete-a-tete?"

"Where about at noon?"

James opened his arms out like Al Jolson about to burst into song, "The bookies! Where else?" he said.

"Okay," Eddie agreed. "Before you go," Eddie uncrossed his arms and scratched his head. "I have to say that all this mumbo jumbo you've told me, I think you're wasting your time."

James nodded and smiled. "You're entitled to your opinion. But I would like to leave you with one question. A question I hope you'll ponder over before we have our noon rendezvous tomorrow. Call it a bit of homework."

"What's that?"

"I've now had six wins in a row at the bookies…How many have you had?" he asked, before heading for the front door, stopping briefly to say "Goodbye" to Stacy who was still chatting to her new friend.

Eddie sat and finished his pint.

CHAPTER SIX

When Eddie arrived home and entered the kitchen, the smell of freshly made coffee and perfume was wafting about the room. It was the smell of perfume Eddie was interested in, not the coffee, as he didn't recognise it as the cheap stuff Joan normally put on in the morning. He took a couple of sniffs. No, it smelt like the pricey stuff she used for special occasions. Eddie also saw Joan was dressed up wearing a short black skirt and white blouse. This wasn't the outfit she wore to work.

What's going on here?

Joan was sitting at the kitchen table, looking into a small compact mirror, as she applied some lipstick. Her hair was tied back in a ponytail and Eddie noticed she had on the gold earrings Steven gave her for Christmas; the pair that were incredibly expensive. Well, they would be, if he bought them. It's no problem for Steven splashing out a few hundred quid on earrings for his Mum. All his Dad got was a *Best of Tom Jones* cd.

What's New Pussycat?

"What are you doing home?" Joan asked as she took her eyes off the compact mirror.

"Surprised to see me?" Eddie asked as he eyed Joan up and down.

"Yes," Joan said as she turned her attention back to the mirror. "You're rarely home at this time of night when you've been paid your dole money. You haven't spent it already, have you?"

"No, I haven't. I just have a few things on my mind, that's all. And I didn't feel like drinking anymore. Where are you off to?" he asked as he made his way across to the fridge, still not taking his eyes off Joan.

"I'm going to Steven and Kathy's for a meal."

"Oh!" Eddie said as he opened the fridge. "Is there nothing to eat?" Eddie immediately changed the subject after surveying the fridge's sparse contents.

"I haven't done a weekly shop yet. I'm still waiting on you giving me some money to put towards it," Joan said as she applied the finishing touches to her lipstick.

Eddie slammed the fridge door shut. "I'm starving! There must be something to eat in here?"

Joan closed her compact mirror. She put the mirror and lipstick into her Dolce and Gabana handbag; another expensive gift, this time from her parents. "You could always come to Steven and Kathy's. You'll get something to eat there," Joan said.

"I won't bother." Eddie stuck his head in the freezer attempting to find a morsel to eat. "You just go on your own. I'd rather starve than go and visit those two."

"What about money for shopping then?" Joan asked.

"Money for shopping?" Eddie's head quickly came out of the freezer. "I've hardly got two pennies to rub together."

Joan shook her head. "Here we go again," she said as she got up from the kitchen table. "So how are we going to afford the shopping this week?"

Eddie shrugged his shoulders, "I don't know."

Joan tutted. "You never do," she said. "And there are the bills and the mortgage. Where's that going to come from?" Joan put her hands on her hips. "My pay can't cover everything. As for savings? That's almost gone as well."

Eddie just shrugged his shoulders again. "Stop moaning. I only came home for something to eat, not to listen to you go on and on."

Joan laughed. "You've such a hard time of it."

Eddie didn't want to hear. He stuck his head back in the freezer. *I wish this was the oven,* he thought cheerfully to himself.

"Looks like I'll just have to ask my parents for a loan again this month," Joan said as she picked up her black leather jacket from the back of a chair.

"They can afford it," Eddie said as he continued to rummage about the freezer.

"They wouldn't have to if you got yourself a job. My Dad's offered you one several times at the oil company he works for."

Eddie stood up quickly, just managing to avoid banging his head on the inside of the freezer, and pointed at his chest. "I've too much pride to accept your Dad's charity," he said.

Joan laughed again. "You're unbelievable," she said.

"Thank you," Eddie replied.

"That certainly wasn't meant as a compliment," Joan said "You don't have too much pride to let your wife work, while you spend all day in the bookies and pub, do you?"

"Hmmph!" Eddie couldn't be bothered to reply. He looked at the clock on the wall, a wedding present from his Aunty Sam, which has hung in the same place for over twenty years. "Isn't it about time you were going?" he said.

Joan also looked up at the clock. "Yes." She put on her jacket. "I take it you're not coming?"

Eddie bent down to have another look in the freezer. "No. Because my son thinks I'm a bum. Him and his precious Kathy. They both look at me as though I'm a piece of..." Eddie stopped himself as he thought there was something in the freezer to eat. When he realized it was only a packet of fish fingers, he continued his tirade. "With their high paying jobs which they just love telling us all about. I wonder how much bonus they'll get this year. Not that we'll have too long to wonder. As soon as they get it, I've no doubt they'll let us know."

"Look, I've told you. They don't think you're a bum. Steven is always asking how you're getting on."

"I'll bet he is," Eddie said, and took his head out of the freezer. "I know what questions he'll be asking." He pointed his finger at Joan who was, standing by the sink, getting a piece of kitchen roll.

"He'll be snooping to see if I'm working yet, that's what he'll be doing. Then he'll give a snide comment about how long it is since I've worked, and isn't it about time I got a job by now? That's all he's ever interested in when it comes to speaking about his own father. It's all fine and dandy for him with his fancy job in I-B."

"I-T," Joan corrected him. "It's I-T he works in, not I-B." Joan threw the used kitchen roll into the bin.

"It's what?"

"I-T," Joan repeated.

"I-T. I don't even know what that stands for?" Then, after a slight pause, his face lit up. "I know," he said, "It probably stands for Ignorant-Twat."

Joan rolled her eyes, "Just as well it wasn't I-B he worked in, then, isn't it? As I wonder what you would have said the B stood for. I get the picture." Joan went back across to the kitchen table with the sound of her high heels echoing round the kitchen. She picked up her handbag and put it over her shoulder. "I better go, as I said I would be there for seven. I'll just give them the usual excuse for you not turning up. But I think it's getting a bit worn out by now." Before Eddie could get the final word in, Joan added, "There are a couple of microwave meals in the bottom compartment you could maybe have. Goodbye..." She walked out of the kitchen. A few seconds later Eddie heard the front door open and close.

"Goodbye," he muttered, before opening the bottom compartment of the freezer.

A chicken curry was found in the furthest, darkest, and deepest corner of the freezer. Eddie didn't like chicken curry that much, but thought he better have it as the only other option was to starve. He also found a couple of cans of lager in the fridge and a can of coke. Unusually for Eddie, he decided to go for the non alcoholic choice to wash down his curry. Once the meal was ready, he took it and his can of coke through to the living room, where he slumped on his favourite brown leather recliner. He turned on the TV and quickly flicked through the channels; *Coronation Street* was about the only thing that could be classed as watchable. Eddie threw the TV controls on to the floor, and thought he better attempt the curry; even though, to him, it looked as tasty as Clive, strutting his stuff and shaking his tush, in a skin tight cat-suit. Eddie shivered at the thought. After a few mouthfuls he decided it wasn't that great, but was still better than it looked; probably because the only thing he'd had to eat all day was a nourishing slice of toast and some paracetamol in the morning. With all the events of today that had happened, Eddie hadn't found time for a nutritious black pudding supper.

Once Eddie finished his meal, he put the plate on the floor beside the TV controls and had a sip of coke. He hoped the coke would wash away some of the aftertaste of the curry, but it didn't. Eddie leaned back in his chair and put the foot rest up. On the TV screen was tomorrow's weather forecast-rain coming in from the North Sea, the plump, middle-aged, balding forecaster cheerfully told everyone. "What a surprise!" Eddie moaned. "More bloody rain." He yawned. Then, with the can of coke sitting precariously on his lap, closed his eyes.

The rain was hard and Eddie was wet. He had no idea where he was. When he looked down at the ground he had no socks or shoes on. Despite this, Eddie continued along the road he found himself on, with no idea where he had come from, or where he was going.

Eddie trudged along the road as the rain got heavier and the skies got darker. Occasionally, he would have the urge to head back the way he had came, yet, somehow, knew he couldn't. Going off the road wasn't an option, either. There was a shadowy, menacing forest on either side of the road, with sinister sounding noises emanating from it, which sounded like nothing Eddie had heard before. Eddie didn't want to find out who, or what, was screaming, and he definitely didn't want to find out why they were screaming. So, the only way to go was forward.

Eddie walked on, and on, cursing and muttering under his breath, with his head down, staring at his dirty, wet feet, as he battled against the almost horizontal rain. Suddenly, as if from nowhere, the road forked off into two. Standing at the fork in the road, dressed in the unusual attire of a white suit, was Clive.

"Hello, Eddie," Clive said in a cheerful manner.

Eddie found it so nauseatingly cheerful that his first instinct was to hit Clive flush in his chubby-cheeked face. "Wh…what's going on, Clive?" Eddie managed to restrain himself. "Why are you wearing that white suit? And where the hell are we?"

"A lot of questions there," Clive said "Sorry, I can't answer any of them."

"Why not?" Eddie asked as he wiped some rain from his eyes.

"Because you're not ready yet."

"Ready for what?" Eddie felt a hand on his shoulder. It was Douglas, and he was also wearing a white suit.

Douglas smiled. "Fine weather," he said as he strolled past Eddie towards Clive. The two men, dressed identically, shook hands.

"Will one of you tell me what's going on here?" Eddie demanded. "And why are you both dressed like that? Are you going to a Saturday Night Fever convention?"

Douglas laughed. It was a laugh Eddie found even more nauseating than Clive's cheerfulness. "Very good, I did like that one," Douglas said. "As the man has already told you. We can't say. I better hit the road, but it's been good to see you again. 'A Hard Rain's a-Gonna Fall', and I've a long way to go. Pity you can't come yet, maybe, one day you will?" Douglas walked along the road Clive was standing at.

Eddie watched Douglas leave. He marched up to Clive, "What does he mean I can't go along that road yet?" Eddie asked.

"What he means, is that you can't go along the same road he has gone. You have to go along the other road for now."

Eddie put his face right up to Clive's; they were eyeball to eyeball, "What if I do decide to take the same road, are you going to stop me?" Eddie kept his right hand down by his side as he clenched it into a fist.

I don't need to stop you." Clive did not flinch. "You'll never make it."

"Do you think so?" Eddie was ready to hit Clive.

"I mean, look at the road." Clive stepped back.

Eddie could now see a road, which he could have sworn only moments ago had been flat. Now it ascended upwards, for as far as the eye could see, till somewhere in the great distance it seemed to finally merge into the brooding clouds. Douglas, who no more than thirty seconds earlier had started off along this never ending road, was now nowhere to be seen.

Eddie unclenched his fist and opened his mouth wide. "Douglas," he muttered slowly. "The road wasn't like that. He's just….disappeared! What's going on?"

"Some people make their way along the road quickly, while others don't. For them it can be a long hard struggle. No matter how dark the clouds get, or how hard the rain must fall, and in every life it will. Just remember, you can always depend on him."

"Depend on who?" Eddie shouted. "I just don't understand any of this."

Eddie's confusion wasn't helped as James was now standing next to Clive; the two of them were like a couple of bookends side by side in their matching white suits.

"Hello again, Eddie," James said. He had a beaming smile upon his face which seemed to light up the darkness. "'Midway life's journey I was made aware that I had strayed into a dark forest and the right path appeared not anywhere.'"

"What?" Eddie asked.

"*The Divine Comedy,*" James replied.

"You might think this is a comedy," Eddie was not impressed, "but I'm not finding it funny. Where am I?" he asked.

"You're on the road to nowhere," James said. "It's still not too late to get on the road to somewhere, if you make the effort."

"That's helped. Cheers." Eddie wiped some more rain out of his eyes with the back of his hand; it was starting to sting now.

"Only you can help, Eddie. Only you can," James said.

"I'm givin' up," Eddie sighed and his shoulders slumped.

"That's not the bulldog spirit we want to hear," James said. "You have to take the other road for now, but it doesn't mean you always have to take it."

"What other road?" Eddie was barely able to ask as he lowered his head.

"That one." James pointed to the other fork in the road.

Eddie, with some exertion, lifted his head to see the other road

70

wound down hill. In the gloomy distance there were some lights shining dimly.

"You better hurry along," James said. "You don't want to be late for our seaside rendezvous tomorrow."

"What's along this road?" Eddie asked, despite being certain of the answer.

"It's the pub and the bookies, my good friend," James said with a twinkle in his eye. "Off you go. If you're quick enough you may even make it right on opening time."

Eddie started along the road with his head bowed and shoulders hunched again. All he could feel was the rain stinging his eyes. All he could hear was James and Clive laughing in his ears.

CHAPTER SEVEN

For Eddie, up, showered, fed, and out of the house by 11-38a.m. on a non-signing on day was almost unheard of. He was almost skipping along the road, in the morning sunshine (Not for the first time, the TV weather forecast had been wrong), head buzzing with anticipation about what today had in store. James obviously had some sort of fool proof system for the bookies he was about to share. Why he had decided to divulge this information, Eddie didn't know? He also didn't really care. What mattered was that James had had an incredible six wins in a row at the bookies, which could not be down to luck alone, or some mumbo jumbo about visualising your horse winning. James had a system, or, like Brody, is part of some syndicate. Whatever it was, it worked, and today was going to be the day James shared his special little secret. Eddie felt a tingle of excitement, and sang Lou Reed's 'Perfect Day', as the bookies came into view.

When Eddie entered the bookies, at almost noon on the dot, James was already there in his now familiar white, and de-rigour, suit. Eddie stopped in his tracks when he saw who James was standing with. Clive was beside him, which was ok. It was the third member of the group Eddie wasn't impressed with. Bully boy Douglas, himself. Eddie stood and watched the three men laughing together. James turned towards Eddie and gave him a wave beckoning him to come across. Eddie reluctantly and slowly made his way over towards the three men. When Eddie joined them, James and Clive said their greetings. There was then an uneasy silence as Douglas and Eddie said nothing to each other.

Douglas finally spoke. "All right, Eddie," he said.

Another couple of uneasy seconds passed before Eddie replied, "Yeah."

Douglas turned his attention quickly to James. "I better go," he said, "but cheers for today."

"It was a pleasure," James answered

"I'll see you later," Douglas said.

"You most certainly will," James replied.

Douglas turned to leave, stopped, and said, "Clive."

"Yes."

"That was a pretty good joke." Douglas nodded then left.

Eddie was almost speechless at what he'd just witnessed. "What is going on?" he asked. "Why are you speaking to that clown?

Clive, have you suddenly forgotten all the things he's said to you?"

"No." Clive said. Today he had on his purple, figure hugging, Jerry the Berry t-shirt. A particular favourite of Clive's, despite it appearing to get tighter by the week. Either Gloria's washing wasn't up to scratch, or, like Eddie, Clive's less than hectic lifestyle was having some effect on his waistline. "Douglas was standing with James when I got here, and James asked me to come over," Clive said. "To be honest, I still don't like him, but he didn't seem too bad today."

Eddie was speechless as he stood open mouthed.

"I did tell you," James said as he put his arm round Eddie's shoulder. "The seed has been planted."

"I know what I would like to plant," Eddie said. "A right hook into that fat face of his."

James took his arm off Eddie's shoulder. "There's no need for violence," he said.

"No wonder," Eddie said. "I came in here and the two of you are chuckling away with him, as though you're all best mates."

"I think you might be exaggerating," James said.

"Anyway, what was so funny?" Eddie asked.

"Clive's joke for the day," James said. "It's absolutely hilarious."

"That'll make a change," Eddie replied. As usual, he didn't actually want to hear it, but thought he better ask, "Ok. What's today's joke?" Eddie didn't get the answer he expected.

"I'm sure you'll survive without hearing it, as I have to go," Clive said. "Gloria's got a day off work and James has persuaded me to spend the day with her."

"Spend the day with…What has come over you?" Eddie could not believe what was going on. "First you're standing laughing with that bald-buffoon. Next you decide to spend the day with Gloria. Are you ill?"

"I'm absolutely tickety-boo," Clive said. "See you both later." Clive marched out of the bookies in his tight fitting t-shirt and jeans.

"What have you done to him?" Eddie asked as he watched the bookies door close.

"I haven't done a thing. Just a little word in Clive's ear, that's all. It's a beautiful day outside. I simply pointed out to him that maybe he would like to spend a little quality time with his beloved wife, instead of spending it here in the stuffy old bookies."

"With Gloria? But why?"

"I met her the other day and found her charming." James lowered his voice, "Don't tell Clive, but I also found her rather an attractive woman."

"Gloria's all right," Eddie admitted. "I remember back at Secondary school she was Rose Queen one year, and practically had the pick of any boy she wanted."

"And the boy she wanted was Clive."

"Hmmph. For some reason," Eddie grunted. "I'm not the only person who wondered how Clive managed to get her."

"How do you think he managed to get her?" James asked.

Eddie shrugged his shoulders. "I don't know. Voodoo? Black magic?"

James tutted. "Whatever he's used has worked, as he tells me they've been happily married for almost twenty five years now."

"Miracles happen, I suppose. But to go and meet her when you're on that winning streak? He must be mad?"

"Clive's not mad. In fact, I don't think I've met anyone saner. And who can blame him for leaving? As it has been said, 'there are more things in heaven and earth Horatio', than a win at the bookies."

"What?"

"It's the Bard. Good old Shakespeare," James said. "That was a quote from *Hamlet.* Well, maybe not the bit about the bookies." James strode across to a poster with today's horse meetings on it and sat down.

Eddie followed and sat beside him.

"Tell me," James said. "How long have you known Clive?"

"I met him on my first week at the cannery."

"And have you been friends ever since?"

"I suppose so."

"If you don't mind me saying, but I've noticed you're rarely very complimentary towards him?"

"I don't mean to be. It's just the way I am. And, anyway, he can be pretty annoying."

"What I've noticed, is there doesn't appear to be a bad bone in Clive's body." James stroked his moustache as he finally had a glance at the poster with today's meetings on it. "What I also find interesting, is your claim that you can't help the way you are," he said.

"I can't."

"Would you consider Clive to be your best friend?" James asked as he touched the poster with his left hand. Eddie noticed a ring on his wedding finger.

"I don't know about that," Eddie said.

"Really?" James sounded surprised. He faced Eddie. "Are there many other candidates for that prestigious title?"

Eddie took his time to answer. There were lots of other people he spoke to in the bookies and the pub, which was basically the extent of his social circle. But, in all honesty, they would be considered more acquaintances than proper mates. People he spoke to only through a common liking they all shared for drinking and gambling. While the more cynical may add, they also have something else in common, namely, a severe dislike for work in any shape or form. Depressing as it may seem to Eddie, the short list for candidates as his best friend was the grand total of one person. "I don't suppose there are many other candidates," Eddie finally and painfully admitted.

"So, the person you moan about and criticise, probably on a daily basis, is actually your best friend?"

"I suppose so. But what's this got to do with picking a winning horse?" Eddie asked.

"I'm just doing some essential background research," James said with a twinkle in his eye. A twinkle Eddie thought he had seen before.

"It doesn't seem very essential to me," Eddie moaned.

"It will," James said.

Eddie started to tap his fingers on the side of his chair. He was expecting a horse to be picked by now. Instead, all he's had, so far, is the Spanish Inquisition. And nobody expects the Spanish Inquisition, not when they're at the bookies, they don't.

"You and Clive must have spent some good times together?" James asked yet another question.

Eddie stopped tapping his fingers; he had to think about this. All that normally springs to Eddie's mind when Clive was mentioned, or when he's in his company, is the naff jokes and the tight t-shirts. Yet there's a lot more to Clive than that, and Eddie knew it. When James said he didn't think Clive had a bad bone in his body, he was right. Clive would do anything for anyone. He's also done a hell of a lot for Eddie in the time the two men have known each other. "In the early days, we had some good times." Eddie sighed, "And I still haven't forgotten how he helped me after what happened to Jenny." As soon as Eddie said that, he regretted it. He'd simply thought it out loud.

"What happened to Jenny?" James, the super snoop, predictably asked

A familiar feeling returned in the pit of Eddie's stomach, which he hadn't felt for some time. This wasn't your typical, run of the mill, butterflies in the stomach, harmlessly flapping about on a pleasant summer's day feeling. Oh, no. Eddie could handle that. This was more like ravenous vampire bats furiously searching for flesh blood on a dark, stormy night. "I don't want to speak about it. Okay?" Eddie said as he grimaced.

"Very well," James said. "Obviously something very distressing happened, and you don't have to speak about it, if you don't want to. But how exactly did Clive help?"

Eddie didn't want to speak about this, either. But it would be easier than speaking about Jenny. "Clive somehow made me laugh. I don't know how, but he did." Eddie said, as his stomach began to settle. The bats were retreating again. Yet, they would return. They always do. "He would also listen," Eddie added. "I would go round to his and we would talk and drink, often till sunrise." An unexpected sound came out of Eddie's mouth. It was laughter. He had no idea where it came from, and, admittedly, it wasn't a full bellied split your sides laugh; yet, it was a laugh all the same, and it sure beat how he felt moments ago.

"What is it?" James asked

"Nothing. I was just thinking back to those drinking sessions and some of the debates we had," Eddie said.

"Such as?" James asked.

"One got very heated."

"What was it about?"

"What was the better Saturday morning programme, *Multi Coloured Swap Shop* or *Tiswas?*"

"Oh yes!" James said with apparent excitement. "The halcyon days of Saturday morning television. Which programme were you for?"

"I was for *Tiswas*. Clive was for *Swap Shop*."

"Who won this fascinating debate?"

"I don't think anyone did. I remember it all hinged on the two females on each show. I thought because *Tiswas* had sexy Sally James, then it had to be the better programme. Clive said it was the Maggie Philbin "factor" that gave *Swap Shop* the edge. The debate raged on till about seven in the morning. Then I finally gave up and left."

"So nothing more was said on the subject?"

"Not exactly," Eddie said. His stomach now back to normal, and, amazingly, he'd even temporarily forgotten about picking a winning horse. "I was determined to get the last word in. So, as Clive was shutting his front door, I shouted out 'I hope the phantom fan flinger gets you!' A phrase that's difficult to say when sober. After a ten-hour drinking session, it's almost impossible."

James laughed so much he rocked back on his stool. As Eddie was about to put his hands out in a reflex action to catch him, James rocked forward again.

"Clive shut the door in my face," Eddie said, with his hands poised to catch James just in case. "I stood there for a while attempting to say 'I hope the phantom flan flinger gets you!' The more I tried to concentrate, the worse it came out. Eventually, I gave up and staggered home."

"Very good," James said.

Eddie took his hands away as it seemed the danger had been averted. He wouldn't have wanted James to fall and bang his head; certainly not before he had picked a horse.

"I take it the all night drinking sessions came to an end?" James, safely sitting on the front of his stool, said.

"They happened less and less. Then stopped altogether."

"So, the only time you spend with Clive is here in the bookies, then across at the pub? Where he usually has a couple of drinks before going home? While you usually stay on and have more than a couple of drinks before going home?"

"Something like that."

"Maybe you should get together in other places apart from the bookies? Get this friendship back where it once was. You could even meet at his house one week, then yours the next. Invite your wives along and make a proper night of it."

"I don't know about-"

James put his hand up. "A little hush, please," he said.

"By Jove-I think I've found it!" James cried out after sitting in silence for about five minutes.

"You have?" Eddie asked, as he felt a different feeling in his stomach. This time it was one of nervous excitement.

"I think so. *The Golden Boy*, one p.m. at Doncaster," James said in triumph.

Eddie had a look at the poster with today's meetings on it. When he saw *The Golden Boy's* odds and recent form, his nervous excitement melted away like snow in the afternoon sunshine. "I don't know about that horse," Eddie said. An all too familiar feeling returned; one of disappointment. "It's seven to one and hasn't won in ages. What about the favourite or second favourite? They're in great form at the moment. Not such great odds. But one of them must be worth a punt?" Eddie desperately attempted to change James's mind.

"*The Golden Boy* is the horse I'll be putting my money on. You are free to put your hard earned money on whichever horse you like." James picked up a betting slip and pen.

"Come on, James," Eddie practically pleaded. "Can you not at least have another look to see if another horse catches your eye? One that could even win?"

"Has not one single thing I told you yesterday sunk in?" James said as he wrote on the betting slip

"What do you mean?"

"I mean, what I told you in the pub?"

"You can't mean that nonsense about picturing the horse winning or just simply believing it will win?"

"You might not believe *The Golden Boy* will win, but I do."

Eddie was in a quandary. He knew James has won something like six races in a row, but Eddie just didn't think a seven to one outsider with such poor form was going to win. As for James's method of actually picking the horse, to say Eddie wasn't too impressed with it would be an understatement. All he did was stare at the poster. Then, out of the blue, he picked a horse. Even Eddie could have managed that.

"You're not impressed?" James asked as he stopped writing.

"Not really," Eddie admitted. "I thought you'd have a fancy method for picking a horse. You don't even seem to have a method, let alone a fancy one. You just looked at the meetings and picked any old horse."

James twirled the bookies pen between his fingers like it was a small baton. "It's my method you're not impressed with? If I tell you why I have picked that particular horse, will it maybe convince you?"

"Maybe," Eddie said, although he doubted even Shania Twain could seduce him into backing James's horse.

"Right. The horse is odds of seven to one. Am I correct?"

"Yes."

"How many horses are in that particular meeting?"

Eddie studied the poster and counted, "Seven," he replied.

"Okay. Look at *The Golden Boy's* form. How many races in a row has he lost?"

Eddie studied and counted again, "Six, I think."

"You're right. *The Golden Boy* has lost six in a row. Let's put it all together. The horse's odds are seven to one. There are seven horses in the meeting. This is the horse's seventh race since it last won. Plus, if I win today, then it will be my seventh win in a row. Can you see any connection?"

"Only the number seven? But how-"

"Exactly!" James shouted out as he threw the bookies pen in the air and caught it in his opposite hand. "The number seven is the connection. It is a highly significant number. That is the point. In Islam, for instance, the prophet Mohammad ascended to the Seven Heavens. Zoroastrians believe the number is seen as the perfect union between man and woman and the spiritual and natural. To the ancient Egyptian's seven was the symbol of eternal life. While in Christianity we have the Seven Deadly Sins, the Seven Virtues, and also the Seven Sacraments."

"What about *Snow White and the Seven Dwarfs?*" Eddie chipped in.

"Yes, that's one. There are obviously seven days in a week. There were Seven Wonders of the World, and *Seven Ages of Man* according to Shakespeare. There are seven chakras in the body, and seven colours in a rainbow. Seven notes are in a musical scale, and the Seventh son of a Seventh Son is meant to be highly significant."

"*The Magnificent Seven?*"

"Yes, *The Magnificent Seven*. And 'The Seven Seas of Rhye' was the first top ten hit the legendary band Queen had. There are countless other examples we could mention, but I think we've covered this subject enough."

"I'll agree with that," Eddie said.

James took out another betting slip. He handed it to Eddie. "Have I convinced you to bet on *The Golden Boy?*" he asked.

Eddie glanced up at the poster on the wall. "Against my better judgement," he said, "I'll bet on *The Golden Boy*."

"I do believe you've made a wise decision." James held a pen out for Eddie.

Just as Eddie was about to take the pen from James, he took it away from him and said, "Before we go any further I have a proposition for you."

"What is it?"

"If we put this bet on and the horse wins. I think you'll owe me something in return."

"Here we go." Eddie sighed. "I knew there would be a catch. What is it you want?"

"Just your time, that's all. If the horse wins, all I ask is we wander down for a seat at Wyndon Park and have a chat in the sun. Not tomorrow or next week. Today, before you go to the pub to celebrate. It doesn't even need to be much of a chat. All you have to do is sit and listen, as I'll probably do most of the talking. Does that sound like a fair deal? If the horse loses we can go our separate ways. If it wins, all I ask is about thirty minutes of your time."

"That's all you expect in return?" Eddie asked.

"That's all. So, my friend, do we have a deal? Or, to combine Noel Edmonds with William Shakespeare, I'll rephrase that and say, Deal or no Deal? That is the question."

"Deal," Eddie immediately said.

At first, Eddie was only going to put a fiver on *The Golden Boy* at each way. After some persuading from James, he eventually bet the princely sum of ten pound on the nose. As one p.m. neared, Eddie felt no excitement in his stomach, or any other part of his anatomy, for that matter. Because he didn't think the horse stood a chance.

When the race started, *The Golden Boy* was, predictably enough, nowhere to be seen amongst the frontrunners. It was languishing back in sixth out of seven horses. Eddie watched the race for a while, but quickly got fed up. He had some change in his pocket, so decided to play one of the bookies bandits. Three fifty pence pieces went into the bandit and nothing came out. Eddie rummaged about in his pocket for more money when he heard James yell. It appeared James was getting excited. Eddie jogged, as fast as he could, across to James. Up on the screen, *The Golden Boy* was somehow neck and neck with another horse coming down the home straight. As soon as Eddie got his breath back, after his brief exertion of jogging for ten metres, he joined in the excitement with James, waving his arms about and shouting at the screen urging the horse on.

The finishing line was in sight, and still neither horse had the edge. Eddie was still shouting when both horses crossed the finishing line with nothing between them. After a few anxious moments, the tension was going to last longer because the commentator announced the race had gone to a photo-finish.

A couple of minutes passed and there was still no decision on which horse had won. Eddie paced up and down, with his stomach now doing somersaults, glancing up at the screen every few seconds hoping for news of *The Golden Boy;* the horse that Eddie had never doubted for a second. Just when the tension was becoming too much for him, there was an announcement. "The winner of the one o clock at Doncaster is." There was a pause, Eddie held his breath, and the announcer said…*"The Golden Boy!"*

Once Eddie collected his winnings (a cool seventy pounds plus ten pound stake), then started to calm down, James mentioned their little agreement. After his long and painful drought, a trip to the park was not how Eddie wanted to celebrate a famous win. The pub was the only place for that. Eddie was even considering buying a bottle of champagne when he got there. He would go with James tomorrow. Today was going to be party time. But James reminded Eddie, several times, that the deal was to go today before the pub. After trying a few lame excuses, James's power of persuasion triumphed again. Eddie eventually relented. With a new found spring in his step, Eddie strolled down to Wyndon Park, in the glorious afternoon sunshine, with his new friend James.

CHAPTER EIGHT

When Eddie and James arrived at the park, James chose a bench beside a couple of trees so they could sit in the shade. When they sat down, Eddie had a look around. He hadn't been to this park in ages and was quite impressed by the condition it was in. There were a wide variety of colourful flowers in full bloom. Plus, the large bandstand, which was the centre piece of the park and hadn't been used for a good few years now (except as a place for the local youths to hang out with their cheap bottles of cider), actually looked freshly painted and graffiti free for once. There didn't appear to be a youth or bottle of cider in sight. Although a group of teenagers were mucking about at the far corner of the park with a football, and a couple of mums with their kids were sitting on another bench. Apart from that there was no one else here.

Eddie sat back on the wooden bench, closed his eyes, and smelt the freshly mown grass. Eddie loved that smell, as it reminded him of when he was a kid, and he would visit his grandparents to help cut their grass. Once they finished, granddad would get two deckchairs out and they would sit in the sun. Gran would then bring out iced lemonade as a well earned treat for the workers. They were great afternoons, sitting there in the garden without a care in the world, lemonade on tap, while listening to granddad's exciting, if slightly exaggerated, stories of the war. It didn't matter how many times Eddie heard the same story; he would still be on the edge of his deckchair hanging on to every word.

Happy times.

"Nice here, isn't it?" James asked after they had sat a while.

Eddie jumped up on the bench and opened his eyes as he came abruptly out of his dream world. "It's all right," he said.

"I come here most days, as I find it relaxing."

"I haven't been here for a while," Eddie admitted.

"You should come more often. It's better than being indoors all day."

"I suppose so," Eddie agreed. Nice as the park was; however, he could still think of somewhere else he'd rather be right now.

"We better get on with things," James said. "You'll be itching to get back to the pub to celebrate your new found wealth?"

"If you don't mind?" Eddie replied. It was almost like James had read his mind.

"You just sit back, relax, and I'll get on with things."

Eddie did as James said. He sat back, relaxed, and watched the teenagers with the football. This was about the third time, since he got here, that they had kicked their ball into a flower bed. Like the previous two times, one of the teenagers ran in to get the ball, flattening at least a dozen daffodils in the process.

"I gather you're happy just now after your win at the bookies?" James asked.

"Of course I am."

"How long do you think this happiness will last?"

"I don't know."

"Let me hazard a guess. It probably won't last very long. It may last beyond tomorrow morning when you wake up with a hangover, and most of your money gone. Unfortunately, I guarantee, it won't last beyond the next time you go to the bookies and back a loser. And how do I know this?"

"I've no idea."

"Because you want to be happy. Let's face it, most of us want to be happy, but most of us aren't. Do you know why?"

"No"

"Because most of us are looking in the wrong place, that's why. Jean–Jacques Rousseau said 'every man wants to be happy, but in order to be so he needs to first understand what happiness is.' You believe that if you win a lot of money, then your life will automatically be perfect. It won't. After the initial euphoria and the big spending spree, you will still be the same old Eddie you were before the big win. It won't be long till you realise, lack of money wasn't the problem in the first place."

"I would rather be miserable with a lot of money, than miserable with no money."

"I'm sure you would. I'm not saying that having money is a crime, far from it. I myself would be a bit of a hypocrite if I said that, considering I spend a fair bit of time gambling for money. The difference is I don't rely on a win at the bookies, or my lottery number to come in to be happy. I would still be as happy today if I hadn't won at the bookies."

"What's the point in gambling?"

"I enjoy it, that's why. It gives me a bit of pleasure," James crossed his legs. "I have learned like many before me, that happiness and pleasure are two different things. Happiness mainly comes from within. Like the old Tibetan saying goes, 'seeking happiness outside ourselves, is like waiting for sunshine in a cave facing north.' There is no doubt we require money to help us with the basic needs such as adequate food, warmth, clothing, and shelter. If these needs are met and we are not in unbearable physical pain, then what reason do we have not to be happy?"

"Hmmph, where do I start?" Eddie said as he had a look at his watch.

"How much will your life actually improve if your old TV became a top of the range one? Or you purchase a new state of the art stereo? Where will it all end? You win at the bookies today, but you won't be content with that. You'll want to keep on winning and winning. It's a never ending cycle that cannot possibly bring you happiness. You want to be happy, yet you don't actually know what will make you happy."

"Right then," Eddie sat up on the bench. "What will make me happy?" he asked.

"You just can't be happy at the click of a finger. You have to work at it. There are ways, and the first way to achieve happiness is not to go looking for it."

"That's just stupid. How am I actually going to find happiness, if I'm not meant to look for it?"

"One way is by realising the only time that matters to you is now. The present moment. Not the past, when your horse came in. Nor the future, where you will be in the pub celebrating your win. That is one of the secrets of what we call happiness, being able to live fully in the present moment. Nowhere else. Your life won't suddenly start when your lottery numbers come in, it is happening now. You have to realise this before it's too late. All life really consists of is your birth, your death, and the bit in between, which is basically nothing more than one moment after another. You can't do something in an hour's time and you can't do something a minute ago. The only time you can actually do something is right now." James stopped talking as he attempted to swat away a bee that was buzzing round his head. After a few swats he continued talking. "Do you like the band Oasis?" he asked.

"I like some of their songs," Eddie said as he swatted away the bee that had gone from annoying James to annoying him now.

"'Don't Look back In Anger' is good advice you should take

on board. But I also mentioned them because of the name of their album 'Be Here Now'. There was a book, written in the seventies, by Ram Dass. It had the same title. I don't know if the album is actually named after the book? What I do know is that you should try to 'Be Here Now' at all times." James thumped his right fist on to his thigh.

"So that's all there is to it?" Eddie shook his head. "I forget about the past and the future, and suddenly my life will become wonderful?" Eddie mockingly threw his hands in the air, "Hallelujah!" he cried out. "I never realised it was so simple?"

"There is more to it than that. But for now, it's a start. You have quite a journey ahead of you, that's for sure. Attempting to live in the present, and not worry about what's happened in the past, or what may or may not happen in the future, is your first step. I bet in the short time since we've sat here your mind has constantly moved backwards and forwards. Thinking about the horse winning at the bookies one moment, going to the pub for a drink to celebrate the next?"

"Maybe."

"It takes time. You can't just suddenly change the way you've thought for years at the drop of a hat. What you must begin to do, is try and remember that now is the only time you have. The past no longer exists, while nothing actually happens in the future. Everything happens in the present moment. Your mind may want to live in the past or the future. Do not let it. Always try to stay focused on the present moment…can you do that, Eddie? Can you forget about yesterday and tomorrow, and just focus on today?"

"I don't think so," Eddie said as he had another look at his watch. The novelty of sitting in the park had quickly worn off.

"Give it a go," James said. "I think you might be pleasantly surprised. If you don't mind me asking? Can you truthfully say you actually enjoy your life? Do you wake up in the morning looking forward to what the day has in store for you, counting your blessings instead of your troubles?"

"Maybe not," Eddie admitted. There was no point in claiming he thought his life was great, when it so obviously wasn't.

"You could if you wanted. I don't think you realise just how lucky you are to be alive. Life's a gift, but a temporary one. The most important thing you can possess is not money, but time. Time won't wait for you, my friend. It is constantly ticking away, and we all have a limited amount of it. When it runs out, that's it. We can't go to the bank and withdraw some more."

"I can't even go to the bank to withdraw money, let alone time," Eddie moaned.

"As soon as you get a lot of money, you won't automatically become a better and happier person. But if you don't become a better and happier person, chances are, you won't get a lot of money, anyway."

Eddie tutted and diverted his attention back to the footballers. They were doing their best to flatten every daffodil in the park.

"Simply living in the present isn't enough to become a better, happier person. You also have to make the most of every single moment. Remembering life is transitory, should remind us to make the best possible use of our all too short lives. Have you heard of the Russian writer Dostoyevsky?" James asked.

"You must be joking? That sounds like a make of vodka." Eddie smiled at his undoubted wit.

"You may well know more about spirits than I do," James said. "When the Russian writer Dostoyevsky faced the firing squad, he came to the sudden realisation just how precious and wonderful life really is. He was given a last minute reprieve, but was sent to do four years of hard labour in Siberia. Dostoyevsky did not care about being sent there, for he was still alive. To him, that is what now mattered. For you, it seems, what really matters is a win at the bookies, then getting drunk afterwards."

"That's not true."

"I'm glad to hear that. Can you tell me what matters more?" James asked. He turned round to face Eddie and raised an eyebrow.

Eddie couldn't answer. He also couldn't look James in the eye. Instead, he scratched his head and diverted his attention to the bandstand.

"I have only known you for about twenty four hours," James said as he turned away. "Yet, in this short time, I can tell that life hasn't turned out the way you would have hoped. You're in a rut and going through the motions. I feel you've been in it for some considerable time. One thing I've noticed by your actions, and the way you talk, even in just one day, is that you're certainly not happy? I could easily be wrong. If your life is a bed of roses, feel free to walk away. Go enjoy yourself in the pub and I won't bother you again."

Eddie didn't reply. Nor did he get up off the bench and walk away.

"When you heard I had won a number of races at the bookies," James said as he crossed his legs again. "How did you feel? Were you happy or envious?"

Eddie took a second to reply. "Envious," he admitted.

"That's very honest of you. As many people don't admit to being envious of others. Even though it's something everyone suffers at some time. We grow up learning to envy other people's car, their house, their wife, or their life. It's just human nature, isn't it? Why should other people have these things, when we don't? Why should other people be happy, when we aren't? We deserve these things just as much as they do, if not more. No one can be happy if they are envious of other people and other things."

"I wouldn't be envious if I actually had a lot of money," Eddie said as he watched another of the youths clamber about amongst the flowers, which were now almost completely flattened, to get their ball back.

"I mentioned the Seven Deadly Sins and the Seven Virtues earlier at the bookies. As you may know, envy is one of the Deadly Sins. To really be happy you should not be envious of others. Instead, you ought to try to help and put their happiness first. If we continue to do that, then our own happiness will inevitably follow. This is an idea that has been advocated from the Bible, to such luminaries as the philosopher John Stuart Mill. Envy is something you must rid yourself of. Try to swap it with kindness, the Virtue which is its opposite."

"Okay, James, whatever you say." By now, Eddie's mind was drifting more and more to his first celebratory drink in the pub.

"To not be envious is to rejoice at all the delights, no matter how big or small, that other people experience. When we are able to do this, and become a more virtuous person by showing some kindness to others. Whilst also managing to live in the present moment, and appreciating what a short time we have on this planet. Once we can do these things, then we are truly on the right road. That is what will make us happy. Not our horse or lottery number coming in, or getting so drunk we struggle to make our way home at night."

Eddie didn't reply. He simply watched the babies with their mothers, on another park bench, and noticed how the babies seemed so happy and content. Eddie couldn't remember what that was like. Yet, he was still sure, despite what James was saying, that a couple more wins at the bookies would definitely help bring back, maybe not total happiness, but at least some.

"I would like to offer you another little proposition," James said, as Eddie watched one of the babies drop a bottle and giggle about it. This brought a smile to their mother's face, and Eddie's.

"What's that?" Eddie asked as he watched the mother pick up the bottle and pat the baby on the head.

"How about we meet same time same place next week? We have another chat, pop up to the bookies, and I'll try to pick another winner?"

"Sounds good to me."

"There are a couple of little drawbacks," James added.

"I thought there would be. What is it?" Eddie asked as he glanced at James out of the corner of his eye.

"The first drawback is the maximum amount you can put on a horse that I pick."

"How much?"

"Twenty pounds."

"Twenty pounds? If I ever bet more than fifteen pounds I usually come out in a cold sweat. That won't be a problem."

"Very good. The second drawback is not too difficult, either. I just want you to try and put into practice what I have told you today."

"Okay-dokey, see you next week." Eddie got up.

"Not so fast." James indicated for Eddie to sit down.

Eddie mumbled to himself. He glanced at his watch and then James. After some thought and double checking his watch again, Eddie sat down on the bench.

"How would I know if anything I had told you today had even crossed your mind between now and next week?" James said. "No. I have a little challenge for you. If you fail with this challenge, I won't be able to try and pick a winner for you again. Our deal will be off."

"That's not fair!"

"Why is it not fair? I am picking winning horses at the bookies for you. I'm trying to give you the benefit, not only of my knowledge, but of greater minds than mine. What exactly are you doing for me?"

James had him there. Eddie had wondered all along what his ulterior motive was, and now he was about to find out. He should have known it wouldn't be out of the kindness of James's heart. You don't get anything in life for nothing. You always have to pay the piper. Now Eddie was about to find out the price he had to pay, as he slumped back on the bench, folding his arms. "What is this challenge," Eddie asked.

88

"I want you to take your lovely wife out for a meal tonight."

"What?" Eddie was sure he had heard James wrong.

"I want you to take your lovely wife out for a meal tonight," he repeated.

"What…But why?"

"Because I think she deserves it. I also think it may have been a long time since you last took her out?"

"Where? I won't be able to get a place booked at this short notice."

"You don't need to. I've booked a table for two at the *Glamis Hotel*, for seven-thirty. I recommend the steak, it's delicious."

"You can recommend what you want. I won't be going," Eddie said. "And, anyway, I can't afford to take Joan out for a meal."

James smiled. "Of course you can afford it. You've just won a nice sum at the bookies."

"I was going to spend that money at the pub."

"It's your choice. You can spend it today at the pub, get drunk, have a bit left over for a flutter tomorrow. If that horse doesn't come in, which is pretty likely, you're right back where you started. Or, you can go out for a lovely time tonight with your wife, have a good meal and a few drinks. Next week we can meet here for a seat and a chat, and hopefully afterwards I'll pick us another winner. What do you think?"

As soon as he had won that money, Eddie's had his whole day planned ahead of him. Part of that plan definitely didn't involve taking Joan out for a meal. James could take her if he's that bothered. Eddie could then get as drunk as possible. But, somehow, Eddie thought he could be killing the goose that laid the Golden Egg if he didn't go along with James's plan. Right now it was a chance Eddie wasn't prepared to take. How would he feel next week when his own dismal solo run at the bookies continued, only to find out James had picked yet another winner? If Eddie believed James was just your average punter punching above his weight at the bookies, then he wouldn't even be thinking twice about this. Eddie would be up to the pub as quick as you like. There was something different about James, and it wasn't just the white suit or cravat. Eddie really didn't have a choice.

"I'll take her," Eddie said quietly.

"I'm glad to hear it. It's booked under the name Ryan. You can tell me next week how it went."

"How do you know that's my surname?" Eddie asked.

89

"Because you mentioned it yesterday," James replied.

"I see," Eddie nodded, but was almost certain he hadn't mentioned it yesterday.

"One last word of wisdom before we part," James changed the subject. "Remember, when you wake up in the morning, it may be for the very last time. So, I'll leave on that cheery note, and let you ponder till next week all the things we've spoken about." James groaned as he got up from the bench. "And if you have any money left after tonight," he said while rubbing his lower back, "maybe you'd like to buy some shopping to cook a meal for your wife. That would be a nice treat for her after a hard day at work."

Eddie didn't say a thing as James walked away. When he had gone about ten yards, Eddie shouted at him, "What if I don't do these things? How will you even know?"

James stopped, turned around, and replied, "Don't worry...I will know." He then made his way out of the park.

CHAPTER NINE

The door made a creaking noise as Eddie opened it. He darted inside out of the pouring rain, making squelching sounds as his feet landed on the carpet. It was warm in the room and there was a familiar sweet smelling aroma in the air as Eddie closed the door, which creaked again as it shut. Eddie surveyed his dark surroundings while breathing in the sweet smell, which seemed to come from a time when life was simpler. The only light in the room came from the orange neon glow of the street lamps outside, which had managed to battle its way through the filthy window. To his left, as Eddie's eyes became used to the light (or lack of it), he noticed a row of shelves on the wall. Further into the room, to Eddie's right, there appeared to be a large desk. Behind it there was some something written on the wall, but Eddie was unable to read what it was from where he was standing. Straight ahead there was also the smallest chink of light at what looked like floor level. For the moment, Eddie wasn't interested in the light or the counter. He wanted to know what was on the shelves.

Eddie walked across to the shelf that was nearest the window, making squelching sounds on the wet carpet as he went. Just before he reached it, something moved and leaped off the shelf in a blur that landed right in front of Eddie's bare right foot. Eddie looked down. At first he thought it was a cat due to its size. It was a large, smelly rat. Eddie hated rats. The rat didn't seem too fond of Eddie, either, as it stared up at him with its horrible eyes, which seemed to glow in the darkness. As Eddie stood motionless, trying to out stare the vermin at his foot, he noticed that its tail was at least a good two feet long. It could be longer as part of the tail was hidden in the shadows of the shelf. As Eddie took his eye off the rat, for the briefest second, while he tried to see where its tail did actually end, the rat quickly lost interest in Eddie. It scurried off towards the chink of light. Eddie inhaled some more of the smell that was filling the room before going to the shelf.

There were numerous items on the shelf. The first one Eddie picked up seemed to be an item of clothing, all covered in dust. Eddie tried to brush most of the dust off before he held the item up in what light there was. It was an item of clothing; a tatty, worn out cardigan, in fact. Eddie, like a child with their favourite blanket, put the cardigan up to his cheek. It felt strangely reassuring and cosy. "Good old Rupert," Eddie whispered. He started to laugh. Once the floodgates opened, Eddie continued to laugh for some considerable time.

With tears of laughter rolling down his cheeks, and his side actually sore, Eddie reluctantly put the cardigan back on the shelf. He walked further into the room, picking up another item from a different shelf. This was no item of clothing. This was a toy model train covered in cobwebs. Eddie turned it round in his hands, admiring the incredible detail and workmanship of the toy, when something slithered out of a carriage window. Eddie froze. It was a worm. Then it was another one and another, oozing out of the train windows. Soon the train and Eddie's hand were covered in them. When the cold, slimy worms began to travel up Eddie's bare arm, he finally threw the train to the floor, brushing a few stray worms from his arm as he ventured to the next shelf.

It was another item of clothing that immediately caught Eddie's eye and he hoped it would have the same affect on him as the cardigan did. How wrong he was. As soon as Eddie picked it up, something didn't feel right. He wanted to immediately throw it to the ground like he did the train, but found he couldn't. His grip got tighter and tighter, so did his stomach muscles. He didn't want to, but he slowly held the item up to his cheek like with the cardigan. When it brushed his cheek, Eddie doubled over and was violently sick all over the floor.

Eddie lost count of the amount of times he was sick. It seemed like one excruciatingly painful wave after another, kneeling on the carpet, in a pool of vomit, with tears in his eyes, which weren't of joy. Eddie had never known pain like this before. He'd had suspected appendicitis when he was younger, but that was nowhere near this feeling on the agony-ometer. It felt like he'd brought up not only the entire contents of his stomach, but the lining as well. However, through the pain and tears, Eddie still kept a fierce grip on the item in his hand.

"Let go of the bloody thing!" Eddie finally screamed. "No, I can't let it go," he answered his own question in between deep painful breaths. "Let go of it. You can't hold on to it for ever!" he screamed again, before attempting to be sick. By now nothing was coming up; only an awful smell from the pit of his stomach. "Let go of it," he could only whisper this time. "Let go."

He finally did, and collapsed backwards on the floor.

An incredible wave of relief came over Eddie as he lay there breathing heavily covered in tears, sweat, vomit, and God knows what else? He managed to summon up the strength and effort to lift his head and look at the thing he'd just been thrown from his hand, half expecting another horrible creature like the rat to appear staring at him. There was no rat, no worms, or any other kind of creature. Eddie slowly got back on to his knees. After a couple more deep breaths he managed to stand up. He looked down. There in a pool of sickness was a small bathing costume. It was too dark in the room to determine its colour; that didn't matter because Eddie knew anyway-it was pink.

He'd had enough of looking at the shelves, so Eddie walked across to the desk by the left wall. As he approached it, apprehensively, after his last experience, Eddie could read what was painted on the wall: "THE MIDNIGHT SPECIAL." When Eddie reached the antique, mahogany writing desk, probably built in 1892 (somehow he knew this, like he knew the bathing costume was pink), there was nothing at all on it except dust and cobwebs. Part of him was relieved about that; a very large part. He went behind it to see if anything was there. He immediately noticed a photo pinned to a drawer. Eddie crouched down; it was a photo of a beauty contest. There were about a dozen women in it wearing swimsuits. At the front of them was a banner, it read-*Miss Skegness, 1962.* Eddie opened the drawer the photo was pinned to. Inside was what appeared, at first, to be a bathing costume? Eddie thought he was going to be sick again. As he braced himself for another wave, it never came. Before his subconscious could warn him not to, Eddie took the item out of the drawer. It was a night dress, too big to be a child's one, and like the cardigan, Eddie felt good as soon as he touched it, but in a different way. A feeling of incredible peace and calmness washed over him. In this light Eddie still, of course, knew the night dress was white.

When Eddie stood up again, he saw a book on the far side of the desk. He could have sworn there had been nothing on it earlier. After neatly folding the nightdress, he carefully put it back in the drawer. Eddie blew some cobwebs off the large and heavy book as he picked it up. On the cover it said Shakespeare's: *First Folio.* Eddie opened the book; something fell out landing on the floor. He put the book down and picked up what had fallen out. It was another photo. Eddie screwed up his eyes as he tried to see what was in the photo. It was a woman with a boy and a girl. All three were smiling. Eddie also smiled. He turned the photo round to see something written on the back. Eddie screwed up his eyes again as he held the photo up in an attempt to read the handwriting: *Georgina, Henry, and Emily. Summer, 1965.* Eddie gently placed the photo on top of the book, and came back round to the front of the desk. When he reached the front, Eddie thought he could hear what sounded like voices coming from where the small chink of light was.

Eddie stood and listened. Yes, it was voices, he was certain of it, and Eddie wanted to know whose voices it was. He walked forward a few paces till he reached what seemed to be the entrance to a long hallway. On the wall, to Eddie's right, was an A4 sized frame. He expected it to be another photo. After wiping some dust off it, he put his face right up to it till his nose practically touched the glass of the frame. It wasn't a photo. It was some sort of award or certificate. There was a motif or emblem at the top of it that Eddie couldn't quite make out, but he could, with a bit of a struggle, read what was written below it:

University of Nowhere
By authority of the Senatus Academicus
the degree of
Master of Arts
was conferred upon
NOBODY IN PARTICULAR
ON 13th JULY 1985

The certificate didn't grab Eddie's attention for long as he wanted to know whose voices it was he could hear, so he set off down the hallway. To either side of him were more and more shelves, from the floor to the ceiling, all seemingly choc a block in dust and cobweb covered objects. Eddie ignored the items on the shelf as he walked down the dark hallway, which was getting warmer as he neared the light. Although Eddie wasn't a great fan of rats, he was starting to hope it was the rat from earlier that he heard shuffling about on one of the shelves. It certainly didn't sound like worms. When a noise was also heard coming from the shelves at the opposite side, Eddie quickened his step.

As Eddie got closer, he realised the light was actually coming from below a door. When he finally reached the door, after the shuffling about on the shelves got louder and more frequent, Eddie put his ear up against it. He quickly took it away again as the door was blistering to the touch. After giving his scorched ear a rub, he put his other ear as close to the door as was bearable. It sounded like two people on the other side; a man and woman, perhaps? Eddie stood listening, sweat now dripping in his eyes, with his ear beginning to burn despite it not even touching the red-hot door. The voices were too muffled for him to understand what they were saying. All he could really hear was laughter; lots of laughter. Whoever was behind the door, seemed to be enjoying themselves. Eddie finally had to take his ear away from the door as the heat became too much. He rubbed his other scorched ear, and retched, as the smell had also gotten worse in the hallway, a hell of a lot worse. Eddie hadn't noticed it till he got to the door, but now he had, it was odds on that the vomiting was about to make an unwelcome return. Eddie retched again. He had to get the door open and out of the hallway. There was no way he could make it back in time before the heat combined with the rancid smell overpowered him. A smell which was like something had died, but only after filling the hall with excrement as its one final act of precious life. Eddie had to somehow open the door.

Eddie fumbled, retched, and sweated in the dark, toxic atmosphere as he tried to locate a door handle. He was practically on his knees, when his right hand brushed against what felt like a handle. Eddie touched it lightly and he was sure it was a handle. It had to be. Because if it wasn't? Eddie didn't want to think about that. He didn't care how hot the handle would be as he grabbed it with both hands and turned it, while trying to push the door open at the same time. The door didn't budge. Eddie felt like screaming. He held his breath, bit his lip, and prepared for one more attempt. If this didn't work, then it was goodnight Vienna. Eddie mustered what little energy he had left; his shoulder crashed against the door as he turned the handle. The door flew open. Eddie didn't feel a thing when some off his skin ripped off while pulling his hands from the handle as he stumbled inside, closing the door behind him as quickly as he could.

The first things that hit Eddie when he entered the room were the bright light, cool air, and the same sweet smell from earlier. Eddie closed his eyes as the cool air smothered him. He took a deep breath and let the wonderful aroma of the room fill his nostrils. It was stronger than before and Eddie now recognised it as perfume. The cool, blissful air and the smell of intoxicating perfume, after the stench and heat, were practically orgasmic.

"Hello, my good friend," a familiar voice said.

Eddie opened his eyes. The light was initially blinding. When

95

Eddie's eyes adjusted to it, he could see the small room was completely painted white. Just in front of him was a white table. Sitting at it was James, looking immaculate in his white suit, and Joan, wearing a red sleeveless dress.

James got up from his seat, "I know it's warm out there" he said, "but aren't you a bit underdressed for the occasion?"

Eddie looked down. He suddenly noticed that the only thing he had on was a pair of blue and white polka dot boxer shorts.

"I'm afraid something is brewing, Eddie," James said, with a serious looking expression on his face. He moved a little to his left and pointed to a yellow teapot on the table behind him, "Fancy a cuppa?" James asked. Then he and Joan both burst out laughing.

Eddie held his hands up. Loose, scorched flesh hung from them, like red strips of wallpaper peeling off a wall. He watched, wide-eyed with fascination, as blood dripped from his hands onto the white, cold floor, while the sound of James and Joan's laughter rang in his ears.

CHAPTER TEN

When Eddie returned to the park, a week later, his t-shirt was almost sticking to him and his armpits were giving off the faintest whiff, which resembled body odour, despite using almost half a can of deodorant this morning. He could also feel the back of his neck start to burn as he surveyed the mass of people here today. There were lot of mums and kids, and the bandstand had a selection of youths gathered at it. The group of teenagers had also returned, playing football in the same corner of the park, with a few groupies now in tow watching them.

As Eddie strode up to the same bench as before, James was already sitting there, dressed in his familiar outfit. It didn't seem to make any difference to him that the day was as hot as Shania twain in her "Man I Feel Like A Woman" video. Most people were wearing shorts and a t-shirt, or even shorts and no t-shirt (only males, unfortunately, as far as Eddie could see). Not James. He still had on his white suit, shirt, and cravat.

Eddie sat down. With pleasantries out of the way, and a good whiff of James's aftershave, Eddie asked, "How come Brenda and Douglas happened to be at a table next to us at the *Glamis,* enjoying a cosy romantic meal for two? You were the one who was meant to be taking her out for a date? Next thing I know, she's sitting in the *Glamis* with Douglas. What happened to his girlfriend?"

"He's left his girlfriend," James answered.

"Never?"

"Yes. It seems he went home after our little chat in the pub, packed his bags, and is now living in a bed and breakfast."

"You're pulling my leg?"

"I can assure you, I'm not pulling anything," James said and wiped his brow with his handkerchief. He seemed to be feeling the heat already, so today's chat could be short and sweet.

"How did he end up at the *Glamis* with Brenda?"

"I had originally booked the table for myself and Brenda, plus another couple I know. Then, when I found out Douglas had left his girlfriend. The more I thought about it. The more I thought he and Brenda would be more suited."

"Why did you think that? He's a loud mouthed idiot."

"He may have had his faults in the past. People can change. I think they could get on very well together."

"We'll see," Eddie said as he shook his head. "And how exactly did you get them together?"

"That's a long and complicated story. The important thing is I did get them together."

"You certainly did," Eddie agreed. "And if you need proof I was there with Joan, then you can ask Brenda or Douglas."

"You're right. I am sure they will vouch for you. However, I must admit. I have a tiny confession to make."

You went to visit Joan at work.

"I may have popped into a certain shop last week, and got chatting to the lovely assistant who works there," James said.

Go through the back for a cup of tea and a good old laugh with her, did you?

"Her name is Joan. And she just happened to mention going out for a meal with her husband to the *Glamis* the night before."

I bet she did!

James looked at Eddie, "You don't seem too surprised with what I'm saying?" he said.

"I'm not."

"Have I made such an impression on Joan that she just had to mention me?"

"I don't think so," Eddie replied and shrugged his shoulders. "I've no idea why I know you were there. Somehow, I just do."

"That's very interesting," James said and nodded. "Very interesting, indeed."

"How did you happen to just visit the shop?" Eddie asked.

"Well," James replied and crossed his legs. "When I was chatting away to Brenda, arranging the dinner date for herself and Douglas. The conversation fleetingly came round to the subject of you and your wife. Brenda told me she was called Joan, and that she worked at a place called *The Purple Shop*."

"What did Joan say to you?"

"I wouldn't say you got a completely glowing report, to be perfectly honest, but Joan did say she enjoyed her meal at the *Glamis*. She also thought you had an ulterior motive behind it all, because she couldn't remember the last time you had taken her out."

"It hasn't been that long," Eddie said, trying not only to convince James, but also himself.

"You don't have to explain anything to me," James said. "But she is a lovely lady and also an extremely attractive one. Who knows?

If I was a bit younger, you may well have had a bit of competition on your hands." James gave Eddie a wink. "You're a lucky man, Eddie, a very lucky man. I think over the years you've forgotten that?"

Both men sat silently and watched all the comings and goings in the park. As Eddie tried to work out how he knew James had been to see Joan, he noticed, not to his great surprise, that a bottle, which could very well be cider, was now being passed around the ever growing gang of youths hanging about the bandstand. His mind drifted away from James and Joan's get together, back to his own misspent youth and misspent adulthood. He may not hang about the bandstand drinking alcohol with his mates anymore, but he does hang about the pub most days drinking it. Not that he has many mates left to hang about with. He remembered the first time he went to the bandstand for a drink, aged fourteen or fifteen; it was like a rite of passage. Laughing and giggling after only about three sups of the stuff. Then, after half a bottle, he was almost comatose and unable to remember being helped home. However, till this day, he has no such trouble remembering the first trailblazing hangover the following morning.

"How do you think the meal went?" James asked, eventually interrupting the silence between the two of them.

"All right. There wasn't much conversation until we had a few drinks. Even then, I wouldn't say the conversation was exactly flowing."

"Did you have the steak like I recommended?"

"No. I just had a burger and chips. Joan treated herself to the steak, probably because it was the most expensive thing on the menu."

James laughed.

Eddie had seen James laugh and smile numerous times since they first met, yet this was the first time Eddie had noticed just how incredibly white and perfect James's teeth were. It reminded him of an episode of *Friends,* where the character Ross got his teeth whitened. It made Eddie wonder if James had done anything cosmetically to get them so pearly.

"Good girl," James said, once he stopped laughing. "Joan told me she'd had the steak, and I've a funny feeling you're right about her motive in choosing it. So the meal wasn't exactly a roaring success. Let's look on the bright side. It wasn't exactly a disaster, either. It's a start. And did you cook her anything, like I suggested?"

99

Eddie didn't answer. He simply brushed a bit of fluff off his, navy blue, sports shirt.

"I'll take that as a no," James said. "What about the rest of your winnings? I gather that was spent in the pub and the bookies?"

Eddie didn't answer. He brushed another bit of fluff (this time imaginary) off his sports shirt.

"I also gather you didn't have any success. Because if you did, I don't think you would be sitting beside me right now. Am I correct?"

James finally got an answer, an almost inaudibly mumbled, "Maybe."

"What about the things I told you last week. Did any of that sink in?"

"I tried listening to what you said. But I didn't exactly jump out of bed next day, skipping round the bedroom shouting out how wonderful it is to be alive."

"At least you took Joan out for a meal. That was our deal. Anything else would have been a bonus." James stroked his moustache and ran a hand through his dark greased back hair. "Do you remember the programme *Challenge Anneka*?" he asked, completely out of the blue.

"*Challenge Anneka*? Yes, I remember it," Eddie was taken back at the topic of conversation. "I didn't like it very much. But I did like *Treasure Hunt*, and Anneka Rice was also in that."

"She certainly was. The reason I asked about *Challenge Anneka*," James said, "is not because I have a thing for Anneka Rice. It's because I have a challenge for you that we could call *Challenge Eddie*. I could even get a nice, colourful jumpsuit for you to run about in, if you like?"

"I'm not sure I have the figure for it, "Eddie said, and they both laughed. "What's the challenge?" he asked.

"I will set you a challenge every week. If you are up to it, then I will go to the bookies with you and try to pick a winner. If the horse wins, then you have to do the next challenge. If, however, the horse loses at any time, then you are free to stop the challenge. In fact, you are free to stop any time you wish. But the moment you stop, is the moment I no longer choose a horse."

"What sort of challenges are you going to give me?"

"It's nothing drastic. Certainly nothing like the challenges in the film *Saw*, that's for sure," James assured him. "In fact, to be perfectly honest. For a lot of people, the challenges I set wouldn't even seem like a challenge, yet they might to you."

"What do you mean they might to me?"

"I only asked you to cook a meal for your wife last week. I might as well have asked you to climb the Matterhorn. It turned out to be such an impossible task."

"That wasn't part of the deal. I could have cooked a meal if I wanted to," Eddie slumped back on the bench and folded his arms.

"That's the whole point. You could have, but you didn't. It was your choice and no one else's. I don't doubt for a second that you're not incapable of rustling up some kind of meal for you and your wife to enjoy. The bottom line is you couldn't be bothered."

"I had other things to do."

"I'm sure you did. So are you up for the challenge or not?"

"Let me get this straight?" Eddie sat up again and pointed at James. "You set me a challenge every week. If I do it, you'll pick a horse at the bookies? If you keep on picking a winner, you'll keep on setting a challenge?"

"Not for ever. We'll have to set a time scale."

"For how long?"

"Seven weeks," James shouted with some excirement. "And seeing as you have already had one challenge in which you succeeded. Then there are now only six weeks and six challenges remaining. We must meet here the same time every week. Like last time, we'll have a chat. But you have to try and put into practice some of the things I say. If you do take some of it in, and at the same time, meet the weekly challenges. I honestly believe that, at the end of the seven weeks, you'll be a better person who enjoys life more. If you don't listen to anything I say, or meet any of the challenges. You'll simply be the same person you are now and your life will be just as enjoyable. So what exactly do you have to lose?"

"Nothing, I suppose," Eddie said. Then he asked the million dollar question, "Why are you doing this? What's in it for you?"

"I have my own incentive," James replied. "I believe you could be more than you are at this moment in time. I also believe you owe it to yourself, your wife, and everyone you come into contact with, to at least try and be a better person than you are right now."

"There are reasons my life has turned out this way," Eddie said as he stared at the ground. "Reasons I'm the way I am…it wasn't always like this." Then, Eddie whispered, almost to himself, "There are reasons…"

"Everyone in life has a reason for the way they are," James said. "It's always out of their hands. Blame it on fate. I don't doubt things have happened, but that's something we might discuss later. Right now, I don't think either of us is ready to delve too deeply, into what happened in your past. At the moment, what I'm interested in is your present." James rubbed his hands together, "Right then, my good friend," he said. "Are you prepared to take up my challenge?"

"I guess so," Eddie said with minimum enthusiasm. "As you said, what exactly have I got to lose?"

"You have nothing to lose, and so much to gain," James said as he held out his hand. "So, do we have ourselves a deal?"

Eddie briefly thought about the question before replying, "We do," he said, and shook James's hand with a firm grip.

"Okay," James said. "I'm going to tell you something extremely important. A person's life is basically what their thoughts make it to be. The person you are, and the life you live, is down to the thoughts you have. This is something that has been said from the Stoics, to such writers as James Allen, and Emerson. A great man has great thoughts. A poor man has poor ones."

"That's because they've no money. No wonder they have poor thoughts," Eddie butted in. He could emphasis with poor men having poor thoughts.

"I don't mean poor as in monetary terms. I mean poor as in character."

"Hmmph."

"As I mentioned back in the pub, we let other people upset us, when really, it is the thoughts in our own minds that does the damage. The Stoic, Marcus Aurelius, was a firm believer that in life it's not what happens to us that's important, it's how we react. External events cannot affect us, unless we allow them to. Like the line from *Hamlet,* 'there's nothing either good or bad but thinking makes it so'. Are you getting the point yet?" James asked.

"Not yet, no," Eddie said as he watched some of the young mothers who were in the park with their children. Some of them were not bad looking.

"The point is," James said. Obviously not taking such an interest in today's view as Eddie was. "What's important isn't what happens in your life, be it good or bad. What's important is the way you think about it, how you react. According to the *Dhammapada,* 'All that we are is the result of what we have thought. It is founded on our thoughts, it is made up of our thoughts. Let the wise man gaurd his thoughts. There is no fear in him while he is watchful.' And Pascal says, 'Thought constitutes the greatness in man.' So you see, Eddie. Your life at this very moment can be as good as you want it to be, or it can be as bad as you want it to be. The only difference is in how you think."

Right now all Eddie could think about was one mother, in particular, who had stripped down to a yellow bikini. Eddie wasn't close enough to tell if it was a polka dot one, or not? He wouldn't mind getting a better view to find out. Eddie was beginning to feel hot and bothered, which he didn't think was due to the weather.

James continued, still not appearing distracted by the sight of bare flesh, merely yards away. "The good news is that it's possible to change your thoughts, and therefore, change the man."

Eddie wouldn't want to change the thoughts he's having right now. He really ought to start coming here more often if this is the sights that are on view.

"Do you have great thoughts, or not so great thoughts?" James asked.

"My thoughts normally aren't too great, I suppose," Eddie admitted, after finally taking his eyes off the bikini-clad-beauty. "No wonder," he added, "I mean, my life is far from great. So why should my thoughts be any better?"

"'Our thoughts make us what we are', claimed Emerson. 'A man is what he thinks about all day long'. You can have miserable thoughts all day long. Or, you can change your way of thinking and have better, more positive thoughts all day long. Like Milton wrote, 'the mind is its own place, and in itself can make a Heaven of Hell, a Hell of Heaven'."

"Is that the poem thing about the Pimpernel?" Eddie asked. "I saw the film about that when I was younger."

"Aaahh, the foppish Sir Percy Blakeney. Alias, The Scarlet Pimpernel. No, that was nothing to do with him. The poem about the Pimpernel went something like this." James put a hand up to his mouth and cleared his throat. "He seeks it here, he seeks it there. Poor Eddie seeks happiness everywhere. Is he in Heaven? Or is he in Hell? Alas, for Eddie, it is sometimes hard to tell."

Eddie scowled.

James, inevitably, had a wide beaming smile on his face. "I thought that was good? Maybe some people don't appreciate poetry?"

103

"You're to poetry what Clive is to comedy."

"Thank you."

"It wasn't a compliment."

"Really? I thought it was. Anyway, enough of this hilarity."

"What hilarity? You're the only one who's laughing."

"I better move on. I think someone's been out in the sun too long. They're getting tetchy."

"I was all right till someone decided to recite their made up poetry."

James put his hand on his heart, "I promise there will be no more poems today."

"Good."

"Back to business. And, according to Aristotle, 'we are what we repeatedly do. Excellence is not an act, but a habit'. Over the years, you, like many, have picked up a number of bad habits. The habits, along with your thoughts, have to be changed."

"How do I do that?"

"You replace your old thoughts and habits with new ones. This is one of the most important things I will mention. The only thing in this world in which you have complete control is your mind and power of thought. You-control-your-mind," James pointed to his head. "Your mind does not control you. You can keep a constant vigil looking out for any negative, weak, or critical thoughts that try to enter your mind. When they do, you try and immediately change them."

"That sounds like a full time job."

"To start with it will be. But it gets easier over time. One important thing you must also remember is that a thought is only a thought. It's not real. The only power a thought can have is the power you decide to give it. You don't have to believe and listen to everything you tell yourself. Like the voice in your head that tells you to lie in bed all day long."

"But I like to lie in bed."

"I'm sure you managed to get up early in the morning, in the dim and distant past, when you did actually work for a living?"

"Yeah."

"So, obviously, you can do it if you want to? At first you have to slowly replace your present unbeneficial thoughts, and replace them with better, new, self improving ones. When you do this, your new way of thinking will start a chain reaction that will, eventually, change your habits. Then you're really on your way."

"Where to?"

"To wherever it is you want to go. As the old Chinese proverb says, 'watch your thoughts, for they become words. Watch your words, for they become actions. Watch your actions, for they become habits. Watch your habits, for they become character. Watch your character, for it becomes your destiny.' And the only way all this can happen, is through hard work, self awareness, and self discipline. I mean, let's face it. We've all heard people who say, 'Oh, I couldn't help it, it's just my temper'. Or, 'I didn't mean what I said'. And, of course, 'I can't help it if I lie in bed all day'. It's just the way I am-"

"Some people can't help it." *Like they can't help their randy thoughts when a young floozy puts sun tan lotion over her nice, slim body. I wonder if she needs any help with those hard to reach places.*

"That's a cop out," James waved his hand in the air like he was swatting an irritating little fly. "By becoming aware of the thoughts you have, the things you say, and the habits you have, along with some self discipline, then you can eradicate these negative traits. That's if you can be bothered to? The easy option, which many people take, is to simply be at the mercy of their thoughts and slavish bad habits, even though it has created their current miserable existence. It is said that one definition of madness is to repeatedly do the same thing, and expect a different result. So, if your current way of life isn't bringing you any happiness or success, how do you expect your future to have any happiness or success? How can it possibly change for the better, if you don't? No one else can do it for you. Only you can." James stopped talking and gave out a loud sigh.

"What's wrong?"

"Oh, nothing's wrong. It's just when I said 'Only you can', it reminded me of the band Fox as that was the name of one of their songs."

"Who?"

"You don't remember Fox?" James asked in apparent disbelief. "They were a band in the seventies."

"Never heard of them."

James shook his head. "Their lead singer was called Noosha Fox. She was very well named as I used to think she was a right little fox back in the seventies. A real foxy lady." James stared at the sky with a smile on his face. "I wonder what she looks like now," he pondered out loud.

Eddie decided to leave James alone with his thoughts about

Noosha, for a second or two, and wondered if Noosha has aged like some of Eddie's pin up girls from the seventies had. If so, then it is probably just as well James didn't know what she looks like now. Eddie was going to mention this, but decided against it. He was happy to let James daydream a while longer as it meant Eddie could sit in peace and watch the girl in the bikini finish putting on her sun tan lotion. Once she put the lotion back in her bag, Eddie asked, "I thought we weren't meant to think about the past or the future, only the present?"

James nodded and wiped some more sweat off his forehead. "There is nothing wrong with occasionally reminiscing about the good times, or looking forward with optimism to the future. The trouble is when you continually live in the past or the future, forgetting that you have a here and a now. Seneca, the Stoic, said 'the greatest hindrance to living is expectancy, which depends upon tomorrow and wastes today'. Remember-Be-Here-Now! For there really is nowhere else you can be. I do think everyone is allowed the occasional daydream about Noosha Fox, once in a while, or whoever tickles their fancy."

I have to agree with you there. Eddie licked his lips.

"I think today's lesson has almost reached its conclusion," James said.

Eddie, meanwhile, continued to watch the girl in the bikini. She was now bending over to pick something up. Eddie's tongue was practically hanging out.

"As always," James said. "I've a few more things I'd like to say before we go."

"You what?"

"I have a few more things to say."

"Great," Eddie replied, with more than a hint of sarcasm in his voice.

"Thank you for your enthusiasm. I'd also like to briefly mention how it is believed your thoughts and health are linked. Negative, stressful thoughts that cause fear, anxiety, and doubt, can, over time, weaken the immune system. This, in turn, can lead to illness and various ailments. Good, healthy thoughts can help in keeping a good, healthy body and immune system. Sick, weak thoughts, on the other hand, can cause a sick, weak body and immune system."

"You're trying to tell me happy people never get ill?" Eddie asked as diplomatically as he could. *What a load of crap,* is what he really thought.

"No, I'm not saying that if you have good, healthy thoughts then you will never get ill. Some people, for instance, with a terminal illness, are the most positive and cheerful people you can meet. Sometimes, unfortunately, the illness is just too much. Although, I'm almost sure that in a lot of cases, people's moods of optimism and healthy thinking may have helped them survive longer than science or medicine would have believed possible. Even if it is only one day more, that one day can mean so much."

What James just said made Eddie think about Jenny. What he wouldn't give to be spending the day in the park with her. Of course, he probably wouldn't have realised just how precious that day was, and would've taken it for granted like most of the other wonderful days they spent together. Eddie felt a flutter in his stomach. *Here we go again*, he thought

"In a way, it may sound heartless," James said. "Perhaps there is one positive you can take out of yourself or a loved one having a terminal illness. You can suddenly appreciate every single moment you have with them, and realise how precious each day is."

You can also say goodbye. Something I never got the chance to do. Eddie braced himself for the return of the vampires as he gripped the edge of the bench with both hands.

"Then again," James continued, "maybe we shouldn't have to wait till our loved one's, or, we ourselves, get a terminal illness before we appreciate our time together. Maybe we ought to do it anyway. Because we never know when we will be taken away to that great gig in the sky, or wherever it is we go. What we do know, for sure, is that we will be taken away someday, and so will everyone we know and love." James got out a white handkerchief and delicately dabbed his neck. "It's rather hot, isn't it?" he said.

"It's a scorcher," Eddie agreed, as he let go of the bench, relieved that the flutter had simply been that, and nothing more.

"As you know," James said as he put the handkerchief back in his pocket, "we all laugh when something amuses us. We cry when we find something sad, and we blush when we find something embarrassing. We may also start to shake a bit when we become nervous. Always, it is a thought which brings these different reactions to our bodies. There is definitely a relationship between the thoughts we have and its effect on the body. Our minds interpretation of the situation we find ourselves in."

Eddie noticed that the more James sweated, the smellier his

aftershave became. The scent now seemed to be coming out of his every pore, it was that strong.

"If we were lucky enough to meet Noosha Fox," James said while shifting about on the bench. "I'm sure my heart would skip more than a beat and I would be tongue tied. She may not have the same affect on you, but if you call yourself a red blooded male, she should."

"I'm a red blooded male, all right," Eddie said. "It's just that it would take something more exciting than a pop star I've never heard of, who could be at least sixty, to push my buttons."

"I don't doubt your masculinity for a second. Let's hope you're not *too* red blooded?" James said.

Eddie shifted uneasily on the bench. For some reason, he felt uncomfortable. Eddie glanced at James, but saw a strange look in his eye, which didn't help Eddie's feeling of unease. Eddie diverted his gaze to the ground. *There's something funny going on here. I actually think he's reading my bloody mind. That's what he's doing. Like that book I read, in English class, at school. What was it? The Big Friendly Giant? Don't be stupid. Willy Wonka? No. It had a bird in the title. Robin Hood? Come on? You're supposed to be helping. Okay then, how about, The Cuckoo's? Yes, it's the cuckoo's, but I need more. Don't you always? The Midsummer Cuckoo's? That's better. It's close, but you still don't win a coconut. The Midwich Cuckoo's? That's it. He's some sort of alien Midwich Cuckoo who can not only read my mind, but also knows every emotion, experience, and feeling I've ever had or ever will have. Wow, Eddie. That's quite a conspiracy theory you have there. Next you'll tell me they never landed on the moon. Of course they never, the moon's not even real. Okay, Eddie. But, hey, this James sounds like a real talented guy. As a concerned friend. Don't you think it's time you laid off the booze a little? I mean, tell too many people about this mind reading lark and you'll be straight up to Abernethy.*

Eddie raised his head and immediately felt better (or saner?) as he saw the girl in the bikini threw a ball to her daughter. He felt even better when she bent over to pick the ball up, giving Eddie probably the view of the day so far. *What was that all about?* he thought as the girl dropped the ball and had to bend over to pick it up again. *What a shame. She's such a butterfingers. But talking about cuckoo's. I think I'm the one going cuckoo. I've definitely been out in the sun too long. And I need a drink.*

"People's minds interpret situations differently," James said, with the supposed, strange mind reading look no longer in his eye.

It must've been a trick of the light? Yeah, okay Eddie. That's the official story we'll stick to.

"This, in turn, can lead to their bodies reacting differently," James continued, oblivious to Eddie going slightly mad for a moment. "Which just goes to show how incredibly important our thinking is. For the way we think really does determine how good or bad our lives will be. And also which road we will choose-"

"What did you say?" Eddie asked.

"What? About which road we will choose?"

"Yes. Have you mentioned that before?"

"Probably. I speak so much, it's more than likely I end up repeating myself."

"You're probably right," Eddie agreed. *But I don't think you are? The Road to Nowhere can become the Road to Somewhere.* Eddie scratched his head.

"I think you need to get up to the bookies?" James said.

"I think you're right," Eddie agreed. *I also need to get to the pub for a drink.*

"Okay then. On to the challenge. As I have told you, the way you think can have an effect on your whole life, including your body and your health. Do you know what else can have an effect on your body and health?"

"No."

"Exercise!" James cried out excitedly. "Now we have this week's challenge."

Eddie did not share in James's excitement. James had mentioned climbing the Matterhorn earlier, so who knows what he had up his white-suited-sleeve?

"What is it?" Eddie asked, almost certain he would not like the answer.

"Last week, the Sin I mentioned was envy and the Virtue was kindness. This week's Sin is gluttony and its Virtue is temperance. I'm going to be honest with you, I feel you drink too much-"

"But…" Eddie tried to interrupt.

James put his hand up. "Before you say anything, please let me finish," he said.

"Okay," Eddie said. He could sense a lecture on the way.

"Thank you," James said. "I think you drink too much. The Sin of gluttony includes the indulgence and over consumption of alcohol, amongst other things. Whereas, the Virtue of temperance is about practicing self-control and moderation. I could tell you to cut down on your drinking, but at this stage, I honestly don't think you could manage it."

Yes, it's a lecture.

"It would also be difficult for me to find out how much you actually did drink. So I don't feel that would be a suitable challenge. Not only is your mind of utmost importance, but so is your body. Therefore, I not only want you to train your mind this week, I also want you to train your body."

"How do you expect me to do that?"

"During my chat with Joan she informed me about going to the gym. Therefore, I want you to go with her every day she goes this week. That is your challenge."

"She goes almost everyday and sometimes at nine in the morning," Eddie protested. "I'm out of shape. I won't last five minutes in the gym."

"If she goes everyday, then you'll join her everyday, and at whatever time. I do have an idea regarding your basic level of fitness, don't you worry about that. When you go, instead of going to the gym to keep fit, you will be going to get fit. That is this week's challenge. If you don't wish to do it, then you know our agreement."

"But most of the time Joan goes to the gym with Gloria." Eddie was still trying to think up excuses.

"Then it will just have to be a threesome," James said.

Eddie had to think about this one. Last week's challenge was only one meal, but this week's challenge could involve him going to the gym everyday this week. He really couldn't be bothered, but then again, if today's horse came in, maybe he could. "Deal," Eddie said while flexing his fingers. "Is that it?" he asked.

"Yes, that's it." James put his hand on Eddie's knee to prevent him getting up. "I want you to remember. I'm not asking you to become like Ned Flanders. You still need to be a realist about life. Life isn't easy, but no-one said it would be. Then again, you also need to realise that perhaps most of your problems aren't as serious as you think they are? Perhaps, life isn't as bad as you believe it to be?" He took his hand off Eddie's knee. "Let's go," James said as he stood up slowly. Again, like last week, he groaned and rubbed his lower back.

Eddie also got up. The two men then left the park together. Eddie, however, managed to sneak a glance at the girl in the bikini before he went, hoping the view would be as pleasing on the eye next week.

When they reached the bookies, James went through his usual routine of looking at the day's races in what was an almost trance-like state. After about five minutes, James picked *Mr Bad Guy,* with odds of six to one. Eddie put fifteen quid on it.

As they watched the race on the TV screen, Eddie was nervous like he always is when watching a horse he's bet on. Yet, this time, there was also a sort of calmness about him as the outcome of the race never at once seemed to be in any doubt. *Mr Bad Guy* led comfortably almost from the start. When it crossed the finishing line, Eddie was ninety quid better off. Not only that. He was also, for the time being, happy with life.

The two men said goodbye, agreed to meet next week, and went their separate ways. Eddie's separate way was across to the pub for a celebratory drink. Only a small celebratory drink, though, for Eddie had every intention of being fresh for the gym tomorrow.

CHAPTER ELEVEN

"Hello. How are you?" a quiet, husky female voice asked.

There was only darkness.

"Hello. How are you?" the voice asked once more.

Still only Darkness. Darkness and that noise. A noise that sounded like a hundred hammers banging away. No. Make that a thousand. Eddie just wished they would stop and leave him in peace.

"Hello. How are you?" the female voice asked for a third time.

Eddie felt a tug at his arm. Well, he thought it was his arm? It's hard to tell in the Darkness as things weren't always what they seemed when you're in there. Eddie didn't want to leave, but he was slowly but surely, slipping out of the Darkness like a child leaving a mother's womb. As he did so, the noise got louder, and Eddie got colder.

Eddie opened his eyes and saw his breath form in the air in front of his face, like dry ice at a rock concert. It was bitterly cold.

"Hello there," the voice said and then coughed badly.

Eddie turned to his left. Sitting beside him was a woman. Eddie assumed she was a woman. The person was practically nothing but skin and bone, so it was hard to tell.

"Hello," Eddie said as he shivered. He looked at the almost skeleton-like creature beside him, wearing a white nightdress, the skin on her face stretched, thin, and pale. It was almost like looking at a skull with nothing except clingfilm wrapped tightly round it, with the odd clump of grey hair stuck on top, for good measure. The eyes were so sunken that, for a second, Eddie thought she didn't have any. But she did. She had green eyes. The body was decaying, yet there was life in those eyes, a lot of life.

"Who are you waiting for?" the woman asked, barely moving her mouth. Yes, it was definitely a woman.

"I'm not waiting for anyone," Eddie replied, shivering.

"Oh!" was all she said and closed her eyes.

Eddie looked around. He was sitting on a platform in a train station. There was no one else about. A number of halogen lamps were lighting up this side of the platform, but the other side was completely dark. Eddie looked up. The noise he heard was the rain battering down heavily on the Perspex roof of a shelter he and his new companion were sitting under.

"You couldn't be a dear, could you?" she said with her eyes still closed.

"What is it?" Eddie rubbed his bare arms for warmth.

"There's a cigarette machine just up the platform. Could you kindly get me some ciggies? I should manage one before he comes," she asked, before coughing again.

Eddie checked his pockets for his wallet or some change. He had none of those things. He didn't even have on any trousers, just a pair of tight, black trunks and nothing else. "I've no money," he said.

"That's fine. You don't need any." She patted his bare leg with one of her bony hands, which surprisingly felt warm.

Eddie got up off his seat and gazed out at the torrential rain. In only a pair of trunks he walked out into it.

The cigarette machine was about thirty long yards up the platform. It was like no cigarette machine Eddie had ever seen, and when he stood trying to fathom out how to work it, a   shuffling-like sound came from the other platform. Eddie spun round. Of course he couldn't see anything, it was too dark. Eddie heard another sound from further up the platform, then one further down, almost opposite from where the shelter was. Eddie turned round again, faced the machine and pressed every lever and button on it till, eventually, he heard a thud. Eddie put his hand in the bottom of the machine. When he took it out, his hand was covered in worms. Eddie threw them off and put his hand in again. He rummaged about amongst the cold, slimy worms. This time the packet of cigarettes was in his hand when he took it out. Eddie hurried back along the platform, as fast as he could, brushing some stray worms off the packet of cigarettes, while the sounds from the other platform got louder.

With a little less than ten yards to go to till he reached the shelter, a high pitched, almost unbearable, piercing sound rung out. Eddie dropped the cigarettes and covered his ears.

"Attention all travellers," a woman's voice said. "Attention all travellers," she repeated.

Eddie reluctantly took his hands from his ears. The voice was coming from a loudspeaker. The piercing sound had been some kind of feedback.

"The Midnight Special shall be arriving very soon. I repeat. The Midnight Special shall be arriving very soon. Have a nice day," the announcer said. Then there was more feedback. Eddie covered his ears again. When he took his hands away there was blood on them.

113

When Eddie returned to the shelter, she was still there and her eyes were open. "Did you hear the announcement? He'll be here soon," she said, with a voice that almost resembled excitement.

"Who'll be here soon?" Eddie asked as he attempted to open the cigarettes.

"He's coming on the Midnight Special. I'm looking forward to meeting him again."

"Who?"

"Not long now." She closed her eyes once more.

There was a loud bang on the roof of the shelter. Eddie dropped the cigarette pack and looked up, "What was that?" he shouted.

"Probably just a rat or a seagull. There's a lot of them about," the woman said as she opened her eyes.

"Are you sure?" he asked, keeping his eyes firmly fixed on the roof. There was now the sound of scratching coming from above along with the sound of the rain.

"Can anyone say they are really sure about anything?"

"I suppose not, no," Eddie said as he managed to take his eyes off the roof and picked up the cigarettes off the wet platform floor.

"Did you get matches," she asked, just as Eddie managed to open the pack, at the fourth attempt, with his shaky hands.

"Bloody hell! No," he said, just as there was another thud on the roof. Eddie almost dropped the cigarettes.

"It's okay," she said. "I don't think I'll have enough time for one, but thank you for going"

Eddie looked at her. The body was thin and painfully weak, but the eyes were burning.

"The Oldie says I shouldn't smoke, anyway," she said, and attempted to laugh. This only managed to start another coughing fit. When the fit eventually stopped, Eddie watched, helplessly, as her frail chest, which was almost buried under the massive looking nightdress, heaved quickly up and down in a frantic attempt to get some oxygen back inside her.

"Are you all right?" Eddie asked, once she appeared to have caught her breath.

She put her bony hand on his leg again and stared at him with those lovely green eyes. A smile even managed to appear on her face. "Don't worry, I'll be fine." She grabbed Eddie's hand and continued to stare into his eyes. "We all reach the end of the line, eventually. But

114

that's not the end of our journey," she coughed again. "It's just the beginning of another wonderful one."

Eddie heard a train in the distance. Then he was back into the Darkness.

CHAPTER TWELVE

There was not another soul around, bar the solitary figure dressed in a white suit sat on the usual bench. Eddie thought the park was as empty as The British Legion lounge, on that infamous night, when 'Clive's Comedy Hour' took place. Clive had hired out the lounge to perform a comedy routine. Regrettably, it wasn't the crowd puller he had hoped. Even his own wife didn't turn up as his 'Comedy Hour' coincided with *Eastenders* on TV. The audience was more than one man and his dog, but not by much. The official attendance figure for that night was actually two men and his dog; Eddie, Fred Williams, and a Cocker Spaniel called *Batfink*. The show got off to a somewhat shaky start. Then, after the quarter hour mark, Clive really began to lose his audience after telling the joke about the Scotsman who was getting abused by the food he'd just bought in the chip shop. Turns out, it was a *Mock-Jock* supper. *Batfink* howled, and it wasn't in laughter. Clive tried to win back his audience with a joke about the new *Star Wars* film, where Luke Skywalker's fallen on hard times, and had to resort to being a Jedi bingo caller. The film was going to be set a long time ago, in a Gala-Hall, far, far away. A minute later, dog and owner were also far, far away. Eddie was once part of the audience, now he was the audience. 'Clive's Comedy Hour' had lasted less than twenty minutes. There was then only one thing to do. Both men spent the rest of the night at the bar and got drunk.

The weather wasn't sunny like it had been the previous two times at the park. This could explain why no one else had bothered to come today. It may have been dull and overcast, yet it was still, officially, t-shirt weather. Eddie had his white, fake Lacoste one on, which he'd bought off Dodgy Derek in the pub a couple of years ago. There was also the added bonus of the wonderful smell of freshly cut grass again, along with almost complete silence, except for the occasional sound of a bird in a tree, or the distant noise of a car as it passed by. The park seemed like a good place to be as Eddie strolled through it, taking in all the sights, sounds, and smells, despite there not being any scantily clad women about.

As Eddie approached the bench, James shouted out, "My! Have you been pumping iron? You look very lean and mean."

Eddie could not think of an answer as he sat down.

James laughed, patted Eddie on the knee, "You know I'm only

joking?" he said. "How did your week go? Don't keep me in suspenders…I mean suspense," James laughed again.

It really seemed to amaze Eddie how often James laughed in a day, particularly, it seemed, at his own attempts at humour.

"It didn't go too badly, at all," Eddie said with some pride. "I have to admit, I didn't go to the gym everyday. But I did go four days. Which is good, considering I haven't been to the gym since school. Even then, I never went all that often, to be honest."

"One of those days you didn't go to the gym, that wouldn't have been the day after the horse came in, by any chance?"

Eddie lowered his head slightly, "It might have been," he said quietly. "I was only going to have a couple of celebratory drinks, but one led to another, and then another. I think you get the picture?"

"Loud and clear," James said and nodded his head. "But let's look at the positives. You did go four times, and, by all accounts, you made an effort while you were there."

"How do you know what kind of an effort I made?" Eddie asked, knowing perfectly well what the answer was going to be.

"I think you know? I might have visited your lovely wife again, a couple of times, in the past week. Believe it or not, the conversation just happened to come round to you going to the gym with her."

"You do surprise me. Mind you, the thought crossed my mind that when I went into the gym you would be there, dressed in your leotard, to keep an eye on me," Eddie joked.

"That's something to be thankful for. Because if you saw me prancing about in the gym wearing my skimpy leotard, there is no way you would have returned. Then again," James put a finger up to his lips, "neither would anyone else." James laughed again. This time Eddie joined in.

"So, do you feel better for going to the gym?" James asked after the hilarity had died down.

"A bit," Eddie said. "I know I only went four times, and my body won't have the Charles Atlas seal of approval, just yet. But…" Eddie flexed a bicep, and jokingly said, "Go and have a feel." Much to Eddie's surprise, and horror, James accepted the offer.

"I'm sure I feel something there," James said as he felt Eddie's flexed bicep. "I'm sure I can. I don't know how to describe it? Maybe like a pea on top of a hill?"

Eddie quickly took his arm away.

"Will you be going back to the gym again?" James asked him.

"At the moment, I've sort of agreed with Joan I'll go twice a week with her. Probably on a Tuesday and a Thursday. Can't say I loved the gym, but it wasn't as bad as I thought it would be. And I feel all right after it."

"So you did some physical exercise, which is great. But what about this?" James pointed to his head with his forefinger, "Did you do any mental exercise last week?"

Eddie took a moment before answering, "I did try. But it's hard."

"I never said it would be easy. Yet, I think you could be underestimating yourself?"

"How?"

"Because your wife has seen a slight difference in you. A positive one at that. The emphasis is on slight, but there has still been a difference, nevertheless."

"What exactly do you talk about with my wife?"

"Just the usual gossip. She even makes me a nice cuppa when I pop in. We're like a couple of fish wives once we get started." James turned to face Eddie, "I do mean this in a nice way. But, in all honesty, we hardly ever mention you."

"Thanks," Eddie said and tutted.

"Don't mention it," James faced forward again. "Plus, I gather from my conversations with Joan, you haven't actually mentioned we know each other? Or the arrangement we have?"

"No. Why, have you?" Eddie sat upright on the bench.

"No, my lips are sealed," James reassured him. "I won't mention it, either. Why have you not told her yourself?"

"That's a good question." So good, in fact, Eddie couldn't think of an answer. He'd thought about telling her, a number of times, especially when she asked him about his sudden interest in going to the gym. Each time he was about to casually mention it in the conversation, something stopped him. Maybe he didn't mention it because he wanted Joan to believe he had taken her out for a meal and gone to the gym with her, simply because he wanted to. There was no ulterior motive. "I don't know why I haven't told Joan." Eddie finally answered. "But I would prefer it if you didn't say anything. At least for now."

"Mum's the word. I won't tell her anything until you want me to."

"Thanks," Eddie said and sat back on the bench.

"Don't mention it. Now, let's get down to today's business. I'm going to talk about money. A subject I know you're very interested in."

Eddie rubbed his hands together and was quickly sitting upright again. "That's more like it. Are we going to talk about putting on an accumulator at the bookies? If we get four or five races in a row on our coupon we would be rich!" Eddie was now almost bouncing up and down on the bench in excitement.

James shook his head, "Sorry, Eddie. Don't you think if I could bet on an accumulator, I would have done so by now?"

"I suppose," Eddie slumped back on the bench, sighed, and asked, "Why can't you?"

"Unfortunately, I can only picture one winner at a time. Believe me, I have tried. I just can't seem to picture more winners," James said. "It's not like a tap you can turn on for as long as you want and then off again. It takes a lot of effort. Even if it was actually possible for me to picture more winners at a time, I think the mental effort would probably be far too great."

"What if we knew the race meetings, say, a week in advance? You could pick one winner a day for a week. Then, on the actual day of the meeting, you would have seven winners on one ticket." Eddie wasn't going to give up easily. "You wouldn't have to pick more than one winner at a time, it would be one every day." Eddie's enthusiasm had returned with a bang. "That wouldn't be too much effort, would it? Just imagine how much we could win. We would be absolutely-loaded!"

"I have tried it, and it's almost…" James paused, like he was thinking of the right words to use. "I don't know how to describe it. This gift, or whatever it is I have. It only seems to allow me so many wins and so much money at a time. If you see what I mean?"

"No." Eddie didn't like this, at all. *There has to be some way we could put on an accumulator to win more money?*

"Let me put it this way." James said. "If I get too greedy, then the gift doesn't seem to work. If I accept it will only work at certain times, and only allow me to win smallish amounts of money when I do win. Then, yes, for some reason, it does seem to work. That's the way it is and I just have to accept it. I mean, I can't picture the lottery numbers or anything like that. Something I've found out to my great disappointment, after many years of trying."

Eddie's enthusiasm had well and truly gone again. He's happy getting a winner picked at the bookies every week, but it would have been extremely nice to get a very big win. Admittedly, on more than one occasion, it had also crossed Eddie's mind that if James could pick winning horses he could also pick the lottery numbers.

"You seem disappointed," James asked.

"I'm okay," Eddie managed to say through gritted teeth, without sounding too despondent.

"No amount of money can bring you real happiness. I can't deny it will make your life easier, but not necessarily happier. In *Ecclesiastes* it says 'the man who loves money can never have enough'. I've given you a winner every week now, yet it isn't really enough, is it? You would maybe like a couple of winners a week, then it will be three, and then four. Where will it end?"

Eddie shrugged his shoulders, "I don't know."

"You're like so many others, never really content and always wanting more. It is believed that one road to contentment is to want what you have, not to try and have what you want. Appreciate what is yours, and forget about what isn't."

"Hmmph," Eddie muttered. "That's easy for you to say. I bet you're loaded? Try living on sixty quid a week. You'll change your tune then."

"I don't know how you manage?" James agreed, his voice almost dripping with sarcasm. "You don't think how lucky you are that you are alive," James said. "That you have a wonderful wife, or that you've had a few good wins at the bookies? What you think about, is how much better your life could be than it is now, if only you had a few more big wins at the bookies. Not that long ago, when you were having your very dry spell, I bet you said to yourself you would be content with just one tiny win? Now, you've had that win, but you're not content with it. You now want more and more wins with higher and higher stakes."

Eddie sat there listening to what James had to say, and it pained him to admit it, but he was spot on; Eddie, however, wasn't going to give James the satisfaction of telling him that.

"The Buddha taught that the root of suffering can be found in our constant wanting and craving," James said. "We all crave things, and when we get these things and the novelty wears off, which eventually it will. Then we crave something else. It's a never ending, vicious cycle. We're all guilty of the sin of greed until we can stop this constant wanting and craving."

"Right then," Eddie asked, "if you're so against wanting a lot of things, and in particular money. Why do you gamble?"

"You're absolutely right," James agreed. "I could be classed as committing the sin of greed by gambling." He raised an eyebrow and said, "I never said I was perfect, did I? I also told you before that I enjoy gambling, but, to me, unlike some, it's not that important whether I win or lose. It's simply the taking part I enjoy. *The Bible* says it is the love of money that is the root of all evil, not the money itself. When the most important thing in your life is accumulating more and more money, that's when you have a problem."

Here we go again. Talking of the Bible, I'm about to get the sermon on the bench- instead of the mount.

"There is nothing wrong with wanting to have money as long as that's not your one and only goal in life," James continued the sermon. "That you've not forgotten all the other important things life has to offer. Did you know? One of the major differences between rich and poor people, apart from the obvious, that one has a lot of money and the other doesn't. It's how they think. Rich people think totally differently from how poor people do. You are not rich at the moment, because your mindset is not geared up for being rich."

"What a load of rubbish!" Eddie moaned. "The reason I'm not rich is because I haven't had any luck, and wasn't born with a silver spoon in my mouth."

"Being born rich does indeed help, I shall give you that," James agreed. "I think you will find, however, that not everyone who is well off was born that way. So let me ask you this. You would like to have more money, is that correct?"

"Yes."

"So what exactly are you doing to earn more money?"

"I... well...I... I'm going to the bookies."

Bravo. That was a hell of an answer. Eddie could hear slow clapping in his head.

James laughed out loud. "I want it all, is a cry you and many more like you make. But, do you ever ask yourself the question, what do I actually do to deserve it all? Do you work hard every day till you ache your bones?"

"I don't see you working?"

Eddie felt some smugness after saying that. *What's good for the goose, James, is good for the gander.* He folded his arms and awaited James's answer.

"No, you don't. You're quite right," James agreed. "Then again, you don't hear me complaining about lack of money. Nor will you see me every two weeks at the job centre, or benefit office, demanding money for doing nothing."

"I'm entitled to that money," Eddie's smugness had lasted a grand total of ten seconds. "I worked hard for years. So don't try and tell me I'm not." Eddie pointed his finger in James's face. "Also, don't try and tell me I don't know what hard work is, because I do. I worked at the cannery for over twenty years before it shut down, and it was bloody hard work. You wouldn't have lasted a day?" Eddie felt better after getting that off his chest. He lowered his finger.

"You're probably right," James said, "I'm not denying that the cannery was hard work. Please do remind me, how long is it since you actually finished there?"

"I can't remember."

James smiled at that half-hearted answer. "I didn't think you would. You expect so much out of life. You deserve this, you're entitled to that. Unfortunately, it seems, you don't think you actually have to do anything to get these things. I bet you even think going to the job centre every two weeks is a bit of a hardship, don't you?"

"Well, I do grudge having to get up..." Eddie started to say, and then decided it may be better if he didn't finish the sentence

"You grudge having to get up what?" James asked, but Eddie had a sneaky feeling that James knew what he was going to say anyway.

"Nothing. I'm not sure what I was going to say," Eddie said as he watched the first person to enter the park. A man in the distance was walking his dog which looked like a black Alsatian. Eddie continued to watch as the Alsatian cocked its hind leg and appeared to relieve itself against the side of the Bandstand. Then dog and owner went happily on their way again.

"I see," James said. "You're certainly not alone. There are millions more like you in this day and age who want so much, while doing so very little. The Welfare State may be a good idea, in principle, but look at the sort of country it has created. A country full of lazy people who expect money, a house, and even happiness, yet don't want to do any of the hard work themselves. Yet, why should they? When they can sit back and expect the state to provide everything for them?"

"So people don't deserve help?"

"When people are given help too often and too easily, then, what generally happens, is people become too dependant on this help. They, ultimately, end up whinging that it's not enough. We live in a country where far too many are selfish, have no dignity in themselves, do not take any responsibility for their lives, and blame where, and what they are, on others."

"Look, what are you getting at?" Eddie was close to shouting. "You're just like my son. He also thinks I'm a bum."

"I don't think anything like that. There are numerous countries which have far worse monetary poverty than here, but I think it will be hard to find many countries that have worse spiritual poverty."

"You're saying people shouldn't receive benefits?" Eddie asked in amazement. "And that I shouldn't be entitled to any money because I don't work? What if I wasn't able to work, do you still think I wouldn't deserve any money? You're like a...a bloody fascist! You'll be goosestepping round the ruddy bandstand in a minute."

James burst out laughing and patted Eddie playfully on the knee. "I have been called many things before," James said. "But that is without doubt the first time anyone has ever called me a fascist! Although, I have been known to read the *Daily Mail,* so you could have a point there? And as for goosestepping, I think the Hokey-Cokey's more my sort of thing. Let me ask you this." James edged closer to Eddie like a python getting ready to strike. "Are you unable to work?"

That was a vicious blow. And Eddie certainly didn't want to answer. The answer was an obvious "No." Eddie, instead, decided to be clever. He's watched the odd documentary on TV. Admittedly, this was a while ago now, but he remembered watching one about the American Constitution. "I would like to take the Second Amendment on that question," he said. The smugness was back.

James laughed. "I don't think you mean the right to keep and bear arms? Well, I hope you don't? I assume you mean the Fifth Amendment? Which includes the refusal to answer the question, because the answer may discriminate yourself in some way."

"Yes, that's what I meant." Eddie cringed. *I'll just say no comment next time.*

"I'll take your answer as a no? What I'm trying to say. Is that yourself, and many others, expect a good house, SKY TV, the latest mobile phone, money, and happiness. Yet seem to expect it all for nothing? As in the name of the New Radicals song, 'You Only Get

123

What You Give'. Sir Isaac Newton's Third Law of Motion states that 'for every action there is an equal and opposite reaction'. Therefore, if you don't do anything, then how can you expect anything in return? Likewise, if you don't do anything for others, then why should you expect others to do anything for you?"

"I do plenty of things for other people."

"Such as?"

"Em…" Eddie thought for a moment or two, but funnily enough, nothing seemed to immediately spring to mind. "No comment," was his eventual, tepid reply.

"I see you are using your right to the Fifth Amendment again?" James laughed. "When was the last time you tried to help other people get what they want?"

"No comment," Eddie said again. He didn't like the way this conversation was going; it was turning into a character assassination. Eddie thought it was about time he stood up for himself. "So what if I don't try to help other people," he almost spat. "Who does actually try to help other people anymore?" Eddie sat up and pointed his finger at James again. "I've a hard enough time trying to look after myself, without worrying about anyone else. I'm no different to most people. If you want to be the next Mother Theresa, then you're more than welcome to it. My priority is to look after myself, because I've been kicked in the teeth just once too often."

"There are a hell of a lot more people in this world who deserve a bit of luck, or a break, more than we do," James said. "Chances are they probably won't get one. Have you ever heard of tithing?" he asked.

Eddie slowly lowered his finger. "Isn't that to do with babies when their first teeth appear?"

"No, not teething…Tithing. It is meant to put you in tune with the universal law of circulation."

"No, never heard of it." Eddie covered his mouth as he yawned.

"It's when you give away the first tenth of your income. This demonstrates that the universe is a place of abundance. In acknowledgement of this fact, you are returning some money back to its source. It's an old custom, and through it, giving opens the way for receiving. In order to receive, one should give. If this is not done grudgingly, then what you give will return blessed and multiplied."

Eddie sat shaking his head. "I don't have enough money for

myself," he said, "let alone enough to give away a tenth."

"That may be so. But, as I said, you only get what you give. This is true, not only when it comes to money, but also in your actions, thoughts, and words. Sooner or later they will all return to you. This is Karma, Sanskript for comeback. We all know the saying what goes around comes around. That's Karma."

"When you said you were going to talk about money, I thought it was going to be about how to make it, not give it away. Now this nonsense about Karma? So far, I can't say I'm too impressed with today's conversation." Eddie tapped his fingers on the bench.

"Helping others should not be an effort and a struggle. It should be a joy. Confucius says 'if a man sets his heart on benevolence, he will be free from evil.' Plus, in the long run, if you really want health, happiness, and even money, it is best if you try to help others. Aristotle claimed 'the ideal man takes joy in doing things for others'. While, I would say, the idle man takes no joy in doing things for others, as well as taking very little joy in doing anything for himself."

Eddie decided he'd heard enough for one day. It was now time for cutting to the chase. "So what do you want me to do this week?" he asked. His fingers still drumming away a steady beat on the bench.

"I have a double whammy for you."

An answer Eddie wasn't expecting or wanting.

"Have no fear," James said, "they are not difficult."

"If it's a double whammy, does that mean you will be picking two winners?" Eddie asked, more in hope than anything else.

"I think you know the answer to that question?"

Yes, Eddie knew full well the answer to that particular question. He stopped drumming the bench as he awaited, with trepidation, the double whammy.

"Benjamin Franklin was a firm believer in being frugal. Yet didn't use that as an excuse for not helping others. Far from it. He also believed we should be charitable towards those who really need it, and if we weren't, it would affect our conscience."

"There's nothing wrong with my conscience."

"Glad to hear it, Eddie. The opposite Virtue of greed is charity. If our horse comes in today, I want you to donate ten percent of what you win to a charity."

Just as Eddie was about to complain, James hit him with another hammer blow.

"I also have a friend who works in a charity shop. He needs someone to help him out for about four days this week, because his usual volunteer is away on holiday. I think you can guess whose services I have volunteered?"

Eddie felt it best he didn't say anything. He took a deep breath and clenched his fists tightly on his lap.

"I know ten percent of what we win today, might not make a massive difference to people's lives. Can you imagine, however, what would happen if everyone gave even as little as say five pound a month, the cost of two pints at the pub?"

Eddie was imagining, not about all the good that could be possible if everyone devoted a small sum of their money to help those less fortunate, but about handing over some of his winnings when he could spend it on himself. Eddie was also imagining being stuck in a charity shop for four miserable days. The more he imagined it, the tighter he clenched his fists.

"Is that it for today?" Eddie grunted.

"Yes."

"Good." Eddie got up and stomped away in the direction of the bookies.

CHAPTER THIRTEEN

Clive was already at the bookies, wearing a yellow Den Perry t-shirt with 'The Banana Grove-Bad Boy!' written on it in blue lettering. Thankfully, this t-shirt wasn't as tight as the 'Jerry the Berry' one. It still, however, wasn't anywhere near being loose fitting.

While James went away to do his thing, Clive remarked about Eddie's trips to the gym this week. He also remarked about Eddie's new muscular physique, and how he now resembled Arnold Schwarzenegger with his new bulging biceps. This conveniently led Clive onto a joke he had just thought up about Arnold Schwarzenegger.

The walk here had managed to calm Eddie down, but not enough that he was in the mood for one of Clive's jokes. Eddie was about to mention this, when Clive started to tell the joke anyway.

"Arnie Schwarzenegger, who hasn't had a box office hit for a few years now, has decided to go and make another Conan film. It is going to be a prequel to the original *Conan the Barbarian*. The start of the film will show how Conan's mum had to go into emergency labour while giving birth to him. And the new film is going to be called…*Conan the Caesarean*."

Eddie laughed. He had no idea why? Neither could Clive, if the look of surprise on his face was anything to go by. But Eddie had, and the last thing he thought he'd be doing at the bookies was laugh at one of Clive's jokes. Now that he had, not only did Eddie feel better, but a look of joy was now etched on Clive's face. "That was a good one," Eddie said, and patted Clive on the back. "I think you must have spent a lot of time thinking it up?"

"No, I just thought it up last night in ten minutes or so."

"It wasn't too bad for only taking ten minutes," Eddie said. And as he did, a realisation occurred to him. It had taken no greater effort to praise Clive, than it would have to criticise him. Yet, the different effect it has had on not only Clive, but also himself, was great.

Eddie and Clive chatted away before James finally came and joined them. Clive repeated the joke for James. Predictably enough, James was in hysterics after hearing it. Once James composed himself, he announced that *La Japonaise*, an outsider at eleven to one, was today's chosen horse. Despite Eddie becoming more and more convinced of James's ability to pick a winning horse, there was still an element of doubt at the back of his mind. Instead of putting on fifteen pounds like last time, Eddie, conservatively, just put on ten pounds. Clive also put a couple of pounds on the horse. That was something Eddie wasn't entirely impressed about. Clive had been given the name of the horse, yet hadn't done any tasks. With some effort, Eddie managed to successfully bite his tongue and not complain.

La Japonaise was in third place for most of the race. Eddie may have initially had some doubts about the horse, but as La Japonaise moved practically effortlessly from third to second, he knew it was going to win. Clive got more and more excited and animated as the horse moved closer to the leader. Eddie, meanwhile, was a picture of calmness, even though he would win one hundred and ten pounds if the horse was first. La Japonaise seemed to glide into the lead while coming down the home straight; it eventually finished some ten yards ahead of its nearest challenger. Clive jumped up and down in excitement, and then gave both James and Eddie a hug. It even appeared, for one horrifying moment, that Clive was also going to give a few celebratory kisses as the emotion of the occasion became too much for him, but he managed to stop himself. All three men then collected their winnings. As Eddie counted his money, for the fourth time, it dawned on him that James always seemed to bet the same amount-the not too princely sum of seven pounds.

James left the bookies, shortly after the race had finished, as he had to go and see about some business, telling Eddie he would see him same time same place next week, if not before. Clive stayed another ten minutes before leaving. He couldn't wait to get home to tell Gloria all about his big win and think up some more jokes, since today's one got such a great response. Also, before Clive left, the two men agreed that Clive and Gloria would visit Eddie's this week for a drink. Eddie definitely felt something strange was going on; first he laughed at Clive's joke, then he's invited Clive and Gloria round to his. Just as Eddie wondered what would be next, Douglas walked into the bookies with Brenda.

"Bloody great," Eddie quietly said to himself when he saw them. "As soon as they turn their backs, I'm out that door."

No such luck.

Brenda clapped eyes on Eddie immediately. She waved and then walked across to him. At least Douglas was still speaking to someone by the front door, so Eddie could make this conversation short and sweet, then get away without having to speak to him.

128

"Hello, Eddie," Brenda said. The first thing Eddie noticed was that she hardly had any make-up on.

"Hello, Brenda," he said, trying not to stare at her practically make-up free face. But failing.

"I see you've noticed something different about me?" Brenda asked.

"Em…yeah…it's your…em…earrings, that's what it is. Are they new?"

Brenda laughed. "Well they are, actually. Douglas bought them for me."

I might have bloody known. He really is Mr Wonderful now.

"I don't think it was my new earrings you were looking at?"

"No," Eddie admitted.

"It's my make-up, isn't it? Or, lack of it? I look terrible, don't I?"

"No, no you don't. You look great, you really do." Eddie said, and it wasn't just some damage limitation exercise because Brenda had noticed him staring at her. She really did look great and at least ten years younger.

"Thank you, Eddie," Brenda said. "You're not just saying that, are you?"

"No. I'm not. You really do look great. But why the new look?" he asked, still quite amazed at how different she looked.

Brenda smiled and brushed her hair back. "It was just something James said to me a while ago, and it stuck in my mind."

He planted a small seed!

"Talking about James," Eddie said. "I thought you were meant to be going out with him for a meal? Yet you turned up with Douglas?"

"I know," Brenda shook her head. "It's crazy, isn't it?"

It's crazy all right.

"I was working that afternoon in the pub and James came in to see me. I can't remember all that he said. But, somehow, he managed to persuade me to go out for a meal with Douglas. At first I told him, in very un-lady like terms, what I thought of his idea. But he can be very persuasive."

"He certainly can," Eddie agreed.

"Do you mind if I have a seat?" Brenda asked.

"Of course not." Eddie pulled out a chair for her.

"Thank you," Brenda said as she sat down.

Eddie pulled out another chair and sat down beside her. "I know James can be very persuasive," he said. "But you knew what Douglas was like. I just can't imagine why you would agree to go for a meal with him? And now, even more unbelievably, you're actually his girlfriend?"

"I know," Brenda nodded. "As I said, it's crazy. Yet James managed to persuade me to go for the meal with Douglas. And I'm so glad I did. It was a wonderful evening. Since then things have got better and better. I couldn't stand him before, but he really does seem like a changed man."

For now, Brenda, he might. Unfortunately, I have a sneaky feeling it's all going to end in tears.

Brenda could obviously sense Eddie's doubt. "You don't seem too convinced?" she asked.

Eddie shrugged his shoulders. "I'm not saying anything. As long as you're happy, that's the main thing," he said.

Brenda played with her new earrings. "I'm incredibly happy. I don't know if you can remember what I said that day in the pub?"

"What thing?"

"About when James held my hand."

"Sorry, I don't." Eddie had a glance across to see if Douglas was still occupied.

"That's okay. It was when James held my hand in the pub. I told you and Clive that I felt a tingle, like a small electric shock. But also at that moment, I no longer felt like a barmaid struggling to meet ends meet, with two failed marriages behind me. A barmaid with so little self-confidence I had to hide behind layers of make-up everyday. Right then I felt I was someone special, with a future that was worth looking forward to. Since that day, and since I started seeing Douglas, I now feel like that almost all the time."

"Good for you," Eddie said as he noticed Douglas starting to make his way over towards them. "Can I ask you one more thing?"

"What's that?"

"James managed to persuade you to go for a meal when he came into the pub. What's the story behind James persuading Douglas?"

Brenda shook her head. "I don't know the full story, "she admitted. "Douglas has been vague about it."

I bet he has.

"That night when Douglas packed his bags and left Yasmin."

"Yasmin?"

"That's his ex girlfriend's name."

"Oh, right." Eddie didn't know her name, but he knew her to look at, as he'd seen her out on the town wearing the shortest skirts imaginable.

"According to Douglas," Brenda continued, "when he packed his bags and left, he went to the bus stop. And guess who just happened to be there?"

"James?"

"That's right. He started talking to Douglas, although Douglas won't tell me what they talked about. Next thing you know, we're going out for a meal and are now girlfriend and boyfriend."

Just then, Douglas appeared before Eddie could make his escape. "Hello, Eddie," he said.

"Douglas," Eddie replied. It was only one word, yet it still stuck in Eddie's throat as he said it. Brenda may think Douglas is the greatest thing since Pop Tarts or Soda Stream; Eddie didn't. Douglas was a long way down on Eddie's list of great things, just sneaking above the Bubonic Plague, but still well below haemorrhoids and diarrhoea.

Douglas took Brenda's hand and helped her up from the chair.

My, what a perfect gentleman.

Brenda and Douglas said goodbye as Eddie, with a bitter taste in his mouth, watched them leave the bookies holding hands.

CHAPTER FOURTEEN

"Hello again," a familiar sounding female voice said.

Eddie was in the Darkness. He hated leaving there.

"Are you not going to reply?" the voice said.

Eddie slowly opened his eyes and left the Darkness behind. This time it seemed so much easier. There were no deafening noises, it wasn't cold, and there was the voice; familiar, yet somehow different; more alive, more seductive, more tempting. Eddie had to see who it belonged to.

Eddie was not disappointed.

When he opened his eyes, Eddie was sitting at the same shelter, at the same train station. He looked to his left, but there was no-one on the bench beside him.

"I'm just having a cigarette. I hope you don't mind?"

Eddie looked out. On the platform was one of the most beautiful females he had ever seen; with black hair which curled just where it brushed her shoulder. This creature was wearing a white silk dress; it wasn't obscenely tight, just tight enough to show off her voluptuous figure and short enough to show off some of her legs; yet it was still long enough to show she had class. The vision in white took a long puff of her cigarette, a simple action that was one of the most sensual things Eddie had ever seen. All he could do was watch with his mouth hanging open.

"You don't remember me, do you?" she asked, then threw the cigarette on the ground, stubbing it out under one of her high heels, before strolling back towards the shelter, like a model on the Paris catwalk, her footsteps echoing out around the nearly deserted station.

Eddie's heart raced as she got closer.

"The weather's a bit better this time, don't you agree?" she asked and looked up to the black, starless sky.

Eddie finally managed to speak, "Yes, it is," he struggled to say. His throat was dry.

"The last time it wasn't raining cats and dogs, more like rats and seagulls," she said, and laughed. What a wonderful sound her laughter was.

She sat down beside Eddie, on the bench, and he immediately smelt her perfume, it was intoxicating. He looked at her flawless face, which had merely a hint of make up on it. She put a hand on his bare leg and an electric current flowed through his body up into his brain.

Almost all his senses were being overwhelmed like never before. The sight, sound, smell, and touch of her was almost too much. Heaven knows what affect the taste of her would have?

"You're a lot quieter this time," she said. "I still don't think you remember me, do you?"

Eddie looked at her blemish free face, "Sorry. No, I don't," he answered while inhaling the wonderful aroma of her perfume.

"I didn't think you did," she said, and smiled.

What a smile.

"I may look slightly different from the last time you were here. But I can assure you we have met. Not just here by the line, either, but elsewhere, briefly. Although, it was just one of those many meetings we all have in our lives which seem meaningless at the time."

"I think I would've remembered if I had met you," Eddie said. He still didn't recognise her, but there was something about her eyes. He had definitely seen those green eyes before.

She took her hand off Eddie's leg and took a cigarette out of the blue and white Regal packet she was holding in her other hand. "Would you hold this a second, please?" she asked, and gave the cigarette to Eddie.

Eddie tried to take the cigarette with his right hand, but it was shaking so much he had to use both hands.

She took a lighter out of the packet, and then, carefully, put the packet down on the bench. The lighter was an old fashioned looking brass one, but it suited her perfectly. For her clothes, hairstyle, and whole demeanour seemed from days gone by. She was more silver screen Goddess than size zero model-a Jane Russell not a Kate Moss. "Just as well I have a lighter this time, isn't it?" she said, whilst taking the cigarette back again.

"I suppose so." Eddie couldn't help but stare into her green eyes.

"The Oldie said these would be the death of me someday," she said, and blew out some smoke. "At least he was finally right about something," she added, and laughed a loud booming laugh. "He was on the train as well, but he told me it wasn't quite my time yet. Tonight it is."

"Is it?"

"When it's finally time you leave your tired, weak, and disease ridden old body behind, like the metamorphosis of a butterfly. That's why you see me like this, not how I was before."

"I don't really know what you mean," Eddie said as he at last managed to stop looking at her eyes. His gaze didn't travel too far. It was now firmly fixed on her chest. The dress she had on was tight in just the right places.

"You go back to how you want to be," she had another puff of her cigarette and stared into Eddie's eyes.

Eddie tried to divert his eyes to the floor, but he was too late.

"I see something appears to be grabbing your attention?" she said.

All Eddie could do was look across at the other platform, which was completely dark.

"You have been busted!" she shouted out. "Which is pretty appropriate, considering what you were staring at," she took another puff of her cigarette, and then laughed.

"No, I wasn't," Eddie tried to protest. "I was looking at…"

"Don't worry," she assured him. "I haven't had a young man stare at my bust for many a year." She touched Eddie's leg again. The current flowed through his body feeling even stronger than before.

"This is how I looked when I was an awful lot younger. I must admit, I did have many a male admirer in those days."

"I can believe that."

"My, you are a charmer."

Eddie blushed.

"I even won a beauty contest once," she said, and dropped her cigarette on the ground, again stubbing it out under one of her heels.

"Was it Miss World?"

She laughed again and patted Eddie's leg. It felt like a series of small electrical pulses.

"You really are a smooth talker, if only I were about forty years younger," she said, and gave out a sigh.

"Forty years-" Eddie attempted to reply. He quickly covered his ears with his hands.

A high pitched piercing sound filled the air. Even though Eddie had covered his ears in time, the sound was still intolerable. He kept his ears covered as the noise stopped.

A female voice spoke softly over the station speaker system, "Attention all travellers." There was some more feedback from the speakers, then she repeated, "Attention all travellers. The Midnight Special shall be arriving very soon. Have a nice day." The noise could be heard again for a few seconds. Then there was silence.

Eddie slowly took his hands away from his ears.

"Oh well," the vision in the white silk dress said, "it's almost time to go." She stood up and Eddie had an inevitable glance at her posterior. It seemed as perfect as the rest of her. "I'll just wait by the edge of the platform." She pulled down the hem of her skirt as it was showing almost an inch of leg above the knee. "Bye then," she said, and strolled off with a wiggle.

"Wait!" Eddie cried. "I don't even know your name." he tried to get up off the bench, but couldn't. The Darkness was returning.

She stopped and turned round, "Don't worry...you know," she said, and blew him a kiss, just as the sound of a train could be heard in the distance.

Eddie went back into the Darkness. This time he didn't want to go.

CHAPTER FIFTEEN

Eddie had a spring in his step as he strutted into the park, with his head up and chest out, whistling "It's A Kind Of Magic". He wasn't sure if it was due to something called endorphins kicking in, which Joan had told him about as he had been at the gym this morning, or if it was due to a lack of alcohol consumption in the last week. The only time he really had a lot to drink in the past seven days was the night Clive and Gloria came round. Then again, the spring in Eddie's step could simply be down to today's glorious warm weather. Whatever the reason? Eddie felt good. He quickly felt even better when he noticed his young female friend was back. She didn't have her bikini on, but the day would surely get warmer?

Before Eddie even got to the bench, James asked him, "I hear you got on well at the charity shop this week?"

"I did," Eddie answered and sat down. "I've also agreed to go there and help out a couple of times next week." Eddie took in James's aftershave, which again, seemed to be stronger on a warm day.

"So I've heard. My, you are getting a busy schedule," James said.

"I wouldn't say it's exactly hectic." Eddie laughed. "But the gym and helping out at the shop have kept me out of the pub."

"You were also entertaining guests this week as well, I hear?"

"You don't miss a thing, do you?" Eddie laughed again. "We had Clive and Gloria round. It was a good night. I wonder how you know that."

James gave a wry smile. "I might have been in to see your lovely wife again for another chit-chat. And I hear our little secret has been discovered?"

"Yes," Eddie nodded. "On the night he was round, Clive let the cat out of the bag that we know each other. Joan just thinks it's because of the bookies, she doesn't know anything about our weekly meetings…unless you've said anything to her?" Eddie asked.

"Of course not," James said and patted Eddie on the knee. "I wouldn't dream of telling her the change in you is because you're getting a winning horse picked at the bookies. I'll just let her believe you have miraculously seen the light. The positive changes in your life, and yourself, is all down to your own motivation to try and become a better person, nothing else."

Eddie did not try to dispute what James had just said. What would be the point? It may sound devious, but it was true.

"Joan really is a wonderful person," James said as he stroked his pencil-thin moustache. "She also appears to be very strong. I don't mean physically strong because she goes to the gym, but mentally strong. Plus, I hope you don't mind?" James looked Eddie in the eye. "Joan has confided in me about your daughter."

Eddie immediately lowered his gaze. *Yes, I do mind. She had no right to tell you about Jenny as I haven't even told you yet. What else do the two of you talk about?* Eddie clenched his fists and took a deep breath. It didn't seem to work.

Eddie's response (or lack of one) must have been enough to let James know whether he minded or not. "I'm sorry to bring it up," he said. "I can see by your reaction you aren't ready to speak about her just yet. We'll not discuss Jenny today. Let's discuss Joan instead."

Give you a few tit-bits so you can charm her yourself? Was what Eddie thought. "What do you want to know?" was his diplomatic reply.

"What about how you first met?"

"It's not very interesting." Eddie took another deep breath.

"I'll be the judge of that."

Eddie sighed. He took another deep breath that seemed to do the trick. Third time's a charm. "Do I have any choice?" he asked, knowing it was a futile question. He may have his suspicions about James and his ulterior motives, but what choice did Eddie really have? For the time being he would have to abide by the rules if he wanted a winning horse picked.

"No, you don't." James sat back and crossed his arms.

Here goes. "I actually went to school with Joan," Eddie said, "And in my teenage eyes, anyway, she just seemed to stand out."

"I take it she was a cutie?"

"She was that," Eddie agreed. "I can't say whether it was her blue eyes, long dark hair, or even longer legs? There was just something about her I liked. Something I wanted to get my hands on, but I just didn't know how."

"You must have learned pretty quickly?"

Eddie sighed. "Not really," he said. "The closest I actually got to speaking to Joan at school, which is pretty sad, was about a couple of months before I left. I had somehow ended up in the library, and I'm still not sure what I was doing there?"

"Really," James said and lifted an eyebrow. "You just so happened to end up in the library. Yet, you don't know how you got there. My, this sounds like a case for Mulder and Scully."

"Okay, okay." Eddie grimaced and shook his head. "I might have followed her one day. Are you happy?"

"Very."

"Anyway," Eddie continued, "I found myself lurking in the literature section, and I can even remember the book I was pretending to look engrossed in."

"Was it *The Broons* or *Oor Willie?*"

"No." *It wasn't the Midwich Cuckoo's, either.* "For your information, it was Shakespeare's *First Folio.*"

"Shakespeare?"

"Not that I read any of it," Eddie admitted. "I just thought it would impress Joan if she looked up and saw me with it."

"Did it?"

"No. Joan was sitting, scribbling into her notepad, at a table just a few feet away. After at least twenty minutes, I realised that to make any contact I would have to actually speak to her."

"You never marched up to her like a swashbuckler?"

"Erm…no, not exactly," Eddie sheepishly said. "I just got more and more nervous, until a couple of Joan's friends appeared. There was no way I was going to speak to her with her friends there. So, relieved, I put the *First Folio* back on the shelf, and quickly made my way out of the school library, for what was probably both the first and last time."

"Alas, poor Edward," James said. "But you did eventually make your move."

"But it would take me three years," Eddie admitted.

"You did do it, however. That's what matters. Yes, it may have taken you a while, but as the Bard himself would say, 'how poor are they who have not patience'. When did you first manage to speak to her then?" James asked as he crossed his legs, appearing engrossed.

"As I said, it was over three years later. Because in Christmas nineteen seventy nine, Pink Floyd weren't the only one's who decided they no longer needed any education."

"What happened?"

"I left school at the beginning of December to start at the cannery where my mum and dad both worked."

"Did they get you a place there?"

138

"Not quite." Eddie fidgeted on the bench. "My dad was a supervisor and my mum a cleaner there. One evening while they were having tea, and I was pretending to be engrossed in *Roobarb and Custard* on the TV..."

"*Roobarb and Custard?*" James put his hand up. A look of confusion was on his face. "Please remind me how old you actually were when you left school?"

"You're never too old to appreciate that cartoon."

"Apparently not," James rolled his eyes.

Eddie cleared his throat and continued. "My mum and dad were discussing how a vacancy had arisen at work. So, that night, I decided to pack in the learning and go and do some earning. I stayed off school the next morning. By ten-am I had been accepted in my first, and currently, only, full-time job. Then by four-pm the same day, I was no longer a pupil at St Peter's School. I left with one O Level in Woodwork as the grand total of the last eleven years of schooling."

"Then three years later you met Joan again?"

"I did. 'Oh What A Night' might've been December sixty three to Frankie Valli, but to me it was December eighty two. On Christmas Eve that year I finally plucked up the courage to speak to Joan. Admittedly, some of my courage was of the Dutch kind."

"Yes, nothing helps quite like alcohol, when it's comes to giving us the courage to chat to a fair maiden."

Eddie nodded in agreement. "Traditionally, the cannery closed at noon on the Twenty fourth, and by one-pm I was on my way along the High Street, scrubbed, fed, and drenched in Denim aftershave."

The mention of aftershave had seemed to make James's smell stronger. Eddie just had to ask. "James," he said and turned to face him. "What is that aftershave you wear?"

"Why, do you like it?"

"Well, it's...."

"*Hi-Karate* it's called. It drives the ladies wild, so I have to wear it sparingly."

"*Hi-Karate!* I thought I recognised the smell. My dad used to wear the stuff, yet I can't remember it driving my mum too wild?"

"It works wonders for me as it's a very manly fragrance."

"That's one way of describing it, I suppose. I didn't think they made it anymore?"

"I can still get my hands on a bottle when required. Would you like one?"

"It's okay. But thanks for the offer."

"Anytime," James said. "Now back to Joan, please."

"Where was I?" Eddie asked.

"You were drenched in Denim aftershave walking along the High street."

"So I was." Eddie chuckled.

"What's so funny," James asked.

"It's not really funny, but there was always a Christmas tree on the High street."

"You're right, Eddie," James agreed. "It's not really funny."

Eddie waved his hand and shook his head. "No, it's what my dad used to say about the tree."

"What did he say?"

"He always complained there wasn't a fairy on top. My Dad used to joke that they should get John Inman. Not only because he seemed a bit of a fairy, but also because of cheapness. When the Council asked how much he would charge, John Inman would simply say, 'I'm free'!" Eddie shook his head. "Mind you," he said. "My Dad was never really one for jokes."

"I've heard worse," James said in Eddie's Dad's defence. "However, I'm not sure when?"

"Yes, my Dad's humour makes Clive seem like some sort of comedy genius. But I finally made it to the pub, and all I was thinking about was getting stuck into my first pint of hopefully many. I wasn't thinking about Joan Rogers."

"Rogers? Was that Joan's maiden name?" James asked.

"Yes."

"So you hadn't thought about her, at all, in those three years since you had left school?"

"Not really. I had even been going out with a girl called Doreen Stuart for a while, but had just split up with her a week, or so, earlier."

"What happened?"

"All she did was nag, nag, nag. She constantly moaned about me going out every Friday for a drink after work. I mean, I was only nineteen at the time. I wanted to enjoy myself."

"You were only nineteen? Which, according to the song, was the average age an American soldier's life ended in Vietnam? You, therefore, decided it wasn't going to be the age your life of drink and debauchery ended, either?"

140

"Exactly," Eddie agreed, although he wasn't entirely sure what James was on about. "After more than a few pints with my Dad," Eddie continued, "and other workmates, the youngsters amongst us headed off to the local nightclub. Normally, you could walk in the place and head straight to the bar. But that night the place was mobbed. I knew it was going to be survival of the fittest if I wanted to get myself a drink." Eddie coughed to clear his throat.

"Are you all right?" James asked. "You appear to have a bit of a cough."

"I should be okay. It's just that I'm not used to talking so much." Eddie whispered, "Unlike some people." But James appeared not to hear, or chose to ignore the comment, so Eddie continued. "I stood in the queue for ages, and had almost given up hope of being served when I somehow grabbed a barman's attention."

"What did they say to you?"

"I can't remember."

"Oh! I thought they may have said *Are you being served?*" James asked. "As in that timeless TV classic starring John Inman." He was barely able to contain his laughter.

A smile came upon Eddie's face. "Very good, James," he said. "Then, just as I was about to tell the barman what I would like to order, a female voice from behind me shouted out. And I can actually remember what she said."

"What was it?" James was now sitting on the edge of the bench.

"They shouted out, 'Two Bacardi and cokes and a Malibu and lemonade, please'."

"What did you do?"

"I turned round intending to tell them exactly what I thought. I had spent the last half hour of my life being shoved and swore at. Trapped without a drink, while being deafened by such Christmas classics as, 'I wish it could be Christmas everyday'. At that exact moment, I was glad it wasn't Christmas everyday, if that particular Christmas was anything to go by."

"What did you actually say?" James asked as he got his white handkerchief out to wipe away some beads of sweat from his forehead.

"I didn't say anything. I just stood there staring at the person who moments earlier had jumped the queue ahead of me."

"I gather it was a certain Joan Rogers?"

"It had been over three years since I last saw her. Yet I

recognised Joan immediately. She had a red sleeveless dress on. Her hair was slightly shorter. And I may not have thought it possible, but she actually looked better than I remembered her looking at school."

"From my experience, a lot of women look better after a few drinks."

"You have a point," Eddie agreed. "But alcohol had nothing to do with it. If I had been stone cold sober, Joan would have looked just as good. Thankfully, unlike in the library years before, I had just enough alcohol in me to calm my nerves. This time I was actually able to say something to her, so I offered to buy the drinks she'd just ordered."

"What a charmer," James said as he dabbed his forehead again.

Eddie decided to take advantage of the interruption. He had been so engrossed in telling his story that he'd forgotten about a certain female. Eddie gazed across the park to see if this certain female was stripped down to her bikini yet. Eddie was disappointed. However, there were four young kids running about her because she was also accompanied by two female friends, and Eddie was more than happy to report, that from this vantage point, the friends also seemed attractive. He was now getting excited at the prospect of three good looking, twenty-something females running about the park in nothing more than bikinis. Eddie had suddenly forgotten all about 'Late December back in eighty two'. But before he started frothing at the mouth, James interrupted him.

"Sorry about that delay," James said. "It's a hot one today."

"Yes…yes it is."

"What happened then?"

"What happened when?"

"That night with Joan. What did you think I was on about?"

"Oh…nothing. Where was I again?"

"With Joan in the nightclub."

"That's right…thanks." Just then, Eddie wasn't with Joan in the nightclub. Instead, he was being chased around the park by three bikini clad young women to the theme tune of *The Benny Hill Show*.

With a smile upon his face Eddie went back in time to December 82. "Joan then asked me if I would like to join her and two friends at a table up beside the dance floor? I think I thought about the invitation for at least a millisecond, before saying 'yes'. We sat at the table chatting about almost every subject under the sun. We also found time to fit in a Christmas kiss at midnight as well as the odd dance."

142

"I didn't know you were a bit of a dancer?"

"If you ever see me you'll know I'm not. I put up a pretty tame fight that night, that's how Joan managed to drag me on to the dance floor. But once I was up there, I happily pranced about not only to the usual Christmas favourites you would expect, but also to such manly tunes as Kelly Marie's 'Feels Like I'm In Love', and the Tweets and their 'Birdie Song'. Which I'm ashamed to admit, I just happened to know all the actions to."

"That's nothing to be ashamed of," James said, "as I know them too."

"Why does that not surprise me? And to cap off two of the best hours of my life, I got a slow dance with Joan just before closing time. Even though it was to Mud's 'Lonely this Xmas', it was still amazing. I can remember smelling her perfume during that dance and almost going weak at the knees."

"Was that due to the perfume or the alcohol?"

"You could have a point there. Maybe it was a combination? Then, two of the best hours of my life became three of the best. I got to walk Joan home. There was a frost on the ground, the sky was clear, and the stars were shining bright as we walked along the road holding hands. I kissed her at her front door, and we agreed to meet the following week. The rest they say is history."

James stroked his moustache. "From that day on, I take it your romance went from strength to strength?" he asked.

"It did, and we became practically inseparable."

"How did you get on with Joan's parents?"

"Pretty well. Mind you, it didn't take me long to realise how well off they were. Well, compared to my family anyway."

"Yes, all families are created equal, but some are more equal than others."

"They seemed a hell of a lot more equal than mine, that's for sure. But they were still down to earth."

"I'm glad to hear it," James said as he wiped his sweaty brow again. "So what was Joan doing at this time? Was she working?"

"She was at University."

"Really?"

"She was doing a Degree in Art."

"Joan never mentioned that."

"She was away at University. So we were apart quite a bit. That was difficult because I thought she was great. I really did."

"Did you think she was perfect?" James said as he put his handkerchief away.

Eddie thought about the question before answering. "I would probably say, almost-perfect. One thing I couldn't understand was her fascination with Terry Wogan. Even way back then. It just seemed weird. I mean, it wasn't the sort of thing you expected from someone her age. She was only eighteen."

"Terry does appeal to all ages. And I'm sure there are worse people she could admire?"

"I'm sure you're right," Eddie agreed. "That reminds me."

"Reminds you of what?"

"During a dinner break, at the cannery, one of my male colleagues, who will remain nameless, told me about this sort of fantasy he had for someone on the telly."

"Who was it?"

"He hadn't told his wife because he didn't think she would understand. I promised I wouldn't tell their wife, or anyone else. My colleague told me he found Mavis Cruet, the fairy from the cartoon *Willo the Wisp,* strangely attractive!"

James burst out laughing. "MAVIS CRUET! You must be joking?"

"I wish I was," Eddie said. He also burst out laughing.

"Did he even realise it was Kenneth Williams who did the voice?" James managed to ask in between laughs.

"He realised. That's what made it all the more worrying. He also mentioned maybe buying a pink fairy outfit for his wife to wear."

"This colleague?" James was almost bent over double. "I wouldn't know him by any chance, would I?"

Eddie burst out laughing again. He hadn't laughed as hard or as long as this in ages. His sides were actually sore when he finally finished. "I'm not saying a thing," he managed to say as he wiped tears from his eyes.

"You don't have to," James said as he got his handkerchief out once more. "You should have looked on the bright side." James also wiped some tears from his eyes as well as giving his forehead a quick dab once again. "It must have made you realise liking Terry Wogan wasn't too much of a problem, after all? I gather Joan hasn't asked you to partake in a bit of *Blankety Blank* in the boudoir? With your good self wearing nothing but a smile and a black wig, singing 'The Floral Dance', whilst gripping *Wogan's Wand* firmly in your hand?"

144

"Wogan's what in my hand?" Eddie shouted in a combination of shock and surprise at what James had just said.

"*Wogan's Wand,*" James repeated, remaining straight faced. "I do believe it's the name Terry gave to his famous stick like microphone he used on the programme *Blankety Blank*. Why, what on earth did you think I meant?" James asked innocently.

"I think you know. I also think we better move on from this subject. Or, I could just finish if you've heard enough?"

"No. Please continue if there's more to tell," James said.

Eddie may have been reluctant to speak about all this in the first place, but now he had started, Eddie was actually enjoying this trip down memory lane. For he hadn't thought, let alone talked, about these halcyon days for a long time and had forgotten how good they actually were.

Eddie continued without much hesitation. "After almost three years of dating, everything was still going perfectly. Then, in the summer of eighty four, Joan fell pregnant. It certainly wasn't planned, but there was never any doubt we wouldn't keep the baby. Not long after, on a holiday weekend in Blackpool, I proposed to Joan while being ridden in a horse and carriage up the promenade, under the illuminations."

"Very romantic," James said, nodding his head in apparent approval.

"I do have my moments," Eddie said, although it may be some considerable time since the last one. "The decision to have the baby meant Joan reluctantly had to give up University that Christmas, with only a year and a half of study to go. She did plan to go back and continue her studies after the baby was born, but that never happened."

"That's a pity...a great pity, indeed," James said.

"Yeah. So the marriage took place at the registrars on a bitterly cold day in January. It was followed by a small reception at Joan's parents' house. A couple of months later our first child, Steven, was born. Joan immediately took to parenting as well as she took to almost everything else."

"How did you take to it?"

"Quite well, I must admit. I didn't even mind changing the odd nappy or two. Life at that time was very good for the Ryan family. Then, in April nineteen eighty nine, it got even better. That's when we had another child. A girl called Jenny..." Eddie stopped talking as a familiar feeling appeared in his stomach, "I'm sorry, James, that's

145

about all I have to tell you," he said.

"I enjoyed that," James said. "And you said your story would be boring? My, your life could be a novel."

"I don't think it would be much of a bestseller," Eddie said, feeling better. He had stopped talking about Jenny just in time.

"You never know. I think they publish anything these days. I could think of a lot worse things to read than your life story."

"What about your life story? Would that make a bestseller?" Eddie asked.

"I doubt it very much," James quickly answered.

"Why don't you let me decide? I've told you mine." Which Eddie believed was a fair point to make.

James stroked his moustache, paused and said, "Alas, there is not much to tell. I was a lecturer at University for a long time, too long, probably. Then, when I retired, I moved back up here."

"What about a wife and kids?" Eddie asked, wanting to know more. Normally you can't stop James from speaking, but he was uncharacteristically quiet

James sighed and gazed up at the cloudless blue sky. "You see, Eddie," he said slowly. "You're not the only person who has have ever lost a loved one, or ones. Some try to move on, whilst others try to use it as an excuse to stand still, or remain firmly in the past. The past is something I feel we have talked about enough for one day." James took his eyes off the sky and focused them on Eddie. The usual glint in his blue eyes appeared to be back. "Let us concentrate on the present," he said, and that ever familiar smile had also returned. "What do you think the subject is going to be today?" James asked as he patted Eddie playfully on the knee.

"I've no idea…surprise me." Eddie realised he had probably been given all the information he was going to get from James.

"The first thing I'm going to mention is meditation," James said.

Eddie sighed.

"What's wrong?" James asked.

"I hate to moan…"

"I had noticed that," James said, and raised an eyebrow.

"Won't talking about meditation and stuff, be a bit…oh, I don't know…em…boring?" Eddie tactfully said.

"Have no fear. I can jazz it up if you want? How about this little song? "Meditation. Meditation. Meditation, that's what you need.

If you want a quiet mind, and leave your troubles behind. Meditation's what you need."

Eddie was speechless.

"That was a little treat for you." James's smile seemed almost illuminating. "Let's discuss someone I am sure you have heard of. That is the Buddha. Or, Prince Siddhartha Guatama, who was born near the Himalayas in present day Nepal. His father didn't want him to become too curious about the outside world, so he ensured the Prince had everything he needed within the confines of the Palace walls. Therefore, he would have no need to venture outside. Eventually, however, he did venture outside, and there he saw sick people, old people, and dead people."

"Like the boy in the film *Sixth Sense?*" Eddie butted in.

"Like the boy in what?"

"The film *Sixth Sense*...he saw dead people too," Eddie repeated.

"He's maybe not the only one?" James whispered.

"What?"

"Never mind," James clapped his hands. "Back to Buddha. Once he saw these things in the outside world, he came to the realisation that life is suffering. So he decided to leave the Palace for good, and realised that we don't only suffer physically through pain and disease, but mentally, through grief, despair, greed, and anger. We can also suffer because we take ourselves and life too seriously. To free us from suffering, Buddha believes we have to reach the state of Nirvana-"

"The state of Nirvana?" Eddie interrupted. In a serious tone, he asked, "Isn't that where Las Vegas is? Why would Buddha want us to go there? I never knew he was a bit of a gambler?"

James clapped slowly. "You are certainly on top form today. I think we both know Las Vegas is in the state of Nevada."

"So where's the state of Nirvana?"

"It's not a place, as such. Which I think you know full well?"

I got you real good with that one.

"It is a state of mind, which can mean an extinguished flame, the cooling of our emotions and desires. It's possible to reach Nirvana in our lifetime, though difficult. We have to change our personality from one full of negative emotions and thoughts, to one that consists only of thoughts of compassion, peace, and contentment. To reach Nirvana, we must become an enlightened person. 'Knowing others is

147

wisdom, knowing yourself is enlightenment,' said Lao-Tzu, the Chinese philosopher. And one of the best ways of getting to know yourself is through meditation."

"I don't have a clue how to meditate?"

"That's no bother. If you are new to meditating, you only have to start with five minutes a day, preferably first thing in the morning. Just sit quietly, observe your breathing, and let whichever thoughts enter your mind to simply pass. Don't consciously try to get rid of them, just let them go. You can try other forms of meditation. As you inhale, count one, and as you exhale, count two. If your mind wanders to the bookies or the pub, then start counting again at one."

"Is that it?" Eddie was anticipating something a bit more exciting than that for reaching Nirvana and an enlightened mind.

"It is not as simple as it sounds. You can start at five minutes then build up to longer. Even that short space of time will be too much for you at the first attempt."

"I can't sit there meditating cross legged on the floor," Eddie protested, "I'm not flexible enough."

"You don't have to sit cross legged on the floor to meditate. You can do it sitting on a chair, or a bench. As you progress, you can do it for longer, and also start to visualise or repeat affirmations."

"I'm not too convinced about this meditation. The only state sitting there quietly and breathing is going to help me reach, is a state of boredom. There must be more to it than that?"

"I wouldn't underestimate what good meditation can do for you. We all need a little break from thinking too much, and meditation is the best way to achieve this. With meditation, we look very deeply inwards and see how we can change ourselves and our life. Peace and happiness are available, if we can only quieten our distracted thinking long enough to come back into the now. Balanced natural breathing will bring you back to the present moment, and we all remember how important living in the present moment is, don't we?"

"Yes. You've mentioned it often enough."

"And I'll keep mentioning it until it finally sinks in. Meditation purifies the mind. And as the *Dhammapada* says, 'No one can do more for you than your own purified mind. The consequences of a purified mind will follow you like your own shadow'."

"This all sounds like hard work?"

"It is. That's the reason we turn to meditation. Not because our minds are strong and we can do it, but because our minds are weak and we require it. "Saint Augustine said, go not abroad-"

"I couldn't afford to, even if I wanted," Eddie chipped in.

James gave Eddie a quick glare and continued. "'Go not abroad,'" he repeated, "'Retire into thyself, for truth dwells within the inner man'. Being able to retire into thyself requires a quiet mind. 'Quiet minds cannot be perplexed or frightened,' said Robert Louis Stevenson. 'But go on in fortune or misfortune at their own private pace, like a clock in a thunder-storm.' The quieter our mind can become, the calmer, contented, and more peaceful we become. Modern man, or woman, has forgotten how to relax and stop the constant chit-chat that goes on in their heads. That is what meditation can do for us. It stops the voice that constantly drones on, and helps us feel perfectly aware in the present moment. It teaches awareness."

"Can I meditate even while sitting on the toilet if I want? Or do I need a special room set up with candles, incense, and all that sort of thing?" Eddie asked, trying his best not to take the conversation seriously.

"You don't need candles or incense," James said, probably realising that Eddie was trying to be funny, but managing to give a serious answer none the less. "All you need is some peace and quiet where you won't be disturbed. If the toilet is the best place for that, then the toilet it is. You can almost do a form of meditation anytime and anywhere. All you need to do is concentrate on your breathing. This can be done while sitting here, sitting on a bus, or simply while you're walking."

Right now it wasn't his breathing Eddie was concentrating on. Talking about how he met Joan had distracted him for a while, but now his eyes and thoughts were firmly focused on the girl and her two friends again. So much for Nirvana, it was a state of excitement Eddie was close to reaching.

"One of the best places to do this is while out in the countryside," James said, seeming unaware that Eddie was paying little attention. "Getting back to nature and reconnecting yourself with the natural world is, without doubt, one of the best ways to put life in perspective. Just getting away from the hustle and bustle of modern life, going back to the peace and tranquillity only nature can provide. It can be amazingly calming and therapeutic for someone who is suffering from the stresses of daily living." James stopped talking, glanced at Eddie, and said, "Don't you agree?"

"What? Yes...yes, that's right," Eddie said without taking his eyes off the girls. One of them who appeared to be red haired, tall, slim, and very attractive, was now rummaging about in her handbag; Eddie hoped it was to get out a bottle of suntan lotion.

James tutted and carried on regardless. "There is nothing like being alone in a forest, or atop a hill admiring a breathtaking view. 'I never found the companion that was so companionable as solitude', claimed Thoreau. I must agree. You have to try and practice putting your mind at rest every day. Go into the silence, for there is a healing power within it. Isn't that right, Eddie?"

"Yes, yes that's right," he repeated, now practically drooling at the thought of these three very attractive ladies wearing nothing but skimpy bikinis, while they rubbed suntan lotion all over their, or even better, each others bodies.

"I'm glad you agree. Don't think, though, that by simply going out into the wilderness for an afternoon's solitude you will come back a fully enlightened and changed man. It takes a little longer than that. People go out into the wilderness to get away from something, and that something is usually themselves. No matter how far into the wilderness they go, the thoughts, worries, and bad habits all follow. That's fine, for that is the first step along the long road to enlightenment." James stopped talking. After a couple of seconds he asked, "I hope I'm not boring you, am I?"

"Yes, yes that's right," Eddie said without taking his eyes off the view. He was on the edge of the bench.

"So I am boring you?"

"What? Yes...I mean, no. What was the question again?"

"Something else appears to have grabbed your attention."

"No...no," Eddie spluttered "I was just, em...I was just enjoying the scenery, that's all."

James looked across in the direction of where Eddie's gaze was transfixed. "I can see what kind of scenery you're enjoying. When I recommended getting back to nature, that's not exactly what I meant."

Eddie had to laugh at that comment. "Good one, James." He nodded. "I get your point," he said while managing to take his eyes off the girls. A task made slightly easier, because the girl with the red hair had only taken a mobile phone out of her handbag, not suntan lotion. "I can agree there must be something in this meditating lark, as a lot of people seem to do it, and it appears to work for them. I just don't think I'm one of those people? I couldn't see myself being able to sit quietly for thirty seconds, let alone five minutes, without something to keep me entertained. I would just be bored. As for getting back to nature? I couldn't think of anything more boring than just sitting on a hill and doing nothing except look at the view."

"Blaise Pascal famously claimed 'All man's miseries derive from not being able to sit quietly in a room alone'. You will also have that problem. Meditation is about taming your mind and showing it who is boss. That mind of yours has run wild for so long now, constantly saying whatever it wants, whenever it wants, that you have been programmed to simply take it all for granted." James pointed at Eddie and said, "YOU have control of your mind and your thoughts, it's not the other way round. It is about time the balance of power was shifted back to the way it's meant to be. Your mind doesn't have to chatter away from the moment you wake up to the moment you fall asleep. It can be taught to be kept quiet when you want it to-"

"Pity you couldn't be taught the same thing," Eddie said.

"I'm glad to see you're taking today's discussion seriously."

"Sorry, James," Eddie tried to apologise. "Carry on," he said.

"Yes, this has been a carry on. I couldn't agree more." James cleared his throat. "Now then, where was I? Oh yes, the inevitable first line of defence from a person's programmed mind, when they first attempt to quieten it, will be to moan that it's bored. Your mind says you would rather do something else. Boredom is not really about not having anything to do. It is more a sign of an untrained and weak mind which is overactive and busy."

"Come on. You can't tell me you never get bored?"

"Never. If you learn to ignore the pleas your emotional mind will sigh, when it's not happy and wants to be listened to, then you won't get bored either. A weak mind is an easily bored mind. The majority of people can't spend five minutes alone with only their thoughts for company, before they complain of boredom. For me, life is far too short to get bored. Hopefully, you will also think the same at some point."

"Let me see." Eddie put his right index finger up to his lips. With a look of deep concentration on his face he said, "I wonder what this week's task could be? Meditating by any chance?"

James patted Eddie on the back, "By jove-old chap. You are catching on. I want you to spend at least five minutes every morning attempting to meditate. I know it will be difficult and you may not do too well at first, but I want you to at least try."

"I'll give it a go."

"Good stuff!" James cried out. "Oh, but there's also something else I require you do to," he added.

"I thought that would be too simple. What is it?"

"I want you to go for a couple of trips back to nature. Here, take this." James handed over a white envelope with Eddie's name neatly written on it in black ink.

"What's this?"

"It's two tickets for the train, plus a timetable and some directions. All the information you need is there for two away days."

"Where to?"

"I don't want to spoil the surprise. All you need to know is in the envelope."

"How will you know if I go on these trips, or if I meditate? Surely there's no way you can check?" Eddie asked as he put the envelope in his back pocket.

"I'll ask you questions about the places. And as for meditating, I'll just have to trust you. But before we go," James put his hand on Eddie's shoulder. "I had completely forgotten about today's Deadly Sin, which is pride."

"Great!" Eddie looked at his watch for the first time since he entered the park.

"Pride can be an excess opinion of one's self. When you get back to Nature and see its wonder and vastness, this makes you realise what a minor part you play in everything. As you see trees hundreds of years old that were there long before you were born. Which will be there long after you die. As you see rivers that will continue to flow, and mountains that will stand long after you have shifted off your mortal coil. It makes you realise you're not quite as important in the great scheme of things as you think, and makes you more humble and respectful of how great Nature is. Whilst humility is indeed a Virtue."

Eddie looked at his watch again. They had been here longer than usual. It may be a lovely day and the view good, but Eddie was now getting anxious about heading up to the bookies. Especially now it looked unlikely that any of the girls would be taking their clothes off in the foreseeable future. If they weren't down to their bikinis by now, then they never would be.

"Sorry to interrupt," Eddie said, "Are we going to go soon?"

James nodded his head. With a grave expression he said, "We most certainly are. Some sooner than others, but we are most definitely going to go soon. Of that there is no doubt."

"That's not what I meant. What I meant was-"

"I know exactly what you meant," James interrupted. "You are in a hurry to get to the bookies. But I have been thinking, maybe I should add one more trip to this week's schedule?"

"Where to now?" Eddie cried out louder than he intended. "How many things do you think I can fit into a week? I only have twenty four hours in a day like everyone else."

"I'm sure you'll have room left in this week's itinerary for one more trip. You don't even have to go out of town."

"Where is it?"

"The local graveyard."

"Why?"

"Because a trip to the graveyard, looking at the gravestones of people who all had the same worries and stresses, while they were alive, that we have now. That can help put your life and mortality into perspective, like few other things. I bet the people there aren't bothered about the small irritations in life? Do you think it matters to them whether that horse they put on at the bookies came in or not?"

"I wouldn't have thought so."

"Whether they were late for an appointment? Or they missed a bus? In the great scheme of things, many of the minor irritations we all blow out of proportion, mean absolutely nothing. We get so wrapped up in our own importance we forget the things in life which matter. When you look at the graves, I don't want you to focus on the year the person was born, or the year they died. What I want you to focus on is the gap in between. That was their life. Just think. All their life now amounts to is the gap between two dates on a gravestone. All the good times and the bad times. The laughter and the tears. They are all gone. One day that's all that will be left of your life, a few words on a gravestone, with two dates and the gap in between. Maybe a trip to the cemetery will help you realise this before it's too late."

"You certainly know how to cheer someone up," Eddie said in a joking attempt to lighten the mood. Eddie didn't want to think too much about what James had just said. As sometimes, like David St Hubbins, from Spinal Tap, found out whilst visiting Graceland, too much perspective is not such a good thing.

James got up off the bench, with a familiar groan, and walked away without saying a word.

Eddie quickly followed, forgetting a final peek at his female friends as he caught up with James.

When Eddie and James made it to the bookies, the place was practically deserted. James went and sat over in the far corner to do his usual thing as Eddie had a look around. Apart from the two assistants at the counter, there was only one other person here, a fat balding bloke, playing a bandit. Eddie vaguely recognised who it was, but couldn't remember his name.

Eddie went and stood by a screen, pretending to watch as he racked his brain as to why this place could be so empty.

After about ten minutes, James came across with today's horse, *Nevermore.* As it was only a four to one shot, Eddie decided to put on his maximum bet of twenty pounds. If it came in he would still have a hundred pounds to play with, which wouldn't be too shabby at all, thank you very much. Eddie handed his slip over to the assistant and mentioned the bookies being so quiet. She told him it was because Brody's wife's funeral was today. Poor Mary MacDowell finally died last week after being ill for years. Almost all of the regulars were at it (Except Eddie, and the fat balding bloke, who, by the sounds of it, had just won the jackpot on the bandit.). That's when it came back to him. Clive had mentioned the funeral when he and Gloria visited. Guess who forgot? *Too interested in other things,* an unfamiliar voice inside his head said. Eddie didn't want to listen, but the voice wasn't going to give up easily. M*aybe it is about time you got some perspective,* it added.

While watching the race, despite having his biggest stake in a long time on this horse, Eddie wasn't paying much attention. Instead, he kept thinking about Mary McDowell. Why he should be so worked up about missing someone's funeral he hardly knew, Eddie had no idea? *Maybe you knew her better than you think you did?* The voice piped up. But it wasn't like Brody was exactly a good mate? *What's the matter with you? You have twenty quid on this horse and you're more bothered about her funeral?* That's better! That's like the Eddie we all know and tolerate. But despite Eddie's best efforts, the more he tried to concentrate on the race, the more his mind seemed to wander onto Mary McDowell and how he should have been at her funeral.

Eddie hardly noticed when *Nevermore* crossed the finishing line in first place.

They collected their winnings. Eddie's was one hundred pounds, while James's was a more modest thirty five pounds. They walked out into the late afternoon sunshine, leaving the fat balding bloke to put all his winnings back in the bandit. As James made his way up the High Street, after both men agreed to meet again next week, Eddie didn't know what to do. The pub was across the road, teasing him, but it was such a lovely day. Surely he could do something else? He looked at his watch. It was far too late to attend the funeral. So, the next best thing he could do was have a drink to celebrate Mary's life. After very little deliberation, Eddie managed to persuade himself to go to the pub for a drink. It was the least he could do for Mary.

CHAPTER SIXTEEN

When Eddie went to the pub he never had only one or two drinks, or even only three or four. He began to lose count when nearing the double figure mark. Nevertheless, Eddie believed it was a moral victory just having second thoughts about going to the pub in the first place. Not that long ago, Eddie wouldn't have thought twice about going in. Progress was being made, small progress, mind you, Eddie would be the first to admit, but progress none the same. It would take time, and Eddie definitely believed he was headed along the right path. It wasn't as though he went to the pub everyday like he used to, so surely he's allowed to let his hair down once in a while?

Eddie still made the gym the next day, but it had been a struggle, much like his brief attempts at meditating. The two trips he went on were more successful. The first was to Seraphina Forest; the second to Howatson Hills. Eddie actually enjoyed both trips, even with no book, magazine, mp3 player, or alcohol for company. Or even any scantily clad females to ogle at.

Eddie had gone on these trips like James had asked. He had even helped out a couple of times again at the charity shop, but there was one thing he had been determined not to do this week. Yet, it was this one thing which had been at the back of his mind most of the time.

Eddie found himself standing outside the large black iron gates at the entrance to the cemetery. The sky had been overcast when he got up this morning and it had been raining lightly, which it still was. Add those factors to a twenty five minute walk from his house, meant that a trip to the cemetery didn't seem like the best way to spend his day, yet here he was. Eddie had repeatedly told himself he wouldn't come here, but there was a sort of inevitability about it all. Like when the very macho named Shirley Crabtree, better known as the wrestler Big Daddy, used to fight on a Saturday afternoon on the programme *World of Sport*. You somehow knew all along what the outcome would be. *Easy! Easy!*

As he stood outside the black iron gates, Eddie was suddenly reminded about the sign you used to see in old films or cartoons. The one that said: *Abandon hope, all who enter here!* Eddie had abandoned hope a long time ago. Maybe today they could have put up a special sign, just for Eddie, that read: *Find hope, all who enter here!* Because he was here looking for something. But then again, is hope really what he needs? If you simply hope things will get better, then isn't that an

156

admission things are out of your own hands? You are being reactive, not proactive as James would say. If you're not happy with your lot in life, just hoping things will change for the better, is surely not enough? So, as far as Eddie was concerned, you could keep hope, he was here looking for something else.

As he felt the drizzle run down the back of his neck, Eddie was definitely rueing the bizarre decision not to wear a jacket, and, with a bit more exertion than he would have liked, he pushed the groaning cemetery gate open. Entering the graveyard, he chuckled to himself when he remembered that cheesy old joke: *I hear the graveyard is a great place to be, because people are just dying to get in. Boom Boom! As Basil Brush would say.*

Still chuckling to himself, Eddie made his way along the path, beneath large, towering trees, which gave Eddie a brief respite from the rain, reading some of the names and dates on the gravestones. Donald Gray: 1898-1935. Alison Warwick: 1902-1948. He stopped at a grave that had fresh white carnations at it. The inscription on the white, marble gravestone had three names on it. Georgina Allan: 1930-1965; Henry Allan: 1955-1965; Emily Allan: 1959-1965.

"They all must have died in some kind of accident?" Eddie said quietly as he looked at the gravestone for a second or two before moving on.

Eddie reached a part of the graveyard that had newer graves. "Bloody Local Council!" Eddie mumbled after almost going over his ankle in a hole in the path. "Too expensive for them to even fill in a hole. I could have broken my ankle there." *Have to cut down on costs so your five a day. Or is it seven a day now? Diversity enhancing, minority loving, wheelie bin snooping, rubbish recycling, fun stopping, light bulb changing, golliwog bashing, global warming worrier, can earn fifty grand a year advising us all how to run our lives. What would we do without them? Except, maybe, fill in a few bloody holes!*

Eddie stopped at another grave after finishing ranting to himself about the Local Council. This one had daffodils at it, which were now more brown than yellow. The inscription read: Bill Donaldson: 1910-1994; and Grace Donaldson: 1920-1997. This time, Eddie thought about some of the things James had told him. It's not the two dates that are important, but the space between them, for that was the person's life. He looked again at the grave and read that Bill and Grace were parents, grandparents, and also great grandparents. Eddie wondered if, in those eighty four years, whether Bill spent a lot of it worrying about the small immaterial things that occurred in his life, like a hole in a path that hadn't been fixed. Was he a happy person? Did he do something with his life? Did he appreciate his loved ones? Or, did he waste most of his fleeting time here getting drunk in the pub, or gambling in the bookies, while he and those around him, whom he cared about, were getting older with each passing day? Somehow, Eddie believed Bill had been a good man, who had led a good life. He didn't know why he believed that? He just did. In one hundred years time when someone happened to stumble upon Eddie's grave, would they say the same thing about Eddie and his life?

Things were getting too sombre. Eddie decided to leave Bill and Grace, who sounded like the lead characters in an American comedy, and head onto his final destination. He was attracted to this destination, like a female over sixty, with a pulse, is attracted to a Daniel O Donnell concert. As he got nearer to it, he read another inscription; Polly Johnston: 1932-1998. The name reminded Eddie of that Monty Python Parrot sketch. *All the people in here are like Polly the Norwegian Blue Parrot. They are dead.* In all honesty, Eddie never found that sketch very funny. He was never that fond of Monty python, and preferred John Cleese as Basil in *Fawlty Towers*. As Eddie continued making his way through the graveyard in the rain, he reminisced about some of the other comedies he liked from the seventies. There was *George and Mildred, The Goodies, It Ain't Half Hot Mum*, plus numerous others. But Eddie's favourite, without any shadow of a doubt, would have to be Leonard Rossiter, with his slippers and worn out cardie, as Rigsby in *Rising Damp*. Eddie laughed out loud, remembering having a cardie just like Rigsby's, which he would wear about the house, while constantly pestering his mum by going up to her, placing his hands on his hips, in a classic Rigsby pose, and saying, 'Oh, Miss Jones!' Eddie was easily pleased back then. He didn't think putting on a cardie, a pair of slippers, and doing Rigsby impressions would have the same affect on him anymore. Times have changed and Eddie had changed with them. Whether or not for the better? Well, that was very much open to debate.

The rain became heavier. Eddie was getting damp, and it wasn't a *Rising Damp*, as he looked up at the sky; the clouds were getting darker by the second. "Great. A hard rain's a gonna fall," he said, and had no idea why?

As the rain got harder, Eddie finally reached the bottom of a small hill. He stopped, took a deep breath, in an attempt to compose himself, counted to three and muttered, "Once more unto the breach, Eddie" before clambering up the small hill. As he did, a familiar feeling in his stomach reappeared. The bats were back. But, of course, Eddie knew they would be. Jenny's grave was the fourth one along. When Eddie reached it, he placed a hand on top of the cold, black marble, closed his eyes, and concentrated on the sensation in his stomach. It wasn't as bad as he'd anticipated. Even that day in the bookies was worse. Slightly relieved. Eddie opened his eyes, took his hand off the grave, and read the inscription on it.

JENNY RYAN
15TH APRIL 1989-16TH AUGUST *2000*
MUCH BELOVED DAUGHTER
SISTER AND GRANDDAUGHER
DON'T WAIT TILL THE CLOUDS PASS
JUST DANCE IN THE RAIN

Eddie was embarrassed to admit he hadn't read those words for over a year now. Joan came here at least once a month, while Eddie tried to come on Jenny's birthday, Christmas, or the anniversary of her death. He hadn't made it this year, but, of course, he had reasons. Good reasons.

The unfamiliar voice in his head spoke. *Yes, you always have reasons. Plenty of reasons. Usually for doing nothing.*

Eddie tried to ignore the voice. He said softly, "Hello, Jenny. Sorry I haven't been to visit you for a long time. I have wanted to, but..." Eddie couldn't think of anything to say. "I think you know why I haven't been here for a while," he eventually said. "I think we both know why I haven't been here."

As the clouds got darker, and the rain got heavier, Eddie stayed by the grave and spoke for the next hour.

When Eddie finally finished saying all it was he had to say, he looked at his watch and saw over an hour had passed. Reluctantly, he decided to make tracks and get home. He had one last look at Jenny's grave, thought about saying something else, but felt he had said more than enough for one day. He left the grave and went back down the small hill, feeling better than he had when going up it not so long ago. Eddie may have been soaked to the skin and in danger of catching pneumonia, yet he was glad he came today. Right there and then, he made a promise to Jenny that it wouldn't be nearly so long before he returned.

As Eddie made his way to the entrance, the sky began to brighten, and the rain died down. Not that it made much difference now as it was doubtful whether he could get any wetter. Eddie decided to go back a different way. Approximately thirty seconds later, he regretted that decision.

Eddie stopped in his tracks the moment he saw Brody MacDowell. Brody, surrounded by an amazing and colourful array of flowers, was kneeling by what Eddie assumed must be Mary's grave. Eddie stood motionless and pondered his options. He didn't think he could slip by Brody without being noticed, so the only other option was to head back before being spotted. Just as Eddie was about to put plan B into action, Brody spotted him and waved. Eddie waved back, and reluctantly headed in Brody's direction.

As Eddie approached Brody, he noticed in the centre of the vast floral display a large love heart of red roses. A fancy arrangement of white carnations also caught Eddie's eye; he thought they were very similar to the carnations at a grave earlier today.

Brody got up, leaning on the grave for support, brushed some grass off his knees, and held his hand out.

"I'm very sorry about Mary," Eddie said, as he shook Brody's hand.

"Thank you, Eddie." Brody appeared to be even wetter than Eddie. It dawned on Eddie that Brody was wearing a black suit, black shoes, black tie, and a white shirt. Not a pair of Jesus boots in sight. Eddie didn't think he had ever seen Brody wear anything else on his feet before? That wasn't the thing that really struck Eddie's attention. It was the clothes Brody had on. They were the clothes you would expect someone to wear to a funeral.

That was five days ago. Surely he hasn't been here since then?

Brody turned his back on Eddie. He crouched down in front of Mary's grave and stared at it.

"I'm also sorry about not making her funeral, either," Eddie said uneasily. "I had intended to, unfortunately…em…something cropped up at the last minute."

"That's all right," Brody said, without taking his eyes off the gravestone. "We never made that holiday off our winnings. I got brochures, which we looked at, but Mary was just too ill."

160

"I'm sorry."

"I try to believe in miracles. Maybe that was one too far? I mean, it was a miracle she lasted so long. As the doctors said she only had a few months to live. That was about two years ago. So I should be grateful for some things."

You're not even grateful for getting a winning horse picked at the bookies every week? Are you, Eddie? That annoying little voice said.

"I knew it was only a matter of time," Brody said, and stroked the large black and white gravestone. "The last week or so before she passed away were the hardest of my life. Mary was in so much pain. I couldn't bear it. But I had to stay strong for her sake. Then, within twenty four hours, my Mary was gone."

"I'm sorry," Eddie repeated. He couldn't think of anything else to say; really wishing he'd gone out the same way he'd came in.

Brody faced Eddie and smiled. "It's okay," he said, and faced the grave again. "About seven days before she went. Mary said he'd visited her and it was almost time. Somehow, she seemed different after this? More peaceful and accepting of things, even though she was in great pain. On her last hour, I held her hand and prayed her pain would soon be gone. I must have dozed off? When I awoke, Mary was sitting up in bed and smiling." Brody sat on his knees. "It was the loveliest smile I think I have ever seen in my life. For the briefest second, Mary no longer looked like the skeleton she had become. Lying in bed was the beautiful girl I had fallen in love with, all those years ago. Mary said she would meet him again shortly. I wasn't to worry about anything as she would be keeping an eye on *Brody the Oldie.*" Brody laughed, "That's what she called me, *Brody the Oldie.*" He tenderly stroked the grave again, almost like he was stroking a favourite pet. "She said we would be together soon, as the end of the line wasn't the real end. It's the beginning of another wonderful journey. She tightened my hand as though trying to reassure me, then closed her eyes. This time I knew they wouldn't open again. My Mary was gone. Thankfully, no longer suffering like she had done for far too long."

As Brody sat quietly and motionless at the grave, Eddie wasn't sure what he should do? Eddie had felt uneasy as Brody told him the story about Mary, and now all he really wanted to do was get out of here. As Eddie was about to walk away, Brody groaned, grabbed on to the grave and slowly got to his knees.

161

"What time is it?" Brody asked, while brushing his trousers again.

"It's about two-forty seven," Eddie replied.

"Really?" Brody sounded surprised. "I better get home soon for something to eat. Mary wouldn't be too happy if she didn't think I was looking after myself."

"I'm just heading back, if you want to get up the road with me?" Eddie asked.

Brody smiled and patted Eddie on the back, making a sort of squelching sound. "Thank you," he said. "I think I'll spend another hour or so here."

"If you're sure?"

Brody didn't answer. He sat down on his knees in front of the grave again.

"Bye then, Brody," Eddie said, not really expecting a reply. To his surprise, Brody put his hand up.

"Bye," Brody said, his hand still up in the air. "Mary says you know him. It's unlucky thirteen, but it'll be lucky in the long run. You little charmer, you." Brody chuckled quietly, while slowly lowering his hand.

At this point, Eddie thought it definitely would be best to quietly slip away.

Eddie left Brody at the grave, hoping he would do what he said and go home for something to eat. Eddie had some doubts. "Surely he hasn't been there for the last five days?" Eddie asked himself out loud. "Sure, he had the same clothes on that he more than likely wore to the funeral. That doesn't necessarily mean he has been at his wife's graveside for five days. Brody didn't look too good, and what he was saying didn't make much sense."

Do you believe in miracles?

It seems Brody did. Just then, a very unwanted image popped into Eddie's head; the image of Brody Mcdowell dressed like Errol Brown from Hot Chocolate. He was wearing a pair of very tight white, shiny trousers, and a silk shirt open to the waist, which showed off a hairy chest and large medallion. As Brody gyrated his hips, far too provocatively for Edie's liking, he sang 'You sexy Thing'. Eddie continued through the graveyard humming the Hot Chocolate tune, whilst trying to get the thought of Brody in a pair of obscenely tight white trousers out of his mind.

When Eddie approached the entrance, he had stopped thinking about Brody. Calmness came upon him, and his mind was empty and clear. He began to sing the hymn 'How Great Thou Art'. It had been one of the songs sung at Jenny's funeral. Eddie hadn't sung it since that day.

Eddie finished the song just as he reached the black iron gates, which groaned again as he pulled them open. When Eddie walked out the gates, he didn't know what he had found today at the cemetery? But he *had* found something, of that Eddie was certain.

CHAPTER SEVENTEEN

Wrapped up in his black, well worn, duffle coat, Eddie surveyed the deserted park, and gave out a loud sigh. He was disappointed. There was no chance of seeing any scantily clad women here today. It was still officially summer, but autumn was waiting just around the corner. Within the next few weeks, the leaves would start to fall from the trees, and it would be even colder. Eddie was glad he had decided to wear his coat, but even with it on, the wind still seemed to cut through him every time there was a gust of it. Cold as it was to Eddie, the weather didn't seem to be bothering James that much. He still had on his usual attire he'd worn since the first day Eddie set eyes on him; a day which seemed such a long time ago.

The two men sat there, Eddie shivering, and James smiling, as Eddie proceeded to tell James about the past week. How he had great difficulty trying to meditate, and the two trips he went on. He decided to keep from James the fact he went on a third trip to the cemetery. Surprisingly, James never asked about it.

Maybe he knew anyway?

"Okay then," James said, once Eddie had finished telling him the edited version of what he had been up to in the past week. "I didn't think you were ready to talk about it last week, but now I think you are."

"Talk about what?" Eddie asked.

"About Jenny…and what happened on that day."

As soon as James mentioned Jenny, Eddie expected that familiar feeling to return in the pit of his stomach. But it didn't. Eddie sat quietly waiting for the bats. They never came.

"Are you all right?" James asked.

"I…I think I am," Eddie replied.

"Good. So, are you ready to talk about Jenny?"

"I don't think so."

"There have been a lot of things you didn't want to do, but have done recently. Each one has been beneficial," James said. "I really think that doing this may also turn out to be very beneficial. Just you speak about it in your own time, and I promise not to interrupt." James paused, patted Eddie on the knee, looked him in the eye and said, "I know how difficult this will be."

Eddie looked into James's strangely reassuring eyes, sighed, and proceeded to talk about the events of August 16th, 2000.

"The day at Liddell River had been good," Eddie said. "I lay there most of the time in the shade of an old oak tree wearing my favourite pair of red, baggy shorts. This reminds me," Eddie gave a smile of sorts. "Before we left that morning, Joan, Jenny, and Steve had given me a present to replace those shorts, because they thought I'd had my red pair too long. When I opened the present, I assumed it was a joke, as it was an extremely small, tight pair of black trunks. It took me about ten minutes to squeeze into them, and even longer to squeeze out again."

"I bet you looked rather fetching?"

Eddie shook his head. "For the brief time I had them on I glanced in the mirror. Instead of looking like Mitch Buchanan, the *Baywatch* character played by David Hasselhoff, I looked more like Frank Cannon, the portly TV detective from the seventies."

"I really don't want to picture that, my good man. I just had lunch before we met." James waved his hand, "Please move on."

Eddie duly obliged. "I headed off to Liddell River, in high spirits, wearing my trusty red, baggy shorts, with Joan, Jenny, her pal Sally, and Steven. Obviously not knowing it would turn out to be the worst day of my life. My time when we got there was spent either dozing off, or checking the race meetings in the newspaper. While music was playing, balls were being kicked or thrown, and the odd barbeque or two was on the go. It was just like a typical summer scene." Eddie paused for a second, "But how quickly it would all change."

"Did you go there often?"

"I've lost count of the amount of times I'd been to Liddell River. Probably every summer since I was a toddler. Even back then, when I would go there with my parents and grandparents, the family tradition was that we would always sit in the exact same spot-a grassy slope just in front of a large oak tree. Down the slope, a few metres, was a large cluster of trees. While below those trees, at the bottom of a much steeper slope, was the river. You couldn't see the river from where we used to sit, but you could sometimes hear it."

"Where was everyone else while you were lounging about under the tree?"

"Joan was lying next to me in a very tight swimsuit, and I do remember feeling frisky. The fact I was surrounded by about one hundred people, many of them children, didn't seem to bother me at that point. I think I must have been in what sportsmen call *the zone*.

All outside distractions no longer existed as one of my hands headed for her tidy little tush. While my other hand was headed somewhere else. Then, just as I was about to make contact, a small hand grabbed my shoulder and shouted in my ear. *"*

"Jenny?"

"Yes," Eddie nodded, "Jenny. I turned round and she was standing there, in her pink swimming costume, with her hands on her hips. When she stood in that pose, it was a sure sign she wasn't too happy about something. At first I wasn't too happy, either, as I had been interrupted. But I remember looking at her, and suddenly realising just how much she actually looked like her mother, with her long brown hair and blue eyes. She was only eleven, and I was obviously slightly biased, but I believed she was a right little cutie, almost a mini version of Joan. She wasn't happy because she wanted to go and play in the river," Eddie stopped for a second and rubbed his eye. He must have had something in it. "Sally, her friend," he continued, "had gone off to play with some other girls. We'd told Jenny before she wasn't to play at the river on her own." Still no bats, but Eddie's heart was beginning to beat faster. "I suggested Jenny go and play with Sally and the other girls, but she didn't want to. I don't think she liked the other girls." His heart was now building up momentum. "I suggested she go and play with Steven for a bit. Jenny said he was playing football, and she hated football more than she hated those girls."

"I don't think it takes Sherlock Holmes like powers of deduction to work out what Jenny was going to ask you next?" James asked.

"Jenny wanted to go in the river. Sally her friend wasn't available. Her brother, Steven, wasn't available, and Joan appeared to be sleeping."

"So you were asked?"

"Yes." Eddie sighed again." His heart felt like it was about to breakthru his chest. "I really didn't want to go. I was happy in the shade. Plus, I also felt I had unfinished business to attend to."

"What did you do?"

Eddie stared at the deserted park. "We came to an agreement. Jenny would go and play with Sally and those other girls for a while. If they didn't want to go in the river, then she was to come back and I would go with her. Jenny reluctantly agreed to this. As she ran off down the slope, I shouted to her not to go anywhere near the river if

166

she couldn't find Sally and the girls, because the current gets strong and it's deep in places. She didn't reply, and kept on running. That was the last time I ever spoke to her or saw her alive." Eddie closed his eyes. The only sound he could hear was the furious thudding of his heart. Eddie took a deep breath and inhaled the smell of James's aftershave. When he breathed out again, his heart began to slow down. Eddie opened his eyes and watched a black cloud creeping in the sky, like a hearse making its way to a funeral.

"Are you all right?" James asked.

Eddie nodded. He took another breath of James's aftershave before continuing. "When Jenny went," he said, "I tried to turn my attention back to Joan. The moment had gone about as quickly as it had appeared. So I read some of the newspaper again. I remember looking at my watch and the time was exactly thirty nine minutes past one. That's when I first heard what sounded like a commotion coming from the river below. It got noisier. I immediately sensed something was wrong down there. It wasn't the normal noise of kids just mucking about."

"I gather you didn't think it was anything to do with Jenny?"

"No. I only realised when Sally appeared at the top of the steps and started running towards me. She was hysterical and I couldn't make out a single word she said. Yet, somehow, I knew Jenny had gone into the river by herself. I ran down the slope and the rickety steps leading to the river side. I was in a complete panic, racing down the steps not thinking about what I was doing. Then, when I got to the bottom, I forgot about a large overhanging branch until I clattered my head against it. I went flying."

"Ouch!"

"I never felt a thing. I'm sure under different circumstances it would have been an amusing sight. There was nothing funny about it that day as I picked myself up, almost as soon as I hit the ground, and ran towards a crowd of people standing by the river. When I reached them, a bearded bloke in a baseball cap spoke to me. It's funny the things you remember, even at a time like that. But I remember as clear as day, that the bloke was wearing a striped blue and white Adidas baseball cap. Funny, isn't it?"

"What did he say?"

"I didn't really listen. But from what I did pick up, he said something about seeing a girl play at the side of the water, while he was further upstream with a group of his friends. He didn't know exactly what happened next, but was sure he saw the girl, in the corner of his eye, go under the water. She never appeared again. That's when some of his friends jumped in the water to look for her. I just walked away and stood by the river's edge. Feeling numb, I didn't know what to do and just gazed at the water, like I was in some kind of trance." Eddie watched the black clouds up in the sky once more. "I don't know how long I stood there for? I became distracted when I heard Joan screaming Jenny's name. That's when I also noticed I'd cut my head on the branch, as there was drops of blood on the rock by my feet." Eddie turned to face James, who appeared to be listening intently. "That's it," he said, not wanting to mention such things as Jenny's body being washed up downstream the next day. Or, how after the funeral, Eddie got very drunk, resulting in him causing a scene and much embarrassment. No, it was best not to say anymore. He'd said enough.

"I gather you feel some sort of guilt?" were the first words James uttered after Eddie had finished. "Because if you had played with Jenny like she had asked, then she would still be alive today?"

"Of course I do," Eddie almost spat out. "If only I-"

"If only you what?" James asked. "If only you played with her that day? Then what about the next day, and the next? Up to that day, did you play with her all the time and never let her out of your sight?"

"No."

"Then how can you possibly blame yourself for what happened?"

"I should have played with her that day…that's why."

"You didn't know what was going to happen," James said quietly, and put his hand on Eddie's shoulder. "Things happen. Sometimes, painful as it may seem, there is nothing we can do to stop it. You could just as easily blame her friend, or the girls she didn't like. You could even blame your parents if you want? If they had never met, you would never have been born and neither would Jenny. Therefore, she couldn't have died that day. Or, why not just blame the weather? If it hadn't been sunny, you wouldn't have even been at the river."

"That's just stupid."

"It's just as stupid as blaming yourself." James took his hand off Eddie's shoulder. "I hate to tell you this, as it will contradict everything you have been telling yourself since that day, but it was *not* your fault. As Lenin said. That's Lenin, as in Vladimir, not John. 'A lie told often enough becomes the truth,' and you have told yourself the lie so often you now believe it."

Eddie didn't say a thing. He just sat and shivered as a gust of cold wind felt like it blew right through him.

"Yes, it was tragic-very tragic. Unfortunately, tragic things can happen to anyone, whether they are young or old, good or bad. No one can tell what's ahead of them, the important thing is to make the most of the short time you have. Jenny had a very short time indeed but, by God, I bet she made the most of it."

A small smile appeared on Eddie's face, "She certainly did," he agreed.

"The best thing you can do for Jenny is to make the most of your time as well. Remember her for the joy and happiness she brought to everyone around her, not for the tragic circumstances of that fateful day." James looked at Eddie and said, "You're not just filled with guilt, though, are you?"

"What do you mean?" Eddie asked, not making eye contact.

"I mean there is also anger?"

Eddie made eye contact now. "Of course there's anger," he said, barely managing to refrain from shouting.

"Anger is a sin," James said quietly as he looked away. "A real test of a person's strength is how they control their anger. It is an emotion which can only cause yourself and others around you pain and misery. It makes us lose our self control, and because of it, we say and do things which we regret later. An old Samurai saying is, 'the angry man will defeat himself in battle as well as in life'. And Importantly, Eddie, no matter how angry you get, it will not bring Jenny back."

"So I'm not meant to feel anything about my daughter's death, am I?" Eddie said and clenched his fists on his lap. "I'm not simply some kind of machine that can just forget about it."

"I'm not saying you have to be some kind of emotionless machine. You must realise the past is past. Continuing to feel anger will not change what happened. All it does is continues to bring you untold unhappiness. You may still remember, as forgetting and forgiving are two different things, and forgiveness is a virtue."

Eddie took some deep breaths to try and calm himself down.

"Are you all right?" James asked.

"Yes," Eddie managed to say in between breaths.

"Good." James brushed his hair back as it was appearing wind swept. Once his hair was as close to immaculate as possible in this wind, James asked, "Do you believe in God?"

Eddie had not expected the question and had been caught off guard. "I don't know," he initially said. After some thought, he added, "No, I don't believe in God. How can I possibly believe a God could exist who'd allow something like that to happen?" Eddie could feel the anger stir in him again.

"You're not alone in disbelieving in God. This country is becoming more secular by the day. But a lot of atheists seem to be as fundamental and intolerant as the deeply religious they are so against. I don't suppose you've ever read *The God Delusion* by Richard Dawkins?"

"No. I don't read many books."

"Dawkins certainly doesn't believe in God, which is fine. But, do you know what I think a better name for the book would have been?"

"I've no idea." Not that Eddie was particularly interested.

"I think it should have been called, *I don't be-lieve it!*" James cried out.

Eddie assumed this was meant to be an impression of Victor Meldrew from *One foot in the grave*. But it was so bad, it was hard to tell. Eddie just had to laugh and shake his head at the awfulness of the impression.

"Then below the title, in brackets," James continued as he crossed his legs," it should also say. *As I am a scientist who is a lot cleverer than you, you shouldn't believe it either!* I'm not saying that anyone must believe in God, or anyone mustn't believe in God. But, I wouldn't tell you, that just because I do or don't believe, you must do the same. We are all free to make our own mind up, and it's not up to any person, not even an intellectual like Dawkins, or the rest of the atheist crowd, to tell us what we must or mustn't believe."

Brody believes in miracles.

"I can't deny religion can be harmful. We've all heard what a, so-called, threat terrorism has become in the name of religion. Yet, do you honestly think that if we all followed the atheist lead and no one believed in God, this world would become a man made paradise? That we would all be living in a perfect Utopian State, and this really would be heaven for everyone?"

"Em…I don't know?" was all Eddie could muster as a reply.

"Now we have entered the Twenty First Century, science has achieved so much, of that there is no denying. It has apparently managed to put a man on the moon, and, likewise, it has also created weapons of mass destruction which have made it so much easier to kill more people at once. What is the point in putting a man on the moon, anyway, when we still haven't learned how to live on this planet? Science has helped many of us to live longer, yet, it hasn't necessarily made us any happier. We're merely prolonging the agony of a miserable existence, by an extra twenty, or thirty years. What benefit is it to us that we can live longer, if we don't actually enjoy the life we have?"

"Em...I don't know the answer to any of your questions," Eddie admitted.

James laughed. "Not to worry, I don't know the answers myself." He brushed his hair back once more. The wind seemed to be getting stronger. "I hope I haven't given the impression that I am against atheism? You can live a good happy life without believing in God. I am just as much against religious people telling us we must believe, and that all societies' problems will be answered if we just follow their religion, as much as I am against atheists telling us the opposite. Do you really, for one moment, think that the yobs who roam the streets in our country, who make the majority of the decent citizens live in fear, are the way they are because they went to Sunday School?"

Eddie laughed. It was obviously a ridiculous statement, but Eddie could see James's point.

"Or, that a person's first taste of communion wine led them down the slippery slope, resulting in this country having a binge drinking epidemic? It was Lloyd George who commented back at the start of the First World War, 'we're fighting Germany, we're fighting Austria, and we're fighting drink. As far as I can see, the greatest of these deadly foes is drink.' It is a battle we are still fighting today. It is also a battle we are losing. In British society, religion is not the opium of the people-alcohol is."

Eddie didn't laugh at that statement. It was, perhaps, too close to home. He looked across at the band stand in the distance. Despite being recently renovated, it had been vandalised again since his last visit. Eddie had a good idea who would have caused the damage; it wasn't likely to have been members of the Salvation Army after one of their concerts had gotten out of hand.

"You don't have to believe in God to be happy," James said as he quickly crossed his legs.

Eddie had noticed the more passionate James seemed to get about what he was saying, the more he crossed his legs. It reminded him of that old Kenny Everett sketch that was "all done in the best possible taste!"

"I'm sure you've seen the religious fundamentalists on television who..."

"Sorry James," Edddie interrupted, with something resembling a smile on his face.

"What is it?"

"It's just when you mentioned religious fundamentalists."

"Yes?"

"It reminded me of an old song from the sixties that my dad listened to."

"What song?"

"It was called, 'Who Put The Bomp In The Bomp, Bomp, Bomp?'"

"I remember that one."

"Well, you could change the title from, 'Who Put The Bomp In The Bomp, Bomp, Bomp?' To, 'Who Put The Fun In Religious Fun-da-men-talist?' Because I could think of a lot of words to describe these people, fun wouldn't be one of them."

James burst out laughing. "Very good!" He slapped Eddie on the back with some force. "You really can be quite a funny guy when you want to be. It's just a shame you don't want to be that often. You're usually too busy moaning and complaining."

"I don't complain all the time."

James raised an eyebrow. "I think we'll continue with the subject of religion. It may be less controversial than the subject of your demeanour."

Eddie was going to respond, but decided against it. He slumped back on the bench putting his hands behind his head.

"To some people religion does help. In a lot of cases, studies have shown that religious people are generally happier and more content than the nonreligious. A belief in God may not prevent bad things from happening to you, but it does give you the strength to cope."

"Well, God wouldn't have been able to help me cope." Eddie felt another gust of wind blow through him. The weather was bitter.

"Who knows if God would or wouldn't? In times of trouble and despair, sometimes there is nowhere else to turn to but a belief in

God. The only thing that helps them recover, in some way, from the death of a loved one, is that they will some day be re-united in another life with those whom they have so tragically lost. If they had no belief in God, nor a belief in an afterlife, then they would have no belief that they will see the smiling faces of those they love ever again. It is the only thing that can give them any kind of solace, and without it, life would be too unbearable. Therefore, for some of us, not all, the famous words of Voltaire are so very true. 'If God did not exist, it would be necessary to invent him'. You never had God to help you through the grieving process, did you?"

"No."

"It seems the only person you have relied on has been yourself. I'm not sure how successful that has been?" James placed his hand on Eddie's shoulder. "What I'm going to talk about now, may seem, at first, a little heartless. Remember? It is to try and help."

Eddie didn't think he wanted to hear this.

"When we are born, we are given no guarantees how long we will be on this earth for. The only guarantee we have is that one day we will die. Like the name of the George Harrison album, *All Things Must Pass*. And they do. Therefore, the question we must ask ourselves, is not if, but when it will happen? Marcus Aurelius said, 'observe how transient and trivial is all mortal life. Yesterday a drop of semen, tomorrow a handful of ashes. So spend these fleeting moments on earth as nature would have you spend them, and then go to your rest with good grace'."

"That's all very well if you live to about ninety! But tell me what's fair about Jenny dying at eleven years old, while some evil sod rots away in jail till they're well past pension age?" Eddie asked, sitting up straight on the bench again, no longer thinking about the bomp, bomp, bomp, or Kenny Everett.

"Who said life was meant to be fair?" James took his hand off Eddie's shoulder. "It's unfortunate. But you know when you bring someone into this world, one day they will die. It's inevitable. I know it's cruel and unfair for a child to die before their parents, but, as I said, there are absolutely no guarantees when a person is born exactly how long they will live for. Epictetus, for example, told his pupils to dwell on a thought as they kissed their wives and children. This thought was that their loved ones were mortal and one day would die. When that day came, no matter how unexpected or terrible it was, they would be ready for it."

"How can you be ready for something like that?"

"Bad things do happen to good people, they always have done, and they always will. What do you do when a bad thing does happen? Do you grieve indefinitely? Do you think that the anger and the self pity will bring them back to life again? Does your constant ranting at how cruel fate is actually make you feel better? I don't think it does? It's incredibly hard, but you have to accept what happened and try to move on. To grieve for the rest of your life is not a sign of affection, by any means. Instead, it is the sign of an unhealthy attachment."

"That's easy for people to say," Eddie said with his fists clenched tightly. "As soon as it happens to them...then they'll change their tune."

"Remember. It's not what happens to us but our response that hurts. What's really important is how we react to whatever adversities or tragedies we experience in life. Two people can react differently to the same event. Joan also lost a daughter that day, yet she seems to have coped with it differently from how you have."

"What are you getting at?" Eddie's fists clenched tighter. His heart was speeding up again.

"Joan was also torn apart when that happened. The difference is, Joan has gradually pulled herself together again and tried to get things back to normal. Well, as normal as you possibly can. One step at a time she went back to work, back to the gym, and slowly but surely regained that certain, what the French call, *joie de vivre.* Obviously, it's impossible for her to be exactly the same person she was before, but at least she has managed to pick herself up, dust herself off, and attempt to start all over again as best she could. Unlike you, Eddie, who up until now, haven't even tried to pick yourself up, let alone dust yourself off."

Harsh words, perhaps? But true. Very true, and Eddie knew it. "You could be right," he said, and unclenched his fists. "You could be right," he repeated.

"Joan is grateful for the times she spent with Jenny and the happiness Jenny brought in the far too short time she was here. Don't be afraid to enjoy life just because your loved one isn't there to enjoy it with you. When we die, we are simply going back to the same place we were before we were born. Everything has a beginning, middle, and an end, including our time on this earth. We have to accept that, no matter how hard it is to do."

"What if you can't accept it?"

174

"Alas, we have to. We know nobody is immortal, yet somehow expect death only to come to other people, not our own families and friends. People die all the time, but we don't care because it doesn't affect us. Then, as soon as it happens to someone we know or love, it's suddenly different. A woman so overwhelmed by the death of her child went to the Buddha. She begged for him to bring the child back to life. The Buddha told her, that to do this he required a handful of earth from a house that has never experienced any death. The woman visited every house in the village, and saw that none had escaped bereavement. She returned to the Buddha to be comforted with words of love and wisdom. Those left behind are devastated and grieve. Are we really sad for them, or are we sad for us?"

Before today, Eddie probably would have told James, in no uncertain terms, just what he though of a statement like that. But, as he sat there, wrapped up in his duffle coat, chilled to the bone on a damp park bench, Eddie said nothing.

"Death affects everyone. Maybe it's necessary? For without it we may not appreciate life. Who wants to live forever? I really don't think it would be too much fun? Enjoy and appreciate life, while, at the same time, accept that, in the great scheme of things, we're not here for very long at all before it's time to move on. And your time will come. One day you'll see."

Eddie nodded.

"You have grieved long enough. No matter how much you grieve you can't turn back the clock, no matter how much you want to. To move on, and make the most of your life, is the best tribute you could possibly give Jenny. Who knows? Perhaps you haven't had the last farewell yet and you will meet her again someday."

"I don't think so." There's no question Eddie would love to think that some day he would be with Jenny again. Eddie didn't believe in God, or an afterlife, so how could it happen? What he was starting to believe, however, was that he couldn't grieve, be guilty with himself, or be angry with the world forever. Maybe it was finally time he tried to move on with his life? As he thought about these things, Eddie noticed the wind had dropped.

"Before we go, I will quickly mention the subject of faith," James said. "You need to have faith that things will turn out as they are meant to, and that you can achieve your aims in life if you try your best. 'According to your faith be it unto you', it says in *Matthew*. Faith lifts us up from the gutter. If we have faith in life, ourselves, and others, we can achieve so much. In the concentration camps Victor Frankl saw that the prisoners who lost faith were, ultimately, the ones who were doomed."

"I don't think I'll ever have faith in a God."

"Who says you have to? You should at least try and have faith in something. It doesn't necessarily need to be in a God, as such. People say there's no evidence, so why should we believe there is a God? But I think that is the whole point in having faith of any kind, you have no evidence, but you still believe. That's what faith is all about, believing something in your heart, even if there is no proof, and others all around you have doubts. As we get on in years, we could all do with a bit of a faith-lift. Even George Michael says you've got to have it. So if it's good enough for Georgie boy, then it's good enough for you."

"You're not going to sing are you?"

"No. I am merely going to tell you about this week's task."

"Which is?"

"One of your children has died. But you have one who is still alive."

"So?"

"So, I want you to make contact with Steven this week, and arrange to meet up with him."

"And do what?"

"Whatever you want."

Eddie shook his head. "I'm not sure about this. I'm just not sure about this at all."

While James was going through his routine at the bookies, Eddie had a seat to think about this week's task. He really didn't want to get in touch with Steven. They had been close at one time, but there had been too many things said; far too much water had flowed under the bridge for them to ever be close again. Eddie would be the first to admit, a lot of the blame lay with him. He had been very pig headed about things on numerous occasions. Yet Steven is far from innocent when it comes to the breakdown in their relationship. Steven changed, but it wasn't Jenny's death that done it. No, Steven changed the day he met Kathy. Eddie had never liked her. As he sat there reminding himself of all the ways she irritated him, James appeared with the name of today's horse.

Khashoggi's ship was a ten to one shot. Eddie put his maximum twenty pounds on it. The race was close all the way. For a time it even looked like this unbelievable winning streak was finally going to come to an end. On the home straight *Kashoggi's ship* appeared to step up a gear just managing to sneak in first. Eddie had just won two hundred pounds, the most he'd ever won on one race. On the outside he appeared as ecstatic as you would expect, giving out a yell for joy, whilst doing a brief, but rather nifty, celebratory jig. On the inside, however, all he could think about was meeting up with Steven.

CHAPTER EIGHTEEN

The time was almost 11p.m. There were three customers left in *The Queen's Head* pub. Two of those customers were a young couple, maybe in their late teens or early twenties, sitting beside the jukebox, who were drunk and couldn't keep their hands off each other. The third customer was Eddie.

The get together earlier with Steven had been a disaster on a par with Jemeni's *nil poi* performance in the Eurovision Song Contest. Eddie hadn't managed to pluck up the courage to phone Steven; he got Joan to phone for him. They arranged to meet at a café for a nice pleasant cup of coffee and a chat. Eddie arrived first, and sat nervously waiting for Steven to appear, not having a clue what he was going to say to him? Their 1p.m. meeting time came and went. By twenty past, Eddie thought Steven had decided not to come. Just when he had made up his mind to wait no longer, Steven appeared. Now, as he sat at the bar, Eddie wished Steven hadn't bothered. Things didn't start off too well. They very quickly got worse. After only fifteen minutes, to the astonishment of the other customers, they were having a blazing row in the middle of the café. Then, before 2pm, Eddie was out of the café and in the pub, where he's remained for the past nine hours.

Eddie hadn't drunk as much as this in a long time. He missed the feeling. The inevitable hangover and wasted day ahead of him tomorrow, was not even thought about. All that mattered to Eddie, at this exact moment in time, was getting as drunk as possible, and hopefully forgetting all about the calamitous meeting with Steven. His first pint today, had been as lukewarm as the reaction he got from his mum and dad, when first telling them the, wonderful, news that he had left school to work at the cannery. That hadn't mattered one bit to Eddie. He had still enjoyed himself at the bar with the drink going down very well despite it not being at the optimum temperature. Another reason Eddie had enjoyed himself so much, was because Stacy was also working tonight, and they'd both had a laugh together, just like they used to. There was also something else. Eddie could be seeing this through his beer goggles? But he could have sworn that as well as a laugh, there had also been some flirting?

"Would you like a quick vodka before we close, Eddie?" Stacy asked as she dried some glasses.

"Only if you care to join me?" Eddie said. A line he wouldn't

178

have dreamt of uttering if he was sober. But Sober or not, he still had enough wits about him to know the answer would be a resounding 'No'. Stacy would want to get cleared up here and back home to her young, good looking boyfriend. The boyfriend Eddie had seen at the gym, prancing about in his shorts and vest, showing off his physique, while lifting weights that almost give Eddie a hernia by simply looking at them.

Not for the first time in his life, Eddie was wrong. Stacy did care to join him, and the night had now taken an unexpected turn.

It was nearing midnight. Eddie and Stacy were the only two people left in the pub. The couple who had been sitting at the bar, had left just after eleven, and Eddie had a fair idea what they were doing right now. Just before they did leave, it actually looked as though they were going to be doing it at the bar. Stacy had told them to calm down, so they hurriedly finished off their drinks and headed off to finish what they had started.

Eddie by now was on his third vodka, as was Stacy. But Eddie had a significant number of pints of lager on top of the vodka, and the combination was beginning to have a serious affect on him. It was taking his drunkenness to another level.

Stacy quickly downed her third vodka and went over to the optic to get herself another. "Would you like one?" she asked.

Eddie's liver would have said a resounding "No", but, Eddie, without any hesitation, said "Yes."

When she came back with the two drinks, Stacy had another question for Eddie, "Once we've finished these drinks, would you like to come back to mine for a drink or two? I have a bottle of vodka at home." A question Eddie may have been asked in his dreams a few times, but he never imagined he would actually hear those words come out of those luscious lips in real life.

Eddie wasn't sure if it was the alcohol that was now making him hear things, but he could have almost sworn Stacy had asked him back to hers? Very drunk and very confused, he said, "What was that?"

Stacy sat down behind the bar directly across from Eddie. "I was wondering if you would like to come back to mine for a drink. I have a bottle of vodka at home?" she repeated. "But if you don't want to. It's okay?"

Don't want to? Of course I bloody want to. "Yeah, I could

come back," Eddie said, trying to sound as nonchalant about it all as he could. Not an easy task, considering the amount of alcohol floating about his blood stream. *Hold on a minute! What about her boyfriend?* The remaining one percent of his brain, which was still functioning rationally, asked him. *Remember him? I don't think he'll be too impressed that you're popping round for a cosy little drink with his extremely attractive girlfriend.* Eddie's heart sunk. *Yes, he's a big bugger. Maybe it's not such a good idea, after all?* Reluctantly, Eddie asked Stacy, "What about your boyfriend? Won't he mind you've invited me back?"

Stacy laughed. "I wouldn't worry about Colin. He's working offshore for the next couple of weeks."

Yabbadabbadooo! Eddie quietly celebrated to himself. "Okay, then. I'll come back and join you for a drink...Cheers!" He lifted his glass, as did Stacy, and the two of them clinked their glasses together.

"Cheers, Eddie," Stacy said, staring into his eyes. Then she took an almighty gulp of her vodka, almost downing it in one go. "What kind of music do you like? As I could put some on when we get to mine?" Stacy asked, and then proceeded to knock back the rest of her vodka.

"All kinds of music," Eddie said, before also finishing off the rest of his drink.

"I'm a big fan of Soul music, Eddie. Do you like Soul?" Stacy asked, as she got up and put her empty glass in the sink under the worktop of the bar.

"I love his music," Eddie enthusiastically answered. Far too drunk to notice the look of bewilderment on Stacy's face, "I do love his music," Eddie repeated again, and then began to serenade Stacy with a rendition of the song 'Silver Lady'.

Stacy stood there open mouthed and asked, "What was that?"

"It's soul music," Eddie said. "David-Soul-music." Then, for an encore, he decided to slow down the tempo and gave Stacy a rendition of that old tearjerker, 'Don't Give Up On Us Baby'.

Luckily for Eddie, the vodkas seemed to be having some effect on Stacy already. If they hadn't, she would've almost certainly 'Given up on us baby', and most likely would have serenaded Eddie with a version of that old Ray Charles favourite, 'Hit The Road Jack'. Instead, she just laughed and shook her head. "Eddie, I have no idea what you're on about?"

"David Soul!" he answered, almost shocked that Stacy didn't

know what he meant. It seemed obvious enough to him. "He was in Starsky and Hutch," Eddie went on. "But I can't remember which one he was? I think he was Hutch, but don't quote me on that."

"Don't worry, I won't," Stacy said as she switched off some pub lights from behind the bar.

Eddie wasn't finished by any means. "Did you also know that way back in nineteen seventy six. Or was it seventy seven? It could have been seventy eight? But, anyway, whenever it was. David Soul was the best selling artist in the singles chart?" Eddie swayed on his stool.

"Fascinating," Stacy said. "Now let's go before I change my mind." Stacy switched off the rest of the bar lights except for a small spotlight that got switched off by the front door. She turned the alarm on, then they had one minute to get out before it went off; with almost half of that minute taken up by Eddie's drunken attempt to get off his stool. They made it out with five seconds to spare. Stacy locked up and they headed off towards her house.

While Eddie made his merry way along the road with Stacy, all thoughts about today with Steven were now far from his mind. As were any thoughts about Joan, his wife of twenty years.

CHAPTER NINETEEN

Lounging on Stacy's white leather couch, as she went through to the kitchen to fix them both a drink, Eddie had a somewhat blurry look around the living room. The first thing to grab his attention, while squinting his eyes, was the large plasma TV fixed to the wall. It seemed like a cinema screen compared to Eddie's. Below it was an expensive looking black cabinet, housing a DVD player, one which was probably top of the range, as well as the obligatory SKY box.

"The bloke goes out with Stacy as well as being loaded. It's all right for some, the lucky bugger!" Eddie muttered.

In the far corner of the room was a tall standing lamp. Stacy had turned it on, something she seemed pretty good at, and the lamp had left the room nicely lit as far as Eddie was concerned; not too bright and not too dark, just filling the room with the right sort of ambience required. The lamp also looked expensive to Eddie's untrained, drunken eye. In fact, practically everything in the room looked expensive to Eddie; from the white leather suite he was sprawled on, like a drunken King of Sheba, to the fancy stereo, which was probably about to have some sweet soul music coming out of its incredibly large speakers.

Eddie turned round. The back wall was completely taken up with a cabinet full of CD's and DVD's. Stacy had been gone a while now. Eddie wondered what she was doing. It shouldn't take her that long to pour a couple of vodka's. He decided to get up and have a look at what DVD's and CD's there were. Just as he attempted to do that, Stacy entered the room. As soon as Eddie saw her, he immediately collapsed back on the couch.

Stacy was now wearing a red, silk dressing gown. The first thing Eddie noticed was the length. It was short-very short. Try as he might, Eddie couldn't take his eyes off Stacy's long, bare legs. He didn't want to look, he really didn't, but he felt like a rabbit caught in a set of headlights and was powerless to stop. Stacy sat down on the couch beside Eddie. She handed over a glass of what looked and smelt like vodka and coke. Eddie attempted to say thanks, but no words came out. He took a long sip of his vodka. This calmed him down enough that he was able to ask. "You, you appear to have changed your clothes?"

"Yes," Stacy said. She edged closer to him. "I usually wear my dressing gown while I'm relaxing in the house. You don't mind?"

"No-not-not at all," Eddie stuttered. He had another nervous drink of his vodka.

Stacy stood up and made her way to the stereo, "Will I put on some music?" she asked.

Eddie had no real idea what she had just asked him as he was still mesmerised by her legs. But he said "Yes," anyway.

"I'll put on some soul, then. Unfortunately, I don't appear to have any David Soul. Will Marvin Gaye do?" Stacy asked. She bent over to pick out the CD.

Eddie's eyes almost popped out of his head at the wondrous view. He was now in another place, and in that other place someone's long legs were wrapped around him like a playful python. With no real idea what Stacy had asked him, Eddie still answered, "I'm not bothered if he's gay," Eddie said, trying to sound serious. "I mean, I'm not a ...I'm not a...a Stereophonic."

Stacy burst out laughing. "A Stereophonic?"

"You know? Those people who don't like gays. I'm not one of them. I mean, I used to like Larry Grayson."

"I'm no expert, Eddie. But I think the word you're looking for is homophobic?" Stacy said, and laughed again as the first notes of Marvin Gaye's 'Sexual healing' came on. "And, did you know," Stacy added, "that amazingly, Marvin Gaye, wasn't even gay?"

"Oh!" was all Eddie could reply. He downed the rest of his vodka. Held the empty glass up and said, "Could I get another, please."

"You are a thirsty boy." Stacy quickly downed her drink and left the room.

Eddie was alone, in the living room, with Marvin, who wasn't actually gay, Gaye, singing about his 'Sexual healing'. As Marvin sung, the room started to spin.

Marvin had been followed by Sam, Jackie, and then Smokey. While these Soul legends sang, Eddie and Stacy drank. Eddie got to the stage where he had heard enough Soul for one night, (or morning) and requested a change of music. "Something a bit heavier."

Stacy read out almost every CD she had, till, eventually, Eddie opted for Meat Loaf's *Bat Out of Hell*.

The drink continued to flow. Stacy continued to flirt. The flirting then reached the stage where Stacy was sat astride Eddie, whilst slowly unbuttoning his shirt as he lay on the couch. Eddie put up no resistance, although, by this stage, he probably couldn't even if he wanted to. After his shirt was thrown aside, it was the turn of his socks and shoes to follow. Then the trousers were unzipped. With a struggle, Stacy pulled them down, showing off Eddie's fetching, blue and white polka dot, boxer shorts. This prompted Stacy to sing that Eddie was 'too sexy' for his shorts when she saw them.

The trousers swiftly ended up, in a heap on the floor, beside the rest of Eddie's clothes. Stacy went back on top of him and began to kiss his chest. Eddie managed to raise a smile, but, unfortunately, that was about all he looked likely to raise. Eddie had imagined being in this situation with Stacy a number of times, neither of the times when Eddie had imagined it, however, had he been wearing his decidedly, unsexy, blue and white polka dot boxer shorts. Nor had he been almost comatose upon her couch.

As the baseball commentary part of the Meat Loaf song 'Paradise By The Dashboard Light' played on in the background, Eddie too, had somehow managed to get to third base. And, at one point, it did look as though he was actually going to go all the way. Then, as Eddie desperately tried to make it to fourth base, his world plunged into darkness.

Eddie woke up with his head thumping and his throat as dry as Billy Connolly's wit. At first he didn't know where he was. But when he saw Stacy asleep on the couch next to him, some of the hazy details of last night, and earlier this morning, came back to him. Eddie managed to get up off the couch at the third attempt. Still wearing only his polka dot boxers, he made his way to Stacy's kitchen for a drink of water.

The sunlight streaming in through the kitchen window was almost blinding when Eddie first walked in, while the laminated flooring was cold underfoot. There was also the faintest aroma of incense. Patchouli, if Eddie's trained sense of smell was correct. The stuff was sold in *The Purple Shop*, and Joan burnt it at home all the time. Eddie gingerly made his way across to the cupboards in search of a glass. One was found in the first cupboard he looked in. He poured himself a glass of water which felt like heaven as the cool water passed over his throat. The glass was quickly finished in one long gulp. The water had sorted his throat out, but his head still felt like it had been used for footy practice. Eddie closed his eyes and rubbed his forehead and temples. Unsurprisingly, it didn't help. A day in bed and a box of paracetamol would be about the only thing that maybe would.

184

Eddie poured himself another glass of water. He finished this glass in another single, long gulp. He put the glass in the sink and noticed a wooden incense holder on the worktop by the window. Beside the holder was a half full packet of incense. Eddie bent over and screwed up his eyes to read the small writing on the packet. Patchouli. *Well done that man!* Eddie congratulated himself. The congratulations were short lived, however, as the incense and *Purple Shop* reminded Eddie that he would have to explain to Joan where he had been all night. It also occurred to him that Stacy more than likely bought her incense from *The Purple Shop. Let's hope she doesn't get involved in any girl-talk with the chatty assistant next time she's in. Loose lips sink ships.*

Eddie rubbed his head as the early morning sunshine flew in the window, hitting the black marble effect worktop, he was leaning on, causing it to sparkle like it had been sprinkled with fairy dust. Eddie was so deep in thought he never heard Stacy come in.

"Good morning, Eddie," she said.

Eddie, taken by surprise, jumped a little. He spun round to see Stacy still wearing her very short, red, silk dressing gown. She still looked good first thing in the morning. Eddie glanced up at the bizarre clock, shaped like a fish, which was hanging on the wall. It seemed Stacy was still looking good at about eight twenty three in the morning, to be more exact.

"Good morning, Stacy," Eddie said. "I was just getting myself a drink of water. Is that okay?" He didn't want to, but he had to catch a glimpse of those legs.

"Certainly." Stacy came towards him. "How are you feeling?"

"I'm not that bad," he lied. He wanted to take his eyes off those slender, shapely pins, but couldn't. "How are you?"

A sad look came upon Stacy's face and she stuck her lower lip out. "I'm disappointed."

"Disappointed...how?" Eddie asked as Stacy stood directly in front of him. Now he had his eyes on something a bit further up. Her dressing gown brushed against Eddie's bare skin; the silk felt cold.

"I'm disappointed...because we have some unfinished business, that's why," Stacy said, and stroked Eddie's short, greying hair.

"What business is that? I can't remember much about what happened last night."

"I think you know?" Stacy undid her dressing gown and let it drop to the floor.

185

Savage!

The sight of Stacy standing there, in her lacy black bra and panties, was almost too much for Eddie. He swallowed hard and tried to move away, but he had been trapped, in a classic pincer movement, between Stacy and the sink.

"I-I-m not s-s-ure about this," Eddie nervously tried to protest. Now Stacy's hand was somewhere that no female except Joan got to go anymore, and even she hadn't been there for a hell of a long time.

"I b-b-better not," he protested again, and then brought out that old chestnut of an excuse, "I'm a married man!"

"You were a married man last night, yet you came back. And I don't think it was to listen to my music collection. Do you?"

"I was also a drunken man." Eddie's heart was racing.

"So you only find me attractive when you're drunk?" Stacy's other hand was now rubbing his chest.

"No, of course not," Eddie gulped and his throat felt dry again. "I find you very, very, em…very attractive."

"I can see that!" Stacy said, while glancing down at his boxer shorts.

"What about your boyfriend?"

"What about him?"

"Look, I don't want to…I can't," he pleaded. But it was a tame, hollow cry.

Stacy again glanced down at his boxer shorts, "You say you don't want to," she said, "but a very small part of you appears to be saying otherwise."

Eddie looked down at how things were developing. Although he knew anyway, he saw the very conclusive evidence that a part of him was getting excited by the proceedings.

"Get down Shep…Get down!" he whispered, and Stacy looked at him with a puzzled expression. Shep was in no mood to obey. He hadn't had any fun in a long time and wasn't about to start listening now he was this close.

"Ooh, be still my throbbing-"

"Right then, Eddie. Let's do it here on the kitchen floor," Stacy interrupted Eddie before he finished his sentence.

"No, I can't do it here. What if someone looks in the window?"

"Then it will just make it even more exciting." Stacy grabbed Eddie by his boxer's waist band, and tried to gently lead him away

186

from the sink towards a space on the floor, beside her kitchen table.

Eddie was reluctant to move. "At least let me put the kettle on. I like a cup of tea immediately after love making," he said, stalling for more time.

Stacy sighed, "Okay," she agreed. "But this isn't my normal idea of foreplay," she said, before lying down on her kitchen floor and getting comfy.

Eddie, meanwhile, filled her kettle and switched it on. At this point, all hope was not yet lost, for there was still a small element of doubt in his mind as to whether he would go through with the dirty deed. The small element of doubt quickly disappeared as soon as Eddie saw Stacy's bra and panties on top of her kitchen table, while she was lying naked on the floor. Eddie at last had to admit defeat.

No man with a pulse could resist that gorgeous creature lying there, naked as the day she was born, Eddie thought as an excuse for finally cracking. *Well, maybe Dale Winton could?* But Eddie was no Dale Winton. And instead of a *Supermarket-Sweep,* he was about to partake in a *kitchen-floor fumble.*

Eddie took his boxer shorts off, threw them in the air, and joined Stacy on the floor.

"Oh-My-God!" Eddie shouted out, not caring if the neighbours could hear. This had been building up for a long time, far too long, and there was no way he was going to manage to stay quiet when he finally reached his point of no return after this length of wait. He let out a deep sigh of relief, then the kettle he'd put on approximately three and a half minutes earlier, also reached its climax and clicked itself off.

Eddie let out another deep sigh, before slowly getting up off Stacy and heading over to the kettle, naked. He got a bottle of milk out of the fridge, a mug from the cupboard he'd found a glass in, and a tea bag out of a jar on the kitchen worktop. He poured himself a well earned cuppa.

"Would you like one?" Eddie asked.

Stacy was up off the floor and sitting at the kitchen table, with her dressing gown back on. "No," she quickly answered.

It was only tea for one.

Eddie took a sip of the tea; it tasted good. For the time being, Eddie also felt good. His head was better, and any apprehension or guilt he'd had was now replaced by a sense of pride, because he'd just been rolling about, not on the lino, so to speak, but on the laminated flooring with an incredibly attractive young female. What the majority of males in this town, or any town, for that matter, wouldn't give to have been in Eddie's place? They weren't, though, were they? Eddie was rightly proud of himself. Then, that pesky little voice appeared and said, *isn't pride a sin?*

Eddie decided not to listen. He didn't want to spoil this special moment, and had another sip of tea. The guilt and recriminations could come later. "That was great, wasn't it, Stacy?" He asked, standing naked at Stacy's kitchen window, looking out at the glorious sunny morning, with a cup of hot tea in his hand. Life was good.

Stacy did not answer.

Eddie faced her. She took a cigarette, out of a blue and white Regal packet, lit it, took a long puff and slowly blew out ringlets of smoke towards the ceiling. After flicking some ash in to a white bowl, Stacy finally answered. "It reminded me of going on the rides at Disneyland. You're all excited about the ride, and have to stand in a queue waiting for ages and ages. But you don't really mind, because you're imagining just how wonderful it's going to be. The anticipation is incredible." She took another puff of her cigarette, "Finally, at last, it's your long awaited turn to go on the ride. Then, wham-bang, it's over in a matter of minutes. And you think to yourself, was it all worth it?"

"I see," Eddie said. Not quite the answer he was expecting. "But, if you could pick one Disneyland ride to remind you of what we've just done, would it be *Big Thunder Mountain*?"

"No, Eddie." Stacy took a second to carefully think of an answer. "I would say *It's a Small World*, would be much more appropriate."

"*It's a Small World*?" Eddie was no longer savouring the moment. "You can't say things like that about *Lord Love Rocket.*" As soon as Eddie said that he immediately regretted it.

"*Lord Love Rocket*?" Stacy asked. "Who, or what, the hell is that?"

Eddie really wished he hadn't said anything. "Well…that's sort of my nickname I have…you know…for him. Most males have a nickname for their special little friend," he added, in a lame attempt to try and not sound too ridiculous.

"Hmmph," Stacy seemed far from impressed. "I think *Justin* might be a more appropriate name for your *special-little-friend.*"

"*Justin*? Why should he be called that?" Eddie asked,

confused, but with a horrible feeling he wasn't going to like the answer.

"Well, the reasons are twofold," Stacy said, and she gave Eddie the V-sign. "Firstly," Stacy held up one finger (her middle one), "you could call him *Justin*, because he was Just-in, and then minutes later, he was Just-out again. Or, secondly," Stacy held up two fingers again. "You could call him *Justin*, because he was Just-in and no more."

"Come on now, you're being unfair here," Eddie cried, getting more flustered by the second. "You know the saying? It's not the size of the ship that counts-it's the motion on the ocean that really matters."

Stacy stubbed out her cigarette and quickly lit another. "Size-of-the-ship? Well, I would have to say that going by the size of *your* ship, it's more like a dinghy. And as for motion-on-the-ocean? The journey was over so quickly, that we never even got out of the harbour. The kettle took longer to boil than you did, and it had been switched on before you were even called into action."

There was no response from Eddie. His dinghy had been well and truly deflated. He could tell her that normally he was a marathon runner and not a 100 metre sprinter. It was merely because he was out of practice. But there was no real point in saying anything. The best plan of action for Eddie would be to get his clothes back on, get out of here, then on his way home try and think of a believable excuse to tell Joan.

Eddie, sheepishly, picked up his boxer shorts from the kitchen floor and put them on, while Stacy sat and smoked another cigarette. He left the kitchen without either of them saying a word. Once he got fully dressed again, in the living room, the thought occurred to return to the kitchen and say something. But he had no idea what to say, and more to the point, he had no idea what Stacy would say? His pride and ego had been wounded enough. Eddie, therefore, decided to just quietly slip out the front door with his tail firmly between his legs.

While Eddie made his way up Stacy's street, he looked at his watch. Joan would not be at her work yet, and he hadn't thought of any kind of an excuse, so there was no point in going home right now. He could say he'd been at Clive's house, but had his doubts Clive would be able to lie very well. There was also the added problem that Gloria wouldn't lie for him, so that idea was knocked on the head.

Eddie decided to take a detour via the park, which would not only kill some more time, but the fresh air may also help him feel better. Not only were his thoughts muddled and confused, he could also feel his sore head return, so the park seemed as good a place as any to go, for the time being. Eddie also decided that when he got there, he would sit on the bench where he usually sat with James. At least, this morning, he would get the bench to himself.

When Eddie entered the park and the bench came into view, he saw someone sitting on it. "No, it can't be?" he muttered in disbelief. Even from a distance, he could see that whoever was sitting on the bench was dressed in white. As he got closer, there was no doubt, whatsoever, who it was. "I-don't-believe-it!" Eddie muttered, in a Victor Meldrew voice James would have been impressed with.

CHAPTER TWENTY

There were no pleasantries exchanged when Eddie flopped down beside James. "What are you doing here so early?" was all Eddie said

"The early bird catches the worm," James replied. "As Thoreau claimed, 'an early morning walk is a blessing for the whole day.' Likewise, I could also ask what you are doing here? Was it an early night, then up early in the morning, hoping to make the most of your day? By your somewhat dishevelled appearance." James looked Eddie up and down with some disgust, "And the overwhelming smell of alcohol coming off you. I think you were up early in the morning, but doubt you also went to bed early. Has it been a night on the tiles?"

"You could say that." Eddie rubbed his head. *Then again, three minutes on the laminated flooring could be more appropriate than a night on the tiles.*

"I take it the meeting with Steven didn't go too well?" James asked, while continuing to eye Eddie up and down.

"You could say that."

"To make yourself feel better, you decided to find some solace in that old mate alcohol. Like the theme tune to *Friends,* it's always there for you. A man who depends upon alcohol cannot depend upon himself. Alcohol changes good character and throws reason out the window. 'He is intoxicated who drinks more than three cups. And if he is not intoxicated, he has exceeded moderation,' said Epictetus."

Eddie's head started to throb even more. *Great, the perfect hangover cure. Listening to James prattle on about the demons of drink.*

"It was Sir Walter Scott who said," James continued to prattle, 'Of all vices, drinking is the most incompatible with greatness'. You won't find many of life's great successes sitting in the bar getting intoxicated day after day. The first of Benjamin Franklin's thirteen virtues was Temperance in food and drink."

Eddie's sore head had returned with a vengeance. He also had to think of an excuse for where he had been last night, so he was in no mood to sit here and be lectured at by James. Eddie put his hands up. "Sorry James. I'm going to have to stop you. My head's splitting. I don't think I can stomach one of your endless monologues this morning. So I had one too many last night? It's not that big a deal. I haven't been that drunk in ages. I'm allowed to have a drink and let my hair down once in a while, surely?"

James raised an eyebrow. "Of course you can partake in a drink whenever you want. But, was your hair the only thing you let down last night?"

"I don't know what you're on about? I was...em"

"You were what?"

Eddie closed his eyes and rubbed his head.

"What have you been up to, Eddie? You appear a little guilty this morning?"

"How can you tell?" Eddie asked as he struggled to open his eyes

"Because, it doesn't take much powers of deduction to work out you haven't been home by the sight and smell of you. And, I don't think you have been at Clive's house, as this would be some detour if you were walking home from his."

"You're a real Miss Marple, aren't you?" Eddie moaned.

James smiled. "After a good night on the drink, surely you would want to head straight home for a good sleep and maybe a clean up? Yet, I find you here in the park. Alcohol takes away our reasoning and lets our subconscious mind run amok. When this happens, our emotions and actions become almost out of our control. The result is we often do foolish things. Things we later regret." James stroked his moustache. "Have you done a foolish thing you now regret?" he asked.

Eddie sighed a deep defeated sigh. "Yes...yes I have." He might as well admit it. James seemed to know anyway. Like he seemed to know everything else that was going on. If James knew about this, what would stop him going and telling Joan? Eddie had no idea what those two talked about when they were together and how friendly they actually were.

"Women," James said. "What would we do without them?"

"Be happy," Eddie moaned.

"It was Nietszsche who said about the fairer sex, 'they make the highs higher, and the lows more frequent.' But I don't think you believe what you just said?"

"Yes, I do." Eddie folded his arms.

"Really? I would be willing to wager that you have just spent the night with a woman who you were very happy to be with? A woman who works as a barmaid?"

"How...how could you know that?"

"It isn't too difficult to work out. She's a girl with a certain zest for life, shall we say. A girl who was probably working behind the bar last night while you were drunk and randy. The result was almost inevitable. Before a man can become great he must be able to lift himself above the basic animal urges. We are thinking animals, and should not be slaves to our libidos." James tutted and shook his head, "Is this the first time you've cheated on Joan?"

"Yes."

"I hope you at least practised safe sex?"

"Sort of. Her boyfriend is off shore, for two weeks, so it seemed safe enough." Eddie looked at James to see if he smiled at that comment. He didn't. "Anyway," he continued, after realising his attempt at humour hadn't worked, "It was just one of those spur of the moment things, which happened quickly." As soon as he said that, Eddie cringed. He shouldn't have said the phrase "happened quickly."

James shook his head again, "It is said that Socrates breathed a sigh of relief when his sex drive diminished with age. For it allowed him to be able to use his reason alone, and not be ruined by his sexual desire. To reach Nirvana you must extinguish the flame and cool your passions. Remember, those who play with fire always end up getting their fingers burnt."

Eddie looked down at his hands; he could feel a warm, tingling sensation in the tips of his fingers.

"Psychoanalytic theory," James said, "claims the impulses of our libido are the most important forces in a person's life. I can't say I agree. Neither did Jung, for that was one of the main reasons he and Freud split. Freud argued almost all psychological issues stemmed from repressed sexual feelings. Whereas, Jung thought Freud didn't place enough emphasis, if any, on man's spiritual side. Mind you, it's looking pretty obvious which side you were placing your emphasis on last night."

"I was drunk." Eddie flexed his fingers which felt normal again

"I was waiting for that old excuse," James said, sounding unimpressed. "It wasn't my fault. I didn't choose to drink a bucket load of alcohol last night. It was my son's fault because we had an argument yesterday. I can't be blamed. Have you not learned anything?" James leant forward on the bench and pointed at Eddie. "You are responsible for your actions, no-one else. You decided to go to the pub. You decided to get extremely drunk. You decided to go back to her house, and you decided to…well, I'd rather not think about what you decided to do after that, thank you very much." James leant back on the bench. "You're not alone, Eddie, for that's the society we

193

live in today. No-one is willing to take responsibility for their actions. As the Existentialist Sartre said, 'man is fully responsible for his nature and his actions.' If a young yob mugs an old granny, it's not his fault. The bleeding hearts and social workers will all come out the woodwork giving us numerous reasons why it's society we have to blame instead."

"Hold on! You surely can't compare me to some young yob who mugs grannies?"

"Really?" James said and crossed his legs. "Who do you think I should compare you to?"

Eddie was not in the mood to go down this road, so he just said, "It doesn't matter."

"The bottom line is that we all have choices to make in life. No-one can make them for us. We make choices which result in our actions. Kant had a thought experiment he called the *Categorical Imperative*."

"Was that him off the kids programme *Playaway?* I remember that."

"I think you'll find it was Immanuel Kant who had the *Categorical Imperative*. Not Brian Cant."

"Oh!"

"Kant believed it could help a person make a moral decision. When making a decision and following a certain course of action, you should ask yourself, 'would I want everyone else, if placed in my position, to do the same thing?' If you can answer 'Yes', that's great, do it. If the answer is 'No', then you shouldn't do it. What if Joan had been at the pub last night instead of you? And what if she went home with a good looking young barman, then got up to whatever it was you got up to? Would that have been permissible?"

"No," Eddie immediately said.

"Then I think you have just answered the *Categorical Imperative*. Lust is a sin. It can be described as any desire or craving for self gratification, an inordinate craving for the pleasures of the body. Lust is very powerful, and when we are consumed by it we can be blinded to committing serious offences. One of the signs of a strong mind is being able to control our emotions and our lusts. We should be able to refrain from sex, or anything we know is wrong, because as humans we understand the difference between good and bad."

That's easy for you to say, James. You weren't confronted with the sight of a naked Stacy on her kitchen floor.

"There are a few lines from *Hamlet* which go something like, 'virtue, as it never will be moved. Through lewdness court it in a shape of heaven. So lust, though to a radiant angel linked. Will sate itself in a celestial bed. And prey on garbage'. As the philosopher Spinoza said, 'we do not find joy in virtue because we control our lusts. But, because we find joy in virtue we are able to control our lusts.' The corresponding Virtue of Lust is Chastity, but I wouldn't ever tell you to refrain from sex for the rest of your life. As you may be randy-but you're certainly not Ghandi."

Eddie laughed, despite his aching head. "Good one, James," he said.

"Thank you, Eddie. One of the offences against Chastity is adultery. It pains me to say it, but you have now committed that offence. You have free will and what comes with free will is responsibility. You are responsible for your actions."

"So what am I supposed to do, then?" Eddie asked. "It's all very well telling me all this, but it doesn't change the fact I've cheated on Joan. It also doesn't tell me what I should do now. Because I honestly don't know what will happen if Joan finds out?" Eddie put his head in his hands.

"You had been doing well over the last few weeks. Admittedly, it hasn't all been plain sailing, for you have had a few blips along the way. But this is not merely a blip, for you have let yourself down, and badly. We can't wave a magic wand and turn back the clock to change the events of what happened."

"So, what can we do?" Eddie slowly lifted his head.

"What's important is how you react to what has happened as you've reached a low which I hoped you wouldn't reach. Now, the only way is up, as that songstress Yazz used to sing. You are at a low ebb, but it is still not too late for you to turn back the tide. If you want to?"

"Of course I want to. But if Joan finds out," Eddie lowered his head again and shook it, "then I'm not sure if I will be able-"

"What if she doesn't find out? What if we had met at the pub last night? You came back to mine for a drink and just happened to doze off? I don't think Joan will be too upset about that?"

Eddie lifted his head, "You would say that?"

"I would, yes. I would say it, because I truly believe that, deep down, you are a good person. This may just be the kick up the derrière you need, if you pardon my French. I will also say it because of Joan, for she doesn't deserve the pain of finding out her husband cheated on her. She's already had more than enough pain in her life."

"Thank you, James," Eddie said. The false bravado from earlier, after his dirty deed, had swiftly disappeared like common sense at a convention for Political Correctness.

"No need to thank me," James said, and gave Eddie a reassuring pat on the shoulder. "I doubt you will make the same mistake again. I hope you now begin to realise that you are responsible for your own life. You will no longer take the easy option by blaming circumstances. Where you are today is a result of previous thoughts and actions. Many people believe nothing in life is within their own control, and disagree with Bacon's saying that 'the mould of a man's fortune is in his own hands.' Instead, they see themselves as putty in the hands of fate. You are no longer putty in the hands of fate, although you never really were. But you liked to believe it, for that made life easier, as all the mistakes you made were never your fault."

"Don't worry. I won't make that mistake again." Eddie held his left hand up and examined the gold band on his wedding finger.

"Very good," James said, and then stretched out his arms and legs. "This really is the life, sitting here on a glorious sunny and mild autumn morning. Missing out on the remorseless grind, while people are indoors having to work for a living." James then gave out what sounded like a screech.

Open mouthed, Eddie turned round. Just before asking James if he was all right, it dawned on Eddie that James was actually singing. It was hard to tell what it was he was attempting to sing, for James was trying to reach high notes that only dogs would hear.

When James stopped his high pitched screeching, he said "That song was called 'Givin' Up'. Which could be an appropriate anthem for a lot of people, and what they have done with the miserable existence they class as life. Do you know who sang it?"

"It was you."

"I think you know what I meant?"

"I know what you meant. No. I don't have a clue?"

"It was Justin who sang it."

"What did you say?" Eddie asked. Maybe he had misheard, but Eddie could have sworn James had said the name Justin. The very name Stacy had mentioned this morning.

"Justin Hawkins of the Darkness, that's who. Why, what's wrong?"

196

"Nothing's wrong." Eddie felt a sense of relief, "I got a bit mixed up, that's all."

"I won't sing the next part of the song as it gets rather rude. Do you remember the Christmas tune the Darkness had, 'Don't Let the Bell's End' it was called?"

"I do. It was pretty good."

"It's a great tune. And it was a travesty it never made Christmas number one. I would say, in my humble opinion, it was probably the best Christmas tune since 'The Fairytale of New York'. You must also like that one?"

"I do."

"Glad to hear it. Do you know what I think the best part of that song is?"

"I don't know," Eddie answered, not sure where all this was leading. James was getting a bit off the beaten track discussing Christmas songs at this time of year.

"Let me tell you the best part of the song. It's when the tempo slows down about midway through. I can't remember the exact lyrics. But reading between the lines, it's Shane McGowan telling Kirsty MacColl how it's not really his fault he's a drunken bum. How he could have actually been someone and achieved something with his life. Then Kirsty MacColl puts him straight, by letting him know we all could achieve something and become someone special, if we really wanted. It's like in the film *On The Waterfront*. When Marlon Brando's character goes on about being a contender," James attempted another impression, which was without doubt the campest sounding Marlon Brando Eddie had ever heard; it sounded more like Marlon Monroe.

"We could all be a contender," James said, thankfully for Eddie, in his normal voice. "The majority of times we have no-one to blame but ourselves, if we're not. Your future depends mainly upon yourself. It can be as good or bad as you choose it to be. If you are not planning to achieve anything worthwhile in life, the chances are you won't achieve anything worthwhile in life. If you want to drink less and maybe get up at a reasonable time in the morning, you won't if you spend late nights drinking in the pub. You choose what your habits are. Choose good ones then it can be the making of you. Choose bad ones, and I think we've seen the results?"

"Yeah," Eddie said. He gazed at his wedding ring again. For a brief moment he and his new blushing bride were dancing, round her parents' living room, in front of friends and family, to the strains of Julie Rogers singing 'The Wedding'.

Ave Maria

"It requires discipline," James said. "That, my good man, is the hard bit. Without discipline you will get nowhere. Those who have achieved any form of success, or achievement in life, haven't done so by staying in bed most of the day, or by spending the rest of it in the bookies and the pub. Aimlessly going through life, and hoping for it to miraculously become wonderful."

Eddie looked across at the deserted, vandalised bandstand. "Maybe you're right?" he said, "Maybe you're right?

"Of course I'm right," James modestly agreed. "No man can be classed as a failure if he actually tries to achieve something. He can be, if he doesn't even try. Before you can begin to control external conditions, you must first learn to control yourself. A person can look in a mirror and see either his greatest enemy, or his best friend."

Eddie couldn't remember the last time he looked in the mirror and sang 'You're My Best Friend' at the reflection in it.

"No-one else is responsible for the rise and fall of Edward Ryan, except Edward Ryan. You may have numerous reasons for failing but, like Kipling says, you shouldn't have any excuses. 'Our greatest glory is not in never falling, but in rising every time we fall', claimed Confucius. Now is your time to rise like a phoenix from the flames."

"I'll try my best," Eddie said. "But I have a lot to think about today." *My head also feels like it could explode.*

"You do indeed. There's a quote by Elihu Root which says, 'men don't fail, they give up trying'…" James suddenly stopped talking and appeared to be deep in thought.

"What's up?"

James did not reply. Eddie reckoned he must be contemplating something profound about the secret of the universe, or perhaps the meaning of life? After what seemed an eon to Eddie, with his aching head, James finally spoke.

"Have you seen the film *Caddyshack*?" he said.

"*Caddyshack?* No, I don't think-"

"It's a hilarious film, absolutely top notch, as the Judge would say."

"The judge?"

"Judge Elihu Smails, to be more precise," James said excitedly.

198

"When I mentioned Elihu Root, just there, I knew I had heard the name Elihu before. Yet, I couldn't quite put my finger on it. You'll have to watch the film some time and tell me what you think."

"Okay, James." Eddie was very hungover and now very confused. It was not a good early-morning combination.

"There's actually a poem the Judge reads out in the film that's appropriate. It's when he christens his new sloop called *The Flying Wasp*. Unfortunately, I can't remember how it goes?"

"That's a pity," Eddie said.

"Never mind. I'll just have to make up my own version of the poem, with the same meaning behind it."

"That's a bonus," Eddie said as he rubbed his temples.

James cleared his throat, and then spoke in a voice Eddie assumed was meant to be Judge Smails? Obviously, Eddie had no idea what the Judge sounded like, so this could be the best impression James had ever done, and Eddie would be none the wiser.

"It's easy to smile, when things seem worthwhile, and you don't have to go out and beg. But the mark of a man, is when he can do what he can, when his jeans are too short in the leg."

Eddie sighed.

"It's not exactly Shakespeare, I'll grant you that," James said, in between chuckling. "But you get the message behind it?"

"Not to wear jeans that are too short?"

James chuckle became full blooded laughter. "No. The message isn't telling you not to wear jeans that are too short, although, that's also a very good and important one. The message is much the same as what the Stoics said all those years ago. It's not the situations or the events in our life that are important. Ultimately, what matters, is how we react to them. It's easier to be happy when things are going well, but the real barometer of a person is how they react when things aren't going well. Instead of merely reacting to events, why not get out there and create the events yourself. You are not merely putty in the hands of fate. Be proactive instead of reactive. 'Life is too short to be little', according to Benjamin Disraeli. So get out there and become a contender, before it's too late."

At the mention of the word 'contender', Eddie asked, "You're not going to do another impression of Marlon Brando are you?"

"Don't worry. That impression was a one-off. I am going to mention Michelangelo instead."

Eddie was relieved.

"It was Michelangelo who said 'the greatest danger for most of us. Is not that our aim is too high and we miss it, but it is too low and we reach it'. Have a goal in life, a purpose, and aim as high as you can. Be warned. The important part of our goal isn't really whether we reach it or not. It would be great if we do. No, what is most important is the person we become along the way as we strive to reach the goal. Have a goal in your life. As Schopenhauer says, 'we take no pleasure in existence except when we are striving after something.' Try to create the life you want, but, never ever forget what is most important."

"I'll try not to," Eddie said quietly.

"Good." James patted Eddie on the knee. "Some people are waiting for something to fall from the sky. You have also been waiting for something." James paused, "And I don't think it's Godot?"

"What?"

James did not answer. He looked at his watch and said, "My, we've been chatting away for a while. I think it may be safe for you to go home now. Get some sleep, tidied up, and we can meet at the bookies about two. If that's suitable?"

"Yeah." *The sleep and tidying up can wait. I'll be heading straight for the medicine cabinet when I get home.*

"I'll pop up to see your lovely wife to apologise for keeping you out all night."

"Thank you."

"Before we go. I have this week's task. It is simply no alcohol of any kind. Not even a snowball. Also, after today's visit to the bookies, I don't want you to bet at all till we meet again next week. As I think you have still been visiting the bookies, have you not?"

"Yes"

"Have you won?"

"No."

"Okay. That's this week's task. As a change of plan, I want us to meet at the bookies instead of the park next week. Is that okay with you?"

"Sure," Eddie agreed, without wondering why James wanted to meet there. All that now concerned him was getting something for his aching head.

"I may not have the answer to such questions as what is the meaning of life?" But, if you do listen to me, you can change your life for the better. You will, I guarantee, also become a better person. According to Victor Frankl there are actually two types of man. The

200

'decent' man and the 'indecent' man. So, Eddie, it is up to you, which one do you want to be? Mmm-Mmm-Mmm." James burst out laughing.

Eddie sat, rubbed his head, and watched in bewilderment.

"I'm sorry. It's a *Caddyshack* thing," James started to get up and groaned.

Eddie quickly got up before James and gave him a helping hand.

"Thank you," James said, rubbing his back,

"No bother. What's wrong with your back anyway?" Eddie asked.

"I had an accident many moons ago. It never really healed," James replied and put his arm round Eddie's shoulder. "Some things never completely heal, my friend. But you still have to live."

When Eddie got home, he was relieved to find Joan had left for work. After taking a few paracetamols, he attempted a power nap, but quickly found he was too worried about what James would say to be able to sleep. Would he tell her the alibi? Or would he just tell the truth? Eddie couldn't lie in bed any longer, so he got up and had a shower. This made him feel slightly better. He also made some toast, but wasn't in the mood for a cup of tea.

With his mind still on Joan, Eddie decided to watch TV; there was still over an hour till he had to meet James. He sat down hoping that whatever was on would take his mind off things. After flicking through the channels, about the only thing on was either *Bargain Hunt* or *Loose Women*. Spoiled with such a wonderful choice of entertainment, Eddie switched the TV off and decided to visit Joan at *The Purple Shop* instead.

The visit to Joan went well. Eddie was a happy man when he entered the bookies. James had been a man of his word. After Joan's initial shock, at Eddie actually visiting, she told him that James, as charmingly as ever, had apologised for keeping Eddie out all night. Everything seemed hunky-dory. Things became even more hunky-dory when, completely out of the blue, Eddie told Joan he was going to cook a meal tonight, as a sort of apology.

James took longer than usual to pick today's horse. Mainly because of the constant interruptions from Eddie, who felt the need to thank

James for giving him an alibi. James did finally pick a horse, *Brighton Rock,* at odds of eight to one. Eddie put ten pounds on it. Again, like recently, he found himself not getting too excited about the race, almost taking it for granted the horse would win. It did at a canter.

Eddie and James collected their winnings. James then wrote down for Eddie, on the back of a betting slip, the ingredients for cooking a chicken chasseur. James left, and Eddie stayed behind chatting to a few bookie buddies, managing to mention, in almost every other sentence, the winners he'd had recently. Once Eddie decided he'd probably bored everyone enough, it was time to leave for the supermarket. As Eddie walked to the door, a smile crept on his face when he managed to hear one of his bookie buddies, it sounded like the low gravelly tones of Lucky Ron, moan about the "jammy git." The smile quickly disappeared from Eddie's face, however, when someone walked in. That someone was Douglas.

CHAPTER TWENTY ONE

Until a few weeks ago, anytime Douglas walked into a building, Eddie would try and leave as quickly as possible. He had never liked him and doubted he ever would. Since that day in the pub with James, however, and since he had met up with Brenda, the word on the street is that Douglas had changed. Eddie had witnessed the so-called new Douglas, a couple of times, but still thought it was only a matter of time before he resorted back to his old bullying ways. Till then, Eddie was willing to at least be civil to him when they met.

"All right, Douglas?" Eddie said as he brushed past him to leave.

"Fine thanks, Eddie," was the reply. "How are you?"

Eddie, surprised, stopped. He turned while halfway out the door, "I…I'm fine, thanks," he managed to say.

"Glad to hear it. Where are you off to?"

Where Am I off to? Eddie had to think about the question. He was off to the supermarket to buy his chicken chasseur ingredients, but answered, "I'm just going to the pub," instead. *Why the hell did I say that?*

"The pub," Douglas repeated. "I was going to put a quick bet on myself and then go across as Brenda's at her mum's this afternoon. Is it all right if I join you?"

You what? Of course it's not all right. I mean, why would I sit in a pub with you by choice?

"Well, I em," Eddie mumbled and stared at the ground.

Douglas laughed, "It's okay. You go across the road and I'll go to another pub."

"No, no. You put your bet on and I'll meet you there. What is it you're drinking?"

"Just a pint of shandy. Cheers!"

"No problem. I'll see you there," Eddie said, and closed the bookies door behind him.

At first Eddie couldn't believe what he had just agreed to, and was going to do a runner to the supermarket. Instead, he reluctantly went across to the *Queen's Head,* where he bought a pint of shandy for Douglas and a pint of lager for himself. If Eddie had to suffer Douglas's company, he would need to be drinking the hard stuff. He's sure James would allow him one little drink this week, considering the circumstances.

Eddie sat in the pub, nursing his pint, wishing Douglas had changed his mind and wouldn't appear. Much to Eddie's disappointment, Douglas did appear and sat down beside him. After thanking Eddie for the drink and taking a sip, Douglas suggested they move to a table further from the bar as he didn't want anyone to overhear their conversation. Eddie didn't think there was much danger of that; the only other people in the bar were the two regular golden oldie domino players, and the barmaid, Amy, who was far too engrossed in gossiping on her mobile phone to show any interest in Douglas and Eddie's conversation. Eddie obliged, though, so they moved to a different table.

"Cheers for coming across," Douglas said, after both men had sat in an uncomfortable silence for a while.

"No problem." There was silence again.

Douglas took a couple more sips of his shandy. Even the way he slurped his drinks annoyed Eddie.

"I'd like to apologise," Douglas said

"What for?" Eddie asked.

"I'm sure there's lot of things, but that would take too long." Douglas gave a rueful smile. "The thing I would like to apologise for is what I said about your kids, and the rubbish about only having to buy a Christmas present for one."

"It's all right," Eddie assured him.

"Not really. But cheers," Douglas said. He took another sip of his shandy. The glass was almost finished already. "That day in the pub with James, you know?" Douglas continued. "Everything he said to me was true. Every-single-thing. I've asked him how he knew about it. All he tells me is that he knows someone my girlfriend was having an affair with. Plus, he also knows someone I went to school with."

"You don't believe him?" Eddie asked.

"I don't know? I always thought there was more to it than that. After last night, I'm almost certain."

"Why, what happened?" Eddie asked, intrigued, and now forgetting who he was actually sitting in the pub with.

Douglas looked uneasily round the pub. "You're going to think this is mad, but I had a dream last night. I think it was a dream? But I'm not sure?"

"A dream?" Eddie was disappointed. He had expected some juicy gossip.

"I can't say if it was a dream, or not. But something happened last night, something I haven't experienced before. It felt real to me." Douglas shook his head. "It's hard to describe, but it seemed almost as real as sitting here with you right now."

"What was the dream about?" Eddie was getting intrigued again.

Douglas didn't answer at first. He made a loud sigh and looked round the pub once more. Apparently happy nobody was listening, he answered, "Ever since that day in the pub when I first met James, things have changed. I left my girlfriend, then James set me up with Brenda, and things have been great. Not only have things changed. I have as well. I mean, who would have believed we'd be sitting in the pub like this?"

"Not me," Eddie agreed. *But then again, maybe you're not the only one who has changed?*

"Yeah, being with Brenda has changed me a lot. Don't worry, I'm not going to get all mushy with you. I've not changed into a complete pansy!"

"I'm glad to hear it," Eddie said, and then laughed, for a historical first time with Douglas.

"So things have been great," Douglas said. "Then, last week, Yasmin, my ex, started texting me about meeting up. And the more messages she sent, the more I was tempted."

"Surely you're not going to meet up with her?" Eddie asked.

"Not now I'm not. I was tempted. I immediately forget how happy I was now, and how miserable I was then. All I could think about over the last few days was basically jumping back into bed with her. You know what she looks like?"

"I do." *She's a looker all right. Long legs and short skirts is quite a combination!*

"I arranged to meet up with her today. Then the dream or whatever it was? It helped change my mind. So I never turned up."

"What was the dream about?" Eddie asked, and had a sip of his lager after the head had finally gone down, leaving him with barely half a pint. *Too busy chatting on that bloody mobile. She can't even pull a pint right. Stacy, now, that girl knew how to pull a pint. Pity that wasn't the only thing she knew how to pull.*

"As I said before," Douglas said. "It seemed too real to be just a dream. As I lay in bed my mind was in turmoil. I didn't know what to do. I remember looking at the bedside clock. The time was one thirty nine in the morning. Next thing I knew, I was standing in the middle of my Primary School playground. The rain was pouring down and I was surrounded by a group of children who had made it their goal each day, to make my life as miserable as they could. At first I was surrounded by about ten children I recognised from my schooldays. Then, slowly, other kids would appear I didn't recognise. They didn't say anything, and just continued to stand and stare at me with hatred in their eyes." Douglas stopped talking and finished off his shandy.

"Would you like another?" Eddie asked.

"It's okay," Douglas said. "I better get on with this story now I've started."

"Okay," Eddie said, and had another sip of his pint, which was also tepid.

"Out of the crowd," Douglas continued, "a girl appeared who I immediately recognised as my best friend from school…well, she was about my only friend back then. We were inseparable for about five years, but when we went to secondary school we drifted apart. After I left school, I barely saw her again before she committed suicide when she would only have been twenty two. I don't know the whole story about her suicide. I think she had been suffering from depression, and the rumour is that the final straw was when her boyfriend cheated on her. Sonja was her name. She appeared out of the crowd wearing a white dress with a kind of white glow, or something, surrounding her. She smiled at me, just like she used to, and started singing the song 'The Midnight Special'."

"The Midnight Special?" Eddie almost shouted out. That name seemed to ring a bell?

"It's a pretty old song," Douglas said." I think, originally, it was a traditional folk song from the American Deep South? But the reason Sonja knew it was because she was a fan of ABBA, and it was one of their B-side's."

"The Midnight Special?" Eddie said again, scratching his head, "I'm sure I know the name."

"Sonja certainly loved the song, and so did I after hearing it so often. But I haven't heard it in almost thirty years." Douglas picked up his shandy glass to take a drink, forgetting it was finished. He put the empty glass down again. "So, Sonja appeared," he said, "and touched my face here." Douglas pointed to where his scar was.

Eddie had a look. He could have sworn that the scar now appeared smaller and less noticeable than it used to. Almost like it had healed? He stared at it for a moment or two, then finally managed to convince himself it was his imagination playing tricks on him, or his hangover kicking in again-Douglas's scar had always been like that.

"I won't forget that feeling when she touched my face," Douglas said. "It was almost like an electric current. Then she whispered in my ear, 'You have to go now, Douglas, and move on. You can't stay in this playground for ever'. Then she gazed at me with those lovely green eyes of hers, and told me she was still looking out for me, even though I didn't know it. My life was going to be better, because I had become better. She smiled once more and gently pushed me into the crowd. Just as she did that, I could have sworn James was now standing beside her, but the white glow had become so strong I couldn't see properly. Sonja's gentle push carried me through a throng of children, which was about twenty or thirty strong by now. Then, once I was clear, there was only one thing to do-run."

Eddie played with a, faded Tennents, beer mat. A trip to the supermarket for chicken chasseur ingredients probably would've been a more riveting experience.

"I ran and ran. The crowd getting bigger and closer."

Eddie's eyelids were getting heavier and heavier.

"I don't know how far or how long I ran for? When my legs were about to pack in, up ahead was the red front door to my old house I shared with my girlfriend."

Eddie jerked in his seat as he almost dozed off. It didn't appear Douglas had noticed. Eddie pinched his leg, under the table, to try and wake himself up, then had a glance around the pub. Amy, the mediocre pint pulling barmaid, was still happily chatting away on her mobile. It seemed like her conversation was more interesting than the one Eddie was having. He managed to stifle a yawn, had a drink, and attempted to feign interest again.

"When I made it to the door," Douglas said, "I didn't have the strength to open it. The crowd, which appeared in the hundreds, had almost caught up with me. Just when I didn't think I could move from the doorstep, Sonja's voice began to fill the air. She sang *The Midnight Special.'* I don't think I've heard anything so beautiful." Douglas stopped speaking and looked up at the once white woodchip ceiling, which was now cigarette-smoke brown. "And I don't think I'll hear anything as beautiful again," he said. "I scrambled to my feet and opened the door. Went in the house and slammed the door shut." Douglas picked up his empty glass again.

"Are you sure you don't want another drink," Eddie asked. "I think you might need one." *And I could do with getting up and stretching my legs before I fall asleep here at the table.*

"It's okay, cheers."

Great!

"I closed my eyes."

Lucky you.

"Then I heard a floorboard creak. I thought the kids had sneaked in from outside. A floorboard creaked again, and again. Each time getting closer. By now I was crapping myself! I'm not embarrassed to admit, I thought I was going to do something in my boxers."

Eddie jerked again as Douglas laughed, but it was a sound more like a scream. Eddie rubbed his eyes. He didn't think it was that warm in here, yet Douglas's forehead seemed damp with sweat.

"I stood there with my back to the door," Douglas said. "After a few more floorboards creaked I felt a warm breath blow against my neck. Now I really was sure I was about to make a mess of my boxers! Then, a female voice spoke and asked me, 'Hey honey, what's wrong?' It wasn't Sonja's voice, but Yasmin's. A hand stroked my face. This time there was no tingle like an electric current, more like an icy chill. 'Come on, honey, it's me, you're safe now', she said. Reluctantly, I opened my eyes. Yasmin was Standing right in front of me. Her blond hair was wet. She had on a short, red, silk dressing gown, and was wearing bright red lipstick."

A short, red, silk dressing gown? Eddie sat up in his chair. Douglas now had his undivided attention. This conversation had gotten interesting, and also weird. *What? A scar that healed practically overnight wasn't weird enough for you?*

"Yasmin said we should go to the bedroom. I followed her down the hallway, which was my old house, but wasn't. One of the things I noticed was that the carpet and walls were the exact same shade of red as her lipstick and dressing gown. So was the front door and bedroom door. Yasmin told me to go in the bedroom."

At least it wasn't the kitchen she took you to? That would've really been the icing on the cake.

"The bedroom was also completely red, from the walls and carpet, to the red silk sheets on the bed. In the large double bed a man was sitting up. A younger man, maybe in his early twenties, but whatever age he was, I didn't recognise him. He looked as surprised to

208

see me as I was to see him. 'What are you doing here?' he asked. 'It's my turn tonight.' Before I could answer, a voice, I did recognise, shouted out from the corner of the room. 'It's a hard life, my friend. But sometimes it's not as hard as we think it is. As long as you keep passing the open windows, you should be fine'. Sitting on a chair wearing a white suit, with a smile on his face, was..."

"James?"

"How do you?" Douglas looked totally bewildered.

"The white suit was a bit of a give away. Plus you mentioned you thought he was back in the playground."

Douglas hit his damp forehead with the palm of his large, hairy hand. "Of course," he said. "It's just that that this vision, hallucination, or whatever it was? I just don't know what to make of it?"

"I definitely think you need a drink?"

Douglas grinned, and showed off his yellow, stained teeth. (He obviously didn't use the same toothpaste as James.) "Normally, I wouldn't say no. But I'm almost finished."

"No bother."

Douglas wiped some sweat off his forehead before continuing. "So I turned back to the doorway," he said, "Yasmin was still standing there. With a horrendous-looking smile on her face, she spat out the words, 'You're not the Big Man now, Douglas. But we all know you never have been...have you?' Don't worry', she said, the smile looking worse as she brushed her fingers against my cheek, which felt even colder than before. 'I'll always try to help my honey, if I can. I've turned the cooker on for you, so you can go stick your head in it and put us all out of our misery'. Then she laughed. It was a laugh which could easily have been the worst sound I've ever heard in my life. 'Pity it's only an electric cooker', she shouted, and was joined in her now almost hysterical laughter by the young man sitting in the bed. For some support, I looked across at the chair in the corner of the room. It was empty. James had gone. Next thing I knew, I had woken up."

Douglas slumped back in his chair and wiped some more beads of sweat from his forehead. "I could do with a drink now," he said, and got up. "Would you like one?" he asked.

"Go on then," Eddie said. "I'll have a pint, thanks."

Douglas nodded, and headed to the bar. While he was gone, it dawned on Eddie that, in the last twenty four hours, both men had faced the same dilemma; which was whether to cheat on their respective partners or not? Douglas hadn't, but Eddie had. While Douglas was having his so-called dream, which convinced him not to cheat on his girlfriend, of just over a month, or so; Eddie was sprawled out, almost comatose, on some floozy's sofa-a floozy who just happened to be wearing a short, red, silk dressing gown. And when he awoke, Eddie would cheat on his wife of over twenty years.

When it came to the crunch Douglas did the right thing, he followed The Categorical Imperative, which James went on about earlier. Douglas seemed very tempted by his ex, yet, didn't give in to the temptation. It's taken some time. Now, it seems, Douglas has finally realised what is important in life. If someone like Douglas can do that, then why can't anyone? Why can't I?

"There you go, Eddie," Douglas said as he put two drinks down on the table.

"Cheers."

Douglas sat down. "You probably think what I've told you is a load of crap?" he said.

"No-"

"I probably would. But it happened, and I don't think I've ever been more certain of anything in my life. When I woke up this morning, I just knew if I met my ex today, then I would be right back in that playground again. This time, almost certainly, for good. There is no way I would, or will, ever go back there again."

As Eddie had a first sip of his pint, which tasted marginally better than the last, he did now actually believe Douglas was a changed man. He had witnessed the new Douglas a few times and heard about him, yet, till today, Eddie had not been convinced. Today he was. The Douglas sitting across from him was not the same Douglas who walked into the pub that day when Eddie first met James. Eddie didn't really know why Douglas had changed? Nor was he too convinced about the dream Douglas claimed he had last night. What did it matter? Douglas seemed convinced about it. Anyway, surely the important thing was that he had changed for the better? Not why or how? Eddie took another sip of his pint. Then came the question he felt had to be asked, "Why have you told me all this?"

A puzzled look appeared on Douglas's face. "I've no idea?" he admitted. Let's face it, I couldn't tell Brenda. I couldn't really tell James, either, that I had dreamt about him. You were the first person I bumped into today. So I guess you just happened to be in the right

210

place at the right time." Douglas smiled, a smile that didn't seem to contain the slightest hint of smugness, and took a sip of a much needed shandy. "Maybe that should be the wrong place at the wrong time?" he said.

"No," Eddie replied. "I would definitely say the right place at the right time."

Eddie held out his hand and, as Douglas shook it straight away, Eddie caught another glimpse of the scar; he was sure it had healed.

CHAPTER TWENTY TWO

This was the first time Eddie had set foot in the bookies for a whole seven days, a feat he hadn't managed since being paid off. James, inevitably, was already there, dressed in his usual attire, sitting at a table beside some bandits. As soon as James saw Eddie, he beckoned him over with a wave and a smile.

"So this is it," James said as Eddie sat down at the table beside him, "your final task. Are you wondering why I chose to meet here today, instead of the park?"

"A little," Eddie said while being immediately hit by the recognisable whiff of *Hai Karate*. A smell he'd now grown used to over the last seven weeks.

"It's nothing sinister. I just thought it would be a nice sort of symmetry, finishing off here where we first set eyes on each other. I know we first met properly in the pub, but I didn't think that would be such a good place to go, in case your favourite barmaid was there."

"She used to be my favourite. She no longer has that accolade," Eddie corrected him.

"Okay," James said. "I chose not to meet in the pub in case the barmaid, who used to be your favourite, was there. Is that better?"

"Much." Eddie said. He glanced up at one of the many screens, which was showing a race from York, and thought back to the first time he set eyes on James. Eddie now felt ashamed about the jealous, petty, nasty thoughts he had about a man, whom at that time, he never even knew. Yet, seven weeks later, this same man, and it wouldn't be too much of an exaggeration to say this, had changed Eddie's life for the better. And Eddie realises the reason his life has changed for the better, has had nothing to do with winning horses being picked for him.

"I hear the meal you made the other night was a success?" James asked.

"It wasn't that difficult to make. You gave me the ingredients, while the instructions on how to cook it were on the sauce packet," Eddie modestly said.

"That's not the point. You made it and, by all accounts, it was delicious. I also hear things between yourself and Joan have been pretty good this week?"

Eddie stopped watching the screen. "Yes, they have," he said, not wanting to go into too much detail.

"I hear they have been better than…say quite some considerable time. Nudge-nudge-wink-wink," James said with mischief in his voice and a familiar twinkle in his eye.

"What has my wife been telling you?" Eddie felt his cheeks get hot.

"Only little tit bits here and there. It's just that I have been able to read a little between the lines. But, we shall change the subject. I won't embarrass you anymore. Your face appears to have gone rather red," James gave Eddie a playful nudge.

"I think we should," Eddie wholeheartedly agreed. "Joan tells me you encouraged her to take up art again," swiftly changing the subject, "and maybe sell some of her pictures in the shop." Eddie felt his cheeks cool down.

"I did. What do you think of the idea?"

"I think it's good. Joan enjoys her art. Maybe it's time she took it up again."

"I'm glad to hear that," James clapped his hands and gave a very wide grin. "That's fine. We have Joan sorted out for now. The question remains-what are we going to do with you?"

A question, Eddie wasn't entirely sure if he wanted to know the answer to?

"You've done well in the last seven weeks. It hasn't been plain sailing, by any means. Normally, in life, the hardest things to do are usually the most important things. Last week, which I won't mention again, in too much detail, was your lowest point. Yet, in a funny way, I think it was the catalyst for you to finally realise, the life you have just now isn't really all that bad. Also, how lucky you are to still have Joan as your wife. Would you agree?"

"I think I would."

"There's also Jenny. I would like to believe I have helped you come to terms, in some small way, with what happened to her. Maybe made you realise that what happened wasn't your fault?"

"I still miss her, though," Eddie said. He could feel a lump in his throat.

"Of course you miss her. That is human. What isn't human is constantly grieving and putting your life on hold. Using that day in August as an excuse for the way your life, and yourself, had turned out since then. No more excuses. Harsh as it may sound, it is time to move forward. I think that deep down, at last, you do know that?"

Eddie simply nodded his head in agreement.

"There's a saying by Lao-Tzu, 'he who conquers others is mighty, he who conquers himself is wise.' The next stage I think you must conquer is to combat the crippling fear, you seemingly have, of that dreaded four letter word."

"What four letter word?"

"W-O-R-K," James spelled out. "It is now time you got back up in the saddle. Because the longer you take, the harder it becomes. You get too used to the rut you are in."

"I'm sure I'll get a job at some point."

"It's all very well saying you will eventually get a job when the right one comes along. But the right job just never seems to come along. The hours are too long, the hours are too short. It's not enough money. The time for talk is over, now is the time for action. Our final Deadly Sin is sloth-which can be defined as spiritual or actual physical laziness. Putting off what you ought to do. The avoidance of physical or spiritual work. Does any of this sound familiar?"

"Mmmm…maybe a little," Eddie hated to admit.

"Hopefully, as far as you are concerned, sloth will soon be a thing of the past. It will be replaced by the Virtue of diligence-which is an enthusiastic and careful nature in your actions and work. A decisive work ethic, where you budget your time and closely monitor everything you do to guard against sloth or laziness."

Eddie remained silent. He just picked up a bookies pen and started playing with it between his fingers.

"According to Voltaire, 'work keeps us from three great evils, boredom, vice, and poverty'. And Thomas Carlyle believed all work was worthwhile and noble, even cotton spinning."

Eddie put the bookies pen down. "Right," he said. "I'll ask at the Job Centre, next time I'm there, if they have any vacancies for cotton spinning."

James gave Eddie a wry smile. "You may find it slightly difficult to find a job as a cotton spinner, but I think you get the point I am trying to make. People who are unemployed have too much time on their hands to do nothing except think how miserable they are. I do not have any evidence, but I think you will generally find that cases of depression, drug abuse, and alcoholism will be greater amongst the unemployed. 'As a cure for worrying, work is better than whisky', claimed Emerson. So there you have it. What better reason do you have to find yourself a job?"

Eddie was not entirely convinced. It was maybe one step too

far, too quickly. Then again, considering he had been unemployed for almost six years, could he really say it's happening too quickly? "What if I can't find a job I'll like?" was Eddie's eventual answer. Not a particularly convincing one, either, Eddie would be the first to admit.

James shook his head, "Dear oh dear, Eddie. Was that really the best excuse you could come up with? I was hoping for a bit of a debate. Some verbal sparring. A battle of wits. Yet your watertight argument for not getting a job, is, 'What if I can't find a job I will like?' As far as excuses go, it's a pretty poor one. Don't you remember? It's not the situation you find yourself in that's important, but how you react and interpret the situation that counts."

"I remember," Eddie said, and chewed the bookies pen in the corner of his mouth.

"Well then. You can find some enjoyment in practically any job, if you put your mind to it. George Ivanovitch Gurdjieff, for instance, claimed we should all 'love work for its own sake, not for the rewards it brings'."

"You're telling me every job is equally enjoyable?" Eddie said in some disbelief. He put the pen back down again as he didn't want to choke on it if James came out with any more ridiculous statements.

"I'm not saying that. What I am saying, is that you have the capacity to find some enjoyment in almost any job you do. Admittedly, you may have to work a bit harder at it for some jobs more than others. The bottom line is you can do it if you decide to."

"So I take it this week's task is for me to get a job?"

"It is indeed. But we will discuss that a bit later. I have a few more things to say first. If that's fine with you?"

"You take as long as you want," Eddie said as he sat back and slouched on his chair, making himself more comfortable. "I don't have work or anything to rush to."

"At the moment, you don't. This time next week," James shrugged his shoulders, "who knows?"

Eddie sat up again.

"It would be great if we could all do our dream job," James said. "In an ideal world we should all strive for doing something we really love. Unfortunately, it is highly unlikely we will find our dream job straight away. So, initially, we'll have to do something else. Yet, the secret to actually enjoying your job may not be to do something you like, but to actually like what you do. A way to help you like what you do, is to do it to the best of your ability, coupled with plenty of enthusiasm. It doesn't matter what job you are doing, because the principle is just the same. Like in the words of that famous John F Kennedy quote-Ask not what your job can do for you. Ask what you can do for your job. Even if, initially, you do not like the job you are doing. It is still important to try one hundred percent at it, until you are able to move on to the next thing. Usually, the better and more enthusiastic you are at your job, the quicker you will move up the ladder to success."

As James kept on speaking, Eddie's mind became more muddled. Part of him was still hanging on, and wasn't going to give up without a fight. The part which had become far too used to the lie-ins; the days spent in the pub and the bookies. Basically, being able to do whatever he wanted, which, over the time he had been unemployed, admittedly, hadn't amounted to much.

"It's all very well," James said, "someone saying they want to change, anyone can say that. The difficult bit is when they finally prove once and for all that they have changed. The time when action takes over. When that person gets off their backside and actually does something. You have come this far, why not take the next step?"

"I don't know. It's not as if I can get a job tomorrow. If I do decide to get one it'll take a while."

James smiled. "Maybe I've found one for you?"

"You've what?" Eddie rocked back on his chair.

"I've been speaking to Joe at the charity shop. He's been very impressed with you. So impressed that, when Patricia goes off on maternity leave, he wants you to take her place as a full time Assistant Manager. How does that tickle your taste buds?"

Eddie was speechless. He had enjoyed working there and thought he had done okay. But he didn't think he had done nearly well enough to be offered the post of Assistant Manager. When the offer actually began to sink in, Eddie answered, "I still don't know."

James shook his head. "The job won't be available for ever. Listen to Mark Twain, 'I was seldom able to see an opportunity until it had ceased to be one'. The decision is yours. No one else can make it for you. Remember, 'never put off till tomorrow that which you can do today'. Nowadays, mind you, for a lot of people, never do today that which you can do tomorrow, could be appropriate. Or, even better, don't bother doing it at all."

"I'll think about it," was the only response Eddie could muster, because, right now, he genuinely didn't know if he would take the job.

"That's all I ask. Don't forget the statement of Burke, 'All that is necessary for evil to triumph is for good men to do nothing'. And I do firmly believe you are a good man."

"Thank you, James. You're not too bad yourself."

James got up from his seat without replying. As he strolled across to the poster with today's races on it, Eddie saw Douglas and, his new mate, Clive walk in.

Clive and Douglas walked over to Eddie and said their greetings. Clive, wearing a manly salmon pink t-shirt, with Ray Von on it, sat down beside Eddie. Douglas, wearing a less flamboyant plain white t-shirt, remained standing.

"What have you two been up to?" Eddie asked.

"I was helping Douglas move some stuff into Brenda's," Clive said, "as he's moving in with her."

"Moving in with her? Bit soon isn't it?" Eddie asked.

"Normally, I would agree," Douglas said. "But, somehow, it just feels right. Brenda asked me last week and I just thought I should go for it. You know? Why put off till tomorrow-"

"What you can do today," Eddie finished Douglas's sentence for him. "Wise words." Eddie turned his attention to Clive. "How did you manage to help? I thought you had a bad back?"

"Well…" Clive paused. "It was maybe more a supervisory role I had. But I was also in charge of making the cups of tea."

"Chief tea maker? A very important role," Eddie said, and gave a sly wink to Douglas.

"Thank you, Eddie," Clive replied, sounding deadly serious.

"Have you moved in yet?" Eddie asked, changing the subject before he burst out laughing.

"Not yet. Just a few more items. I should be in by Friday at the latest. Which reminds me, I've asked Clive and he's coming along with Gloria. Would you and Joan like to come along to a little do we'll be having at Brenda's on Friday night? It's nothing too exciting, just a few drinks as a sort of celebration for me moving in."

"Yeah, we should make that, thanks," Eddie immediately said. Two months ago he wouldn't have been able to think of a worse way to spend an evening, yet he agreed to it without thinking twice.

"That's great," Douglas said. "It should start at about eightish, but I'll let you know if there's any change of plans."

"Eightish and change of plans?" James asked as he came back to the table and stood beside Douglas.

Eddie noticed he had been a lot quicker picking today's horse than usual.

"Is someone having a party I don't know about?" James asked with a serious expression on his face.

"I was going to invite you, but was going to wait till you came across. I didn't want to disturb you," Douglas said, sounding flustered.

Eddie really did wonder if this was the same Douglas.

James put his arm round Douglas's broad shoulders, "I was only joking," he said. "When is it? And what is the occasion?"

"It's on Friday. Brenda's house at eight. And the occasion is I'm moving in with her," Douglas replied.

"Congratulations!" James shouted with great excitement and shook Douglas's hand. "Friday at eight? If I'm here, I'll be there."

"Why-where are you going?" Eddie asked.

"I don't have anywhere planned at the moment. But you just never know. As I said, if I am here, then I would love to attend your gathering. Thank you for inviting me."

"I've got some cracking jokes I thought up especially for the party," Clive added.

"That will certainly be something to look forward to," James said. Then he walked over and put his arm round Clive's not so broad shoulders. "Can we get a sneak preview of any of your jokes today?" James asked.

"Well, I don't know," Clive answered quietly as he looked down at the floor.

Eddie had seen that look so many times. He knew if Clive was encouraged to tell them a joke, then Clive would tell a joke. "Go on, Clive," Eddie said. "I'd like to hear one of them."

"So would I," Douglas added.

Immediately, Clive looked up and his face was beaming. "Okay then," he said, "if you insist? I only thought of this one as I was having my breakfast, so I'm not sure how good it is? What is the name of everyone's most unfriendly relative?"

The three men thought about it for a while. Eventually, Eddie said, "I don't know."

"The most unfriendly relative is called-Aunty-social!" The punchline was met with a chorus of groans. Clive, undeterred, waved his hands and told them, "Hold on. I've got another one, you may like it more. Did you hear the shocking revelation that the President of the United States is actually gay?"

"No," Douglas answered this time.

"Yes, he finally had to come out of the closet, when it was discovered he had been visiting his very good friend *Camp-David* at the weekends."

This joke, although it didn't exactly have everyone rolling about on the floor in hysterics, did actually manage to generate a few chuckles from its audience. Eddie thought it wasn't too bad, maybe not Frank Skinner standard of wit, but then again, even Frank's quality control drops sometimes; Eddie can still remember the sitcom *Shane*.

"Not bad," Eddie said. "I reckon if I put my mind to it. I could come up with a funny joke."

James's eyes lit up and he raised an eyebrow. "That sounds like a challenge. A real jester's battle. What do you two gentleman say to a little contest amongst friends? Douglas here can pick a subject. Then you both have five minutes each to come up with a joke on that subject."

"All right," Clive answered eagerly.

Eddie wasn't so quick to reply.

"What's wrong, Eddie?" James asked. "Do you not feel up to the challenge?"

No, Eddie didn't feel up to the challenge. Maybe he should have kept quiet. But he couldn't back down, could he? "Okay," he reluctantly said.

"Excellent," James said. "Now, all we need is for Douglas here to pick a subject."

Douglas took some time to ponder over it, "I'm not too sure what to choose," he said. Then, after a bit more consideration, he finally came up with a subject, "Okay. The subject I choose is the programme *Loose Women.* Brenda was watching it earlier this afternoon, and I hate to admit it, but I also like it as well."

"*Loose Women?* I can't stand the bloody programme!" Eddie shouted out. "A bunch of women, all sitting round a desk, twittering on about nothing in particular. What kind of a show is that meant to be?"

"I agree with Douglas," James said. "I rather like it. But it was a joke we required, Eddie, not an actual critique of the programme. Unless that was your effort?"

Eddie did not answer.

"Right then," James said, "The subject is *Loose Women.* The time is five minutes…Go."

219

After the five minutes was up, it was agreed Eddie would go first.

"Here we go," Eddie said. Then, with some apprehension, he told his Magnum Opus of a joke. "With ever increasing crime and yobs taking over our streets, a more serious punishment is needed. It was discussed, that as a suitable severe deterrent, one of the options could be to make the most serious offenders guest panellists on the television show *Loose Women*. After much debate, however, it was argued this punishment may be too much a violation of the criminal's human rights. Therefore, a punishment has been decided on that is less severe and more humane. They are going to bring back hanging instead."

As soon as Eddie said the joke, he realised it wasn't actually as funny as it had sounded in his head. This was confirmed by the lukewarm response it got. James and Douglas smiled, but it was obvious they were only doing that to be kind. At least Clive laughed, a little, although he would probably laugh at anything? So his response wasn't really something to get too excited about. Yes, it was a tame effort. Eddie half expected a tumble weed to go passing by.

"That was pretty good," James said, obviously not trying to kick a man when he's down. "But will Clive's effort match it? It is now time for our second Gladiator to get into the arena and do battle."

"I'm not sure if my joke will be as good as Eddie's," Clive said before he started. "But I've thought of one, although I normally take a lot longer than five minutes to think of my jokes." With excuses now firmly out of the way, Clive told his joke. "One of the presenters of the highly rated, and ever so popular, programme *Loose Women* gave an interview. During which, she was asked if the Loose in the title was actually an acronym which stood for Lousy-Opinionated-Overrated-Smug-Entertainment. The presenter was furious at this suggestion. She cried out, 'how dare you! The show has never been called that before'. The interviewer apologises and says, 'What? Lousy-Opinionated-Overrated, and Smug?' 'No', she replies-'Entertainment'."

This joke was met with much the same response as Eddie's. The kind smiles from Douglas and James. Eddie also gave a token laugh to repay the compliment from Clive.

"Well," James said. "That was a match of mirth Made in Heaven. One that was far too close to call. So I think the fairest result would be a draw. Now let us try and forget we ever heard those two awful jokes, and never mention of them again."

James's words were met not only with laughter from everyone, but also total agreement.

Teo Torriate was the name of the horse James picked, with odds of seven to one. Before Eddie put his maximum bet of twenty pounds on it, James took him aside and told him he had now won twelve races in a row, so this was his thirteenth; which, of course, could be a bad omen. Eddie was now almost at the stage where he believed James's horses couldn't possibly lose, and despite James's reservations about this race, Eddie put his money on it without any doubt in his mind about the outcome. Clive and Douglas put their money on another horse, called *Mother Love,* which had odds of thirteen to one.

When the race got underway, *Teo Torriate* moved into an early lead. By the halfway stage the horse was well in front. As three quarters of the race passed, *Teo Torriate* was still way ahead, almost cruising to victory. Eddie knew the horse would win, thirteenth race or not. He had no idea how James done it? It was obviously some sort of gift, but what a gift.

Eddie sat back and relaxed in his chair. Two hundred yards to go till victory; *Mother Love* seemed to have closed the gap a little, but it was still a more than comfortable lead. One hundred and fifty yards to go; *Mother Love* had chipped away some more at *Teo Torriate's* lead, yet it was still nothing to worry about. One hundred yards to go and now there was maybe something to worry about. The gap had become far too close for Eddie's liking. Now, as they reached the fifty yard mark, *Teo Torriate* still had the lead, but only just. Coming down the home straight the two horses were neck and neck. Eddie couldn't believe what he was seeing. James had picked this horse, so how could it possibly lose? So what if it was the thirteenth race? Superstition or no superstition, there is no way this horse wouldn't win.

But it didn't.

Mother Love just appeared to edge ahead at the line. Even though it went to a photo finish, Eddie knew that *Teo Torriate* had somehow lost. He actually laughed while watching Clive and Douglas do a celebratory dance together as the winner was announced. Sure Eddie was disappointed the horse didn't win as he would have won one hundred and forty quid, but he was far from despondent. Part of him even felt glad for Douglas and Clive when he saw the joy on their faces, something he would never have felt seven weeks ago. Being totally honest, he would possibly admit that the horse losing might not be such a bad thing after all. Now he could make the decision whether to start work or not. Eddie didn't have to do it simply because of an agreement with James.

CHAPTER TWENTY THREE

As he sat in the Job Centre, in his usual chair, Eddie watched the same old goings on around him. Most of the faces were the same ones he saw the first day he walked in here, some six years ago. One face, in particular, was directly in front of him. A face hidden behind a large pair of glasses, beneath a head of hair that could only be described as immense, and out of control. It was Eddie's good friend, Edith Strachan. Appearing as she always had, wearing her obligatory polar neck jumper.

Edith had taken Eddie's file out and was reading it, not as though anything new would actually be in it since their last 10 a.m. get together. She put the folder down then made eye contact with Eddie, for the first time since he had sat down.

"Good morning, Mr Ryan," she said, abruptly, and looked down at his folder again in case she had missed any vital information that may be lurking somewhere in it.

"Good morning."

Edith looked up again, "Well, Mr Ryan, have you-"

Eddie didn't allow Edith to finish her sentence. With great satisfaction he sat up in his chair, looked her straight in the eye, and said, "Actually, I have. And I would like to sign off today, as I am going to start a new job on Monday." Words that Eddie never thought he would utter in here. But he had, and surprisingly, didn't come out in a cold sweat afterwards.

There wasn't a sign of shock on Edith's face, nor any emotion. This disappointed Eddie.

"I see," was the only response Edith gave. She looked at his folder, once more, without saying a thing. When she looked up again, this time there was a smile upon her face. "That is wonderful news," she said, and held her hand out.

Eddie was taken aback. This was not the way he expected her to react. He warily shook Edith's hand, which he noticed was incredibly warm. Somehow, he had always thought she would have icy cold hands.

"Thank you…em…"

"Edith."

"Thank you, Edith."

Edith asked Eddie all about the job he was taking. So he told her the details about how he had been helping out there for a number of weeks, and they had offered him the job as Assistant Manager. Edith seemed very impressed with this. She filled in some paper work and Eddie signed a couple of forms. Then, just as he was about to leave, Edith leaned across the desk.

"Some people who come in here, you can tell that they will never find work," she said quietly. "They are, for want of a better word," Edith looked around her. "I know it's not politically correct," she then laughed a quiet, nervous sounding laugh. "Basically, they are lazy. There's no two ways about it. I never thought that about you. I know the tragic story about your daughter, and I always believed that one day you would move on with your life. Now it looks like you are. I really am happy for you." She held her hand out again. This time, Eddie shook it without any hesitation.

When Eddie stood up, he said, "Could I possibly ask you something, Edith? I hope you don't mind?"

"Of course not," she said, and smiled. When she did, Edith's whole face lit up. Suddenly, Eddie realised alcohol wasn't really necessary. Edith was actually attractive, after all.

"I was just…em…just wondering if you were married?" Eddie asked. Dreading how she would react to the question. But he just had to know.

"Are you trying to chat me up, Mr Ryan?"

"No-em-no-I'm…"

Edith laughed. "Don't worry, I'm only joking," she said. "No, I'm not actually married. But my partner, Trevor, keeps asking me, as we have lived together for about fifteen years now. I'm happy the way things are. So are the kids."

"Oh! You live with your partner and have kids?" Eddie asked, trying not to sound too shocked.

"Yes. But, I am, on occasion, willing to have the odd fling, if you're interested?"

Eddie's jaw almost hit the floor at Edith's comment. As Eddie tried to think of some kind of response, Edith burst out laughing. Eddie breathed a sigh of relief when he realised she was only joking; two flings in as many weeks would have been too much for him. "Take care, Edith," he said, then went outside, took a deep breath, and muttered, "Eddie has now left the building."

While making his way down the steps, outside the job centre, Eddie saw a familiar figure sitting on a wall. The familiar figure, who had his back turned and appeared to be watching the traffic go by, was wearing a white suit. Eddie tried to sneak down the steps. When he got almost within touching distance, James's head spun round, reminding Eddie of the child in *The Exorcist*.

Instead of spouting profanities like in the film, James smiled, and said as pleasantly as ever, "Good morning."

"Fancy meeting you here?" Eddie asked as he sat on the wall beside James.

"Well, I just happened to be-"

Eddie laughed and shook his head. "I know. You just happened to be passing the job centre at my signing on time. Yet another coincidence?"

"I wouldn't call it a mere coincidence, as such. More like synchronicity."

"Synchro-what? Isn't that the swimming thing they had at the Olympics?" Eddie asked, hoping he didn't sound as confused as he actually was.

"I think you'll find that's called synchronised swimming." James corrected him. "Synchronicity is a phrase coined by Carl Jung. It basically means a meaningful coincidence, or, in Jungian terms, an acausal connecting principle. But I reckon we both know it's not a coincidence, or synchronicity, that I'm here?"

"Why is it you're here?" Eddie asked.

"I'm not sure what the technical term for it is. I'm just dying to know whether you signed on or off today?"

"I think the technical term is nosey parker," Eddie said. "But to put your mind at ease, I..." Eddie decided he wasn't going to put James's mind at ease just yet. Eddie took a deep, relaxing breath. "It's a lovely day, isn't it?" he asked.

"It is," James agreed.

Eddie detected frustration in James's voice. It was subtle, yet Eddie was sure he heard it. So, Eddie decided to sit quietly and watch the traffic go by for a while longer, just to let James stew some more.

After about one minute of watching the traffic go by, and listening to James's constant sighing and tutting, Eddie decided it was about time to put James out of his misery. "I suppose I'd better tell you," he said. "At the Job Centre today I..." Eddie glanced down at his shoes and cried out, "Oh dear! One of my shoelaces is undone. I'd better tie it."

"No!" James cried out. "I think you better tell me first, as I am about to burst with the anticipation."

"Okay. At the Job Centre today I…" Eddie scratched his head and said, "What was the question again?"

James gave Eddie a playful nudge, "Get on with it."

"At the Job Centre today… I signed off. I'm taking the job at the charity shop."

James jumped off the wall and clapped his hands a few times. "Excellent-Eddie," he said, beaming. James then shook Eddie's hand with so much force that Eddie thought he would be pulled off the wall. Eddie jumped down as James continued to shake his hand wildly up and down. James said "Excellent" a few more times, let go of Eddie's hand and asked, "Have you told Joe yet?"

"I'm going in to see him today."

"This is tremendous news." James had a quick glance at his watch. I would love to stay and chat," he said. "But I better hit the road. I have things to do and people to see."

"Will you be at the party at Douglas and Brenda's on Friday?" Eddie asked, "I thought it could be a joint celebration."

James dropped his eyes towards the ground. There was a look on his face that Eddie had never seen before, not only on James's face, but on anyone's. It was a look that was impossible to describe; almost a bizarre combination of happiness and sadness at the same time, if that was possible? Eddie felt something hit him square in his solar plexus. At that very moment, he knew, without any shadow of a doubt, James would not be there on Friday.

James lifted his eyes and almost appeared his usual self again, but not quite. There was still something not right. "I'll try to make it, Eddie," he said. "Who knows what will happen between now and then?" James shook Eddie's hand once again, this time with less force, before he left and strode up the High Street.

Eddie had no idea why he suddenly decided to do what he did as he hadn't bothered before. Right now it just seemed important. James knew so much about him, yet Eddie knew nothing about James. Therefore, Eddie decided to follow James to see where he went.

James meandered along the High Street, at a leisurely pace, occasionally stopping to look in some shop windows, while Eddie tried to discreetly keep his distance. This went on for about half an hour till James crossed the road and sat at a bus stop. Eddie crossed the same road and decided to go into a card shop, about thirty yards from the bus stop, thinking that would be a good vantage point to watch from without being seen.

Eddie pretended to browse through some cards, by the window, whilst keeping an eye on James. Just when he was running out of cards to look at, a number thirty two double-decker bus appeared. James got on. Eddie ran out the shop to try and catch it.

He made it on to the bus just as the doors were about to shut. Panting a bit, Eddie got out his wallet and handed over a ten pound note. The driver looked in disgust at it. Without saying a thing, the driver pointed to a sign beside where Eddie was standing. It read-*Exact fare, please.* Eddie checked his wallet. There was no change there. He gave a hopeful glance at the driver who, with his quaff and side burns, looked like Cliff Richard about to embark on a *Summer Holiday.* The driver turned away and drummed his fingers on the steering wheel. *It's not the Devil Woman you've to watch out for, it's the Devil Driver.* Eddie began to sweat as he stuck his hands in his pockets in a desperate attempt to find some change. By now the natives on the bus were getting more restless as Eddie got more nervous. There was a lot of quiet, and not so quiet, moaning going on from the rest of the passengers. Two old ladies, in particular, at the front of the bus were now actually heckling Eddie. "Get a move on!" "If you've no change, get off the bus!" were the less obscene comments they shouted. Eddie was about to follow their advice when he found a pound coin, hidden in an old piece of tissue, in his back pocket. With his hand shaking, he handed the money over. The driver took it without saying anything. He didn't need to. The look on his face said it all.

When Eddie turned to face the baying crowd, it dawned on him if James was on the bottom deck, then there's no doubt he would have seen Eddie; for he hadn't exactly sneaked on the bus, chameleon-like. Eddie surveyed the unsmiling and disgruntled faces on the bottom deck. James was not amongst them. Eddie let out a sigh. With his head down, he scurried past his two elderly new friends, or Waldorf and Statler, from *The Muppet Show,* as Eddie had decided to christen them.

The bus stopped a number of times, but still James hadn't appeared. Although, thankfully for Eddie, Waldorf and Statler did get off, so he wouldn't have to walk past them again. The bus headed out of town reaching a small village a mile or so away. Eddie wouldn't be surprised to find James living here. It was a quiet village, and the houses were expensive. Out of Eddie's league, yet the sort of place you may expect a retired University lecturer to live. The bus drove through the village. It stopped as it neared the outskirts. James came down the stairs, behind a couple of women in Nurse's uniform, and got off the bus. Eddie followed without saying goodbye to the driver.

When Eddie got off the bus, James was already ahead of the nurses who had initially been in front of him, walking towards the hospital that was here. Eddie quickened his stride to try and keep up, whilst at the same time, not wanting to get too close. James entered the gates of the hospital. Eddie, not far behind, stopped and read the large white sign at the gates. *Abernethay Royal Infirmary. Part of the NHS Care Trust,* was written on it in blue writing. It was now called a *Royal Infirmary,* yet, its name had changed over the years from *Abernethay Lunatic Asylum,* to the more politically correct *Abernethay Mental Hospital,* to its present name. Despite the name change over the years, the *Infirmary* still dealt with the same sort of patients it always had. This wasn't where you came if you had an ingrown toe nail. This was the place you came if you had a mental health problem.

The hospital was built over two hundred years ago. A lot may have changed about the place since then, but that didn't matter to Eddie. It still gave him the creeps. There had been the odd new building built in the grounds, yet, on the whole, it was still mainly the large and old buildings they used.

Eddie had been here a few times in the staff dorms. His cousin had been training as a psychiatric nurse, around the late seventies, early eighties. Eddie had been invited to some of the staff parties. They had been good because he got drunk, but not that good, because he never seemed to end up with any of the nurses. No matter how randy people said nurses got, after a few drinks, they certainly never seemed to get randy with Eddie. He'd heard everyone go on about the, so-called, permissive society back then, but wondered if it actually existed. Poor Eddie never seemed to find it, and it wasn't for a lack of looking.

James entered one of the buildings up ahead. Eddie followed, but stopped at the door. He now realised a reason would have to be given for being here. James likely helped out here part time, and wouldn't be too pleased that Eddie had now become his stalker. If James had thought this had been any of Eddie's business, he would have told him about it before. Eddie decided it would be best if he left.

"You look a little lost. Can I help you?" a female voice behind Eddie asked just as he was about to leave.

Eddie spun round to see a young nurse standing there. She was about the same height as Eddie, with shoulder length blond hair. Eddie noticed she was very pretty. Her name badge said Charlotte. Nurse Charlotte reminded Eddie of all those pretty nurses he attempted to chat up, without any success, all those years ago. He also recognised her as one of the nurses who had been on the bus.

"I was looking for someone. I think they came in this building?" Eddie said. "James is his name-" As Eddie tried to think of James's surname, he realised he never actually knew it. "I think he must work here, but I don't want to disturb him. I'll catch him another time." Eddie gave Charlotte as dazzling a smile as he could, but it was not in the same league as one of James's.

The nurse had a puzzled look on her face, "James, you say?"

"Yes."

"And he works in this building?"

"I assume so, as I saw him come in here."

Charlotte the nurse shook her head, "It doesn't ring a bell, I'm afraid."

Eddie was going to leave it at that when he said, "He's got a moustache, and he wears a white suit most of the time," Eddie then corrected himself. "Well, actually, as long as I've known him, he wears a white suit all of the time."

A smile came upon the nurse's pretty face. "James!" she said, and nodded. "But you're a bit mistaken. James doesn't work here."

"Does he not?" Eddie asked.

"No. James is a patient."

CHAPTER TWENTY FOUR

While following Nurse Charlotte into the hospital building, Eddie believed James knew he had been followed here and this was all a joke. Behind the reception was a nurse who appeared in her late forties, or early fifties, with red hair. Eddie also noticed she had a fuller figure than Charlotte. Katie was on her name badge. Instead of bursting out laughing, like Eddie expected, when Charlotte told her James had a visitor, Katie seemed surprised and pointed down the hallway to the left of reception. Charlotte headed off in that direction, with Eddie reluctantly behind her, wishing he never set foot on the number thirty two bus.

As they walked down the hallway, Eddie's eyes almost watered at the strong smell of bleach, or some sort of cleaning agent. He also managed to take his almost watery eyes off Charlotte enough to notice how perfectly white the wall and floor was. Eddie imagined he was walking through a tunnel on the Planet Hoth from *The Empire Strikes Back*, with the cold glow emanating from the fluorescent tubes, on the ceiling, managing to accentuate the effect further. Nurse Charlotte stopped outside a door, which, inevitably, had the number seven on it. At this point, it began to occur to Eddie that this may not be a joke after all.

Charlotte knocked on the door. "I'll just go in first to let him know you're here," she said.

"Okay."

Charlotte opened the door and entered the room. Eddie couldn't resist a glance down at her bottom before she went. In her tight white uniform, a hint of panty line could be spotted. Eddie nodded in approval at the pleasing sight.

While the image of Nurse Charlotte's behind was still fresh in his memory, he heard her say from inside the room, "James, you have a visitor."

"Thank you, my dear. Let them come in," a voice, that was unmistakeably James, answered.

Nurse Charlotte opened the door, "In you come," she said.

Eddie entered the room. Nurse Charlotte left and closed the door. The room was not what Eddie would have expected in a place like this; it was actually homely. While the hallway outside was completely white, the decoration in here was almost completely red; from the walls, which had no pictures or a mirror hanging up on them, to the carpet, and the duvet and pillowcases on the single bed. On the facing wall was a large window which the sun was shining through. To the side of the window was a large bookcase which was overflowing with books. In fact, the whole room was overflowing with books, they were everywhere. James was sitting at a small pine writing desk, in front of the window, and for a second, it almost seemed like James had a white glow of light surrounding him. Eddie rubbed his eyes. It was just a trick of the light as the sun streamed in through the glass.

"If I knew you were coming I would have baked a cake," James said as he took some books off another chair beside the desk, and motioned for Eddie to sit down.

"There would have been no need for that, James. Just a quick tidy would have done," Eddie said as he struggled to manoeuvre past a sea of books. Once he had successfully got to the seat and sat down, he said, "How can you possibly?"

"How can I possibly, what?"

"How can you possibly be a patient here? I hate to say it, but you're probably the cleverest, most sensible person I've ever met."

"Why, thank you. High praise indeed," James said as he crossed his legs and placed his hands on his lap. "They say there is a fine line between genius and madness. But who is it that decides whether someone's behaviour is a mere eccentricity or madness? Someone is classed as mentally ill, or they're not. There is no in-between. It is not up to us to decide which one we are. It is society who kindly decides on our behalf."

"So it's society's fault people are put into places like this?" Eddie asked.

"Not exactly," James said. "It is society who decides who is a genius and who is mad. Or who is normal and who is not so normal. It is society who decides, but it is not society who creates the difference. No, the difference between so called good and bad mental health, according to many of the very knowledgeable doctors today, is nothing to do with our experiences in life and the society we find ourselves part of. Instead, it is mainly due to chemical imbalances in our brain. Therefore, the way we think and the way we act is almost totally out of our control."

Totally out of control? Like the books in this room. Eddie nudged a few out of the way that were at his feet.

"Our behaviour is simply all down to luck and the genes we have been given. Therefore, we have no responsibility at all. It's not our fault. The only thing that can help us is not meditation, as I told you about before, but medication. You could even change the song I serenaded you with about meditation." James began to sing, "Medication. Medication. Medication, that's what you need. If you want a muddled head, and spend all day in bed. Medication's what you need."

Before Eddie could comment on James's attempt at singing, James continued to speak.

"We've been told chemical imbalances are what affect our state of mind. There's too much Dopamine in our brains, or there's too little. Or not enough Serotonin. We're told it makes a difference. Yet, incredibly, in this day and age, nothing has actually been proved conclusively. I want you to help me with an experiment. Okay?"

"Sure."

"They say too much Dopamine or too little Dopamine affects the way we think-right?"

"I suppose so."

"I want you to remember how you felt when we won that first race at the bookies?"

"Okay."

"Well then. How did you feel?"

"I felt pretty good. Well, to be more exact, when I found out our horse had won, I felt great!"

"Right. When you first feared that something had happened to Jenny, how did you feel then?"

"I...I don't know. It's hard to put it into words. But it's without doubt the worst feeling I've ever felt in my life."

"You see. That is two extremes of your emotions which you felt. Now, are you trying to tell me that when you won at the races, your Serotonin or Dopamine just coincidently happened to be very high at the same time? That is how you felt such elation? Or, unfortunately, when that tragedy happened to Jenny, likewise, your Serotonin or Dopamine coincidently happened to be incredibly low at that exact moment? That is why you felt worse than you ever have in your life?"

"I suppose not-no."

"It was the situation you were in and your reaction to that situation, which created your emotions. This may well have triggered a chemical imbalance in the brain, but it did not happen the other way round. Psychiatry is from the Greek *Psyche*, which means soul, and, *iatros*, which means doctor. A Psychiatrist is meant to be a *soul doctor*, but you wouldn't know that these days."

Eddie listened to James, but at the back of his mind was the question that kept nagging away at him, so much so, he felt he just had to ask it, "But why are you in here? What mental problem do you have?"

"Ahh! I was wondering when we would get round to that question. It is, indeed, a complicated answer."

"I thought it would be," Eddie said.

"The doctors are not agreed on what my problem is. Originally, it was claimed I had a minor form of autism, a sort of Autistic Savant, if you will. A bit like the character Dustin Hoffman plays in *Rain Man*, where he can do things like count the cards in Vegas."

"I've seen that. Is that how you win at the bookies?" Eddie asked.

"A bit like that. I don't know how it works exactly, but I can somehow recall the form of most horses and where they finished in practically every race they have ran in. Then, I can also take into account many other factors, such as the ground, and things like that. All these formulas and calculations go on in my brain. Then, a horse appears, which, mathematically should win the race. I can't explain how it happens and neither could the doctors."

"What do you mean could? Don't you mean can?"

"Not really. I mean could, because they don't know I can still pick winners like that. I told them a long time ago I wasn't able to do it anymore."

"That's how you pick the horses?" Eddie said, disappointed. "There's nothing magical or mystical about it?"

"I'm afraid not. Surely it didn't matter to you how I picked the winners, but simply that I picked them?"

"I suppose so," Eddie mumbled and shrugged his shoulders. But he felt let down, cheated even. A bit like when he realised Santa didn't exist, that it was merely his mum and dad who left the presents on Christmas morning. When Eddie first found out Santa wasn't real, the world didn't seem the same magical and special place it had before. Eddie felt the same way now he was finding out the truth about James. "What do the doctor's claim is wrong with you now?" Eddie asked.

"Why, that old favourite, Schizophrenia. They realised none of

232

my so-called symptoms really fitted anywhere in their manuals. Therefore, I was put into that great mental health black hole where almost everything gets thrown into that doesn't fit the other categories. They have given me all the neuroleptics under the sun, from Chlorpromazine to Clozapine, with a little bit of Haloperidol, in between. None of which has had any effect."

"Let me get this straight," Eddie said. The feeling of disappointment wasn't going away. "The person who's helped change my life around for the better, and I don't mean to offend you. This person is actually a mental health patient who suffers from Schizophrenia?"

"What did you think I was, Eddie, some sort of Guardian Angel? This isn't a Frank Kapra film, I'm sorry to say. We're not starring in *It's a Wonderful Life*. I'm no Clarence the Angel, and you are certainly no Jimmy Stewart. Why should you be so surprised I have a mental disorder? Nowadays, it is becoming more and more common. Soon, everyone will have one except for the psychiatrists. I think the lunatics have taken over the asylum, I really do. Although, we don't have asylums anymore, do we? It would be more appropriate to say the lunatics have taken over the Royal Infirmaries, as well as that new favourite Care in the Community."

"So why are you in here and not out in Care in the Community? You don't seem like a threat to yourself, or anyone else."

"I only moved back here a short while ago, as I lived down south. I was originally promised a house in the community, but due to circumstances outside of everyone's control, the house was not available when I moved here. This room was vacant so, for the time being, it's home. As you see, I can more or less come and go as I please. I just have to be here at certain times for my medication."

"And what about being a University Lecturer, is that true?"

"That's true," James said as he got up off the seat. "I haven't told you any lies. It's just that I may have held back little nuggets of information about myself."

While James brewed them both a cup of tea, in a bright yellow teapot, Eddie gazed round the room. It appeared to have most of the normal mod-cons, except for one glaring omission of a television set. Eddie didn't think James would have enough time to watch it, anyway, with all the reading he must do. Eddie also noticed there wasn't a bottle of Hai Karate aftershave anywhere, either. As Eddie picked up a book off the table, a photo fell out. It was black and white with a woman and two children in it; a boy and a girl. All three were smiling.

Eddie was about to ask about the photo when James sat down with two mugs of steaming hot tea. One mug had Kermit the frog on it and the other had Top Cat. Eddie was given the Kermit mug as it had fewer cracks in it.

"I'm sorry about the mugs," James apologised. "I don't get many visitors, so this is my finest china."

"Don't worry about it," Eddie said. "As long as the tea tastes all right, that's the main thing." Eddie took a tentative sup; it tasted better than all right. It was the first cup of tea he'd had since the one at Stacy's house, and it was almost as pleasing to his taste buds as lager.

"Nowadays," James said, "people believe medication is the answer to all their problems. One little tablet can miraculously make a person happy and their life wonderful. Like the wonder drug 'Soma' in Aldous Huxley's *Brave New World*. Instead of therapy and cognitive thinking, pills are popped, which, instead of helping people change their thinking, stop them from thinking altogether." James put his Top Cat mug down on the desk without taking a drink out of it. "Thankfully, you don't know what that's like? Or ever will. You are able to think. It's just that, before, the thoughts you were thinking were of little, or no, use to you. Things have changed."

"They have," Eddie nodded his head in agreement and supped his tea. He couldn't believe how good it tasted.

James continued to ignore his cup of tea and continued to speak. "In the past, people who heard voices were revealed as prophets, saints, or in one very special case-The Son of God. Now, they are ridiculed and silenced by drugs. A person hears voices and is diagnosed as schizophrenic. They are given an antipsychotic to stop those voices in the person's head. Yet we all have voices in our heads telling us what to do, and what we do and don't like."

"You're right."

"That is the voice you've managed to train to do what you tell it, not the other way round. A lot of people with mental health problems don't realise they are able to do that. They believe everything the voice tells them, and mistakenly think it is in charge, that it is real. These people seem to lack insight into what this voice in their head really is. It is inner speech. We all have it, but some seem to think they have no control over it."

"Why do people start to believe that these voices are real?"

"I don't know all the reasons. One, I reckon, is that it makes life easier. We lose responsibility for our thoughts and actions. Everything we do is simply at the whim of what the voice in our head told us. If it is the wrong thing then it's not our fault, as we are too helpless to do otherwise. That is not a hard thing to happen, by any means. For this is the same voice which told you to spend most of the mornings in bed, then the rest of the day in the bookies and the pub. It is a voice in your head which helped create the life you led for the past seven years, or so. Likewise, it is the voice in your head, which after some training, has turned your life around for the better."

"It's you who's helped me turn my life around!" Eddie protested.

"I only helped push you in the right direction. Or, planted a small seed." James smiled and nodded knowingly. "If you had not been able to change your way of thinking and your outlook on life, then you would still be the same person in the same place. I couldn't change your way of thinking for you. There were obviously a few ups and downs on the way. It was you who went and signed off this morning, even though you didn't have to."

James, as per usual, was right. Eddie had made the decision to sign off today, and the reason for that decision was because he now believed it was the right one. The voice in his head had changed from telling him all the reasons why he shouldn't work, to telling him all the reasons why he should. Eddie had more or less changed his life by changing his thinking, his habits, and his actions.

James got up, with a groan, and took away both the mugs, even though he'd only drunk out of his once. He put them in a small sink in the corner of the room, beside the door, and filled the sink with water. "If you had gone to a doctor, seven weeks ago, about your lack of get up and go and your negative thinking," he said. "Then I think the outcome would have been very different. More than likely, you would have been put on some form of medication."

"You're probably right," Eddie agreed, as he looked at some of the book titles strewn across James's desk.

"I'm almost certainly right. Today most doctors are not interested in dealing with the cause of the illness, they normally only treat the symptoms. There is a movement called *Anti psychiatry,* which disagrees with almost all the theories of modern psychology. Thomas Szasz, for instance, wrote a book entitled *The Myth of Mental Illness,* which gives you a fair indication of where he stands on the subject."

"I'm not so sure if I agree it's just a myth," Eddie said as he picked up one of the books on the desk. It was a tatty paperback with pages that had turned yellow. Marcus Aurelius: *Meditations,* it said on the cover. Eddie put the book down again.

"Anti psychotic drugs," James said "are handed out. But still the medical profession, after about fifty years, is not in total agreement as to how they actually work. And, anyway, in about fifty percent of cases, as the Verve would say, 'The drugs don't work'." James stopped the tap and dipped his hand in the water. "Ouch!" he cried. "Bit on the warm side." He turned the cold tap.

"You're saying no-one with a so-called mental health problem, or illness, should be given drugs?" Eddie asked as he picked up another book on the table, Anthony De Mello's: *Awareness.*

"In some cases, especially severe cases, drugs should be given." James stopped the cold tap and tested the water again. "Perfick. Now, what I am saying, however, is that drugs, and only drugs, are certainly not the answer to a lot of people's mental health problems. The Jewish wisdom of *Kabbalah,* tells us that the idea our thoughts are merely chemical reactions in the brain, is down to the creation of our Opponent."

"Our Opponent?" Eddie asked.

"Our Opponent is the shadow who hides in the darkest recesses of our minds. The one who inflates our ego by telling us we're better than everyone else, one minute, then the next minute, tells us we're completely worthless. Our Opponent makes us reactive to people and events, instead of being proactive. There's a whole lot more to the *Kabbalaha* than that, as it is a very interesting subject. Maybe one for another day?"

"I'm looking forward to it already," Eddie joked as he put the book back down.

"I'm sure you are," James replied. He began enthusiastically washing the two mugs. "Back to today, however. If we are all led to believe our thoughts and actions are merely the result of biology and external conditions. Then that form of fatalism can give us an excuse for how we are and how we behave. Victor Frankl agreed most of us are more than simply pawns to heredity and sociological circumstances, that a lot of mental illness is a result of the failure of the sufferer to find meaning, and a sense of responsibility in their life. Don't forget, Eddie? This is a man who was in a concentration camp. Who lost all his family to the Nazis. If anyone had an excuse to believe they were a pawn of outer circumstances, then Victor E Frankl would have." James dried off the mugs with a, fetching bright pink and yellow striped, tea towel, admired how sparklingly clean they were, before hanging them up on a wooden mug rack. He came back to his desk and sat down. Almost at the exact moment his bum touched the chair, there was a knock at the door.

Nurse Katie, who had been at reception earlier, entered the room. "It's time to take your afternoon medication, James," she said.

"Okay, my dear," James said as cheerfully as ever. "I shall be a minute or two. I hope you don't mind?"

Nurse Katie smiled. "No, we'll just wait out here for you," she said, and closed the door.

"I better go," Eddie said, and started to get up off his seat.

James immediately put his hand on Eddie's shoulder and indicated for him to sit down again, which Eddie did.

"I have something to give you before you go," James said. He rummaged about through the pile of books on his desk and picked one up. It was a very small white book with blue writing on the cover.

Eddie took the book from James. It was *As A Man Thinketh*, written by James Allen.

"I want you to read that," James said. "As you can see it's a very small book, but, as they say, size isn't everything."

"No," Eddie agreed, as his mind briefly ventured back to a certain incident, in a certain kitchen, with a certain barmaid.

"People go to see their doctor, psychiatrist, or whoever," James said, "and they expect to be cured. It seems, it is no longer the individual's responsibility to make themselves happy anymore. Instead, it is up to someone else. You are not automatically entitled as a member of the human race to be happy, nobody is. Yourself and society, may mistakenly believe you are, but you aren't. What you are entitled to, is to work for it. Do not forget that. You have to work at it every minute of every day. It doesn't just miraculously happen."

There was another knock at the door. Nurse Katie came in again, "Sorry, James," she said, "but we really have to give you your medication now."

"Certainly," James said as he stood up. "My very good friend is just leaving."

Eddie also stood up. He put the book in his back pocket where he had, luckily, found his pound coin bus fare.

Nurse Katie entered the room with another older, plumper, grey haired nurse. Eddie was unable to catch a glimpse of her name

237

badge as he made his way towards the door. When he reached it, Eddie turned round to see James was still standing by his desk.

Unsmiling, James waved and said, "Goodbye, my good friend."

Eddie waved back. "Goodbye, my good friend," he repeated.

The reply brought a smile to James's face. "Before you go," he said, "I would like to say one more thing. It is something Thomas Szasz touched upon. When we pray, we are talking to God, or some other higher power. When God, or some other higher power, decides to reply and is talking to us, then we have a mental illness...probably schizophrenia."

The smile was no longer on James's face as Eddie closed the door.

After catching the bus back into town, Eddie went to the charity shop to confirm he had accepted the job offer; he then visited the park, where he sat on the usual bench in an attempt to gather his thoughts and try to make some sense of things. It didn't work. Eddie wandered up to the bookies; the place where, a little over seven weeks ago, he had first clapped eyes on James in his ridiculous white suit and cravat.

When Eddie walked into the bookies, he half-heartedly hoped James might've decided to visit after receiving his medication. James was nowhere to be seen. Eddie sat down at a table and stared at a poster with today's race meetings on it, much the same way as James would. Unlike James, however, Eddie could have sat there all day and no winning horse would come. His mind was too muddled; horse racing was far from his thoughts.

Eddie lost all track of time as he sat there, oblivious to the daily goings on of the bookies which carried on around him. He couldn't help think about James and how he could possibly be a patient in a mental health hospital. It didn't seem right. Admittedly, a lot of things haven't seemed exactly right since James came on the scene, but Eddie just couldn't get his head round this latest development. As he mulled things over, Eddie was brought back to reality when a hand grabbed his shoulder. Eddie eagerly glanced up, hoping it was James. It wasn't. After a moment or two, Eddie realised it was the face of Brody McDowell.

"Sorry, Eddie, I didn't startle you, did I?" Brody asked. Looking concerned at Eddie's reaction.

"No." Eddie stared at Brody's neatly trimmed beard and hair.

He didn't look so scruffy now. Definitely not with the smart checked shirt and dress trousers he had on. "How are you?" Eddie asked. Disappointed it wasn't James, but thought he at least better try and make conversation.

"It's still pretty hard. I try to take each day as it comes, and I really do believe Mary is up there watching me, which helps a lot." Brody gazed upwards and pointed. "What do you think of the new clothes?" Brody asked and smiled. When he did, Eddie could almost have sworn there was a pleasant aroma of spearmint coming from Brody's mouth.

"You look very smart."

"Thank you," Brody said, and slowly twirled round so Eddie could get a proper look at his attire.

Eddie nodded. "Very smart," he repeated, and glanced down at what Brody had on his feet. Still a pair of Jesus boots, but a brand new pair by the looks of things, matched perfectly with brown socks.

Brody stroked his neatly trimmed beard. "It was my Mary's idea before she passed away," he said. "With the money we won, she told me to get myself a new wardrobe, and treat myself. Said I deserved it for all I had done for her. Not that I need a reward or anything. I did it simply out of love, and would do it all again without any question."

"I've no doubt you would."

"But I must admit," Brody said, "over the last couple of years, I didn't really pay much attention to my appearance, or things like that. It just didn't seem to matter. I was too concerned about Mary, and spent almost all my waking hours looking after her as well as I could."

"I doubt anyone could have done more for Mary than you did."

"Thank you. I might even book myself a holiday abroad with the money left over. Mary told me I should go for the both of us. It won't be the same, but I still think she'll be there with me."

"You should do that. You deserve it."

"Maybe I will," Brody said. He then appeared to survey the bookies, like he was looking for someone. A frown appeared on his face.

"Anything wrong?" Eddie asked.

Brody had one more look round the bookies. "I was just looking for your friend, that's all."

"What friend?"

"Oh…I'm not too sure of his name, but I've seen him in here a

239

couple of times with you. He wears a white suit."

No doubt who that is? "That's James you're looking for." Again, it dawned on Eddie, that he didn't know James's surname. "I don't think he'll be in today," he said. "What do you need to see him for?"

"Oh! Just about something, that's all." After a pause, Brody added, "I suppose I could tell you about it." He looked round the bookies once more, and sat beside Eddie. "This will probably sound silly. But Mary had a couple of dreams just before she passed on, and she said he'd visited her."

"You told me about it that day I saw you at the cemetery."

"What day?"

"I can't remember the exact day it was. I had been visiting my daughter Jenny's grave. I saw you at Mary's grave. We talked for a bit."

Brody was silent for a few seconds. "Sorry, I don't remember that?" he said, shaking his head.

"That's okay. You were obviously under a lot of stress at the time. I seem to remember you told me someone had spoken to Mary in her dreams?"

Brody clicked his fingers, "That's right, that's exactly what happened." Then he pointed at Eddie and said, "The funny thing is, two nights ago, I had a funny kind of dream as well. Mary was standing at the side of my bed wearing the white silk dress she wore to go on honeymoon, with what looked like a white, sort of, glow surrounding her. It was my young Mary, though, looking just like she did when we first got married. You obviously didn't know her back then, Eddie. She was a real beauty. A right little cracker!"

"I can imagine."

"She was. I mean, my Mary even won a beauty contest once."

"Did she?"

"She did that. In my unbiased opinion she would have won Miss World if she had entered it. The contest she did enter, and win, was Miss Skegness, nineteen-sixty two, when we were on our honeymoon," Brody said, and looked up at the ceiling.

"Miss Skeg..." Eddie felt a calm, peaceful feeling wash over him.

"So, Mary held my hand," Brody said. "She spoke to me softly, and told me not to worry about anything, because she would be looking out for me. She was happy where she was, and wanted me to be happy. I wasn't to grieve. I was to get on with my life, and one day, in the future, we'll meet up again. Then she smiled a wonderful, wonderful smile."

Miss Skegness, 1962, The Midnight Special shall be arriving very soon.

"Mary then introduced me to a person who was standing at the bottom of my bed. At first, I couldn't really see him properly as he was also surrounded by a white glow, but it was a lot brighter and stronger." Brody's hands were getting more animated." At first it hurt my eyes a little." He covered his eyes. "Mary never said his name, only that he was her good friend who she'd spoken to in her dreams." Brody took his hand away from his eyes. "Eventually, my eyes got used to the bright light, and I could see a bit more clearly the person standing at the bottom of my bed. I saw he was dressed in white, like Mary. Then, I managed to actually recognise him. That's when I was really shocked."

"Why were you shocked?"

Brody leaned over and put his hand on Eddie's shoulder. "Because it was that friend of yours, in the white suit, who you say is called James."

CHAPTER TWENTY FIVE

Eddie sat up in bed reading the book James had given him. Joan was beside him engrossed in the latest literary gem from Sir Terry Wogan. While she read, Joan was humming away under her breath the tune she always hummed, but which neither she nor Eddie knew the title of. The two of them had gone to bed early to indulge in a spot of hanky-panky. Although, Eddie had managed to last longer than it would take a kettle to boil, it still couldn't really be classed as a love marathon. Joan seemed happy enough about it, but Eddie was slightly disconcerted at how quickly she had picked up her Terry Wogan book almost immediately after they finished.

That was the least of Eddie's worries as the bedroom light got switched off. Joan, like she did most nights, fell asleep almost the second her head hit the pillow. Eddie was not so lucky. He lay there tossing and turning, listening to the heavy wind and rain batter against the window, while at the same time, trying not to think about James and some of the strange goings on that had occurred. But he couldn't. Occasionally, he would glance at the bedside digital clock. On the latest occasion, the red digital numbers showed the time was now 1:39 a.m. Eddie closed his eyes and tried to get to sleep; the more he tried, the harder it was. Till, over an hour later, sleep finally came.

When he awoke, Eddie was in that all too familiar spot under the large tree. The sun was shining, and there was almost complete silence except for the low murmur of the river nearby, or the occasional sound of a bird singing sweetly in the trees. As Eddie stood up, he noticed he had no shoes on. He was also wearing a white suit.

Drawn as ever towards the river, Eddie made his way down the slope; treading barefoot through the damp early morning dew still on the grass. He stopped at the top of the thirty three steps, glanced through the gap in the trees at the raging water, and made his way down the steps, holding on to the rickety hand rail to his right. At the bottom of the steps, he remembered to duck below the overreaching branch. Eddie stepped along the path, down the moss, twig, and dirt covered thirteen steps that lead onto the red, brown, and green coloured rocks at the side of the river. Once he was on the rocks, Eddie walked towards the rock which stood out like a finger pointing at the river. The rock he knew Jenny had been standing on that day.

Eddie glanced up at the overhead sun as it shone a ray of light through the trees on the far embankment directly on to the special rock. Eddie walked onto the rock and into the light. He closed his eyes and felt the warmth of the sun, while listening to the river angrily making its way downstream. Eddie opened his eyes and stared deeply into the river. The colour of the water was a ghostly white as it rushed past. Eddie glanced upstream at the bridge, which on that awful day had a gaggle of people on it shouting and waving. Eddie could have sworn he saw someone on it? He rubbed his eyes. When he looked again, no one was there. Eddie looked downstream at the other bridge, as he did so, he said out loud, "Water under the bridge."

Time passed as Eddie stood staring at the river. After seconds, minutes, or even hours passed, a hand touched Eddie's shoulder. Eddie wasn't alarmed. He knew who it was. Eddie had to screw his eyes up as the glow of white beside him was so strong. With his eyes half closed, Eddie watched James step into the river. The river was now calm and peaceful as James waded further out until he and the glow surrounding him were under the water.

Eddie fully opened his eyes. He blinked furiously a number of times in an attempt to get rid of the white spots he was now seeing. With his vision back to normal, Eddie stood and waited. He didn't have to wait long. James resurfaced, five seconds later, about three metres from the bank at the far side. Even from a distance, the glow was still practically burning Eddie's eyes, but, with some effort, he was able to keep them fully open. There was no way he was going to miss this. James had gone into the water alone, but he was not coming out of it the same way. There was someone with him, (as Eddie knew there would be) a girl with long brown hair and wearing a white dress. The girl was holding James's hand as she came out of the water, with a faint white glow surrounding her

Eddie's eyes strained against the light as he watched James and the girl, still holding hands, almost hover up the embankment at the far side. When they reached the top they let go of each others hand and turned to face Eddie.

The girl was Jenny as gorgeous as ever.

Eddie felt a feeling in his stomach that he had never felt before.

Jenny and James smiled and waved at Eddie.

Eddie thought his heart would explode.

Jenny and James turned round, held each others hand again, and went into the trees. Then they were gone.

243

Eddie smiled, waved, and whispered, "Goodbye Jenny." Something then dripped onto the rock by his feet. Eddie held his right hand up to his eyes. When he brought his hand down again, it was wet with tears.

In the distance, the sound of a train could be heard.

The room was still dark as Eddie jerked upright in bed. His heart was going faster than one of James's winners going down the home straight (up until yesterday). He took a deep breath as he looked at the bedside clock; it was 6:34 a.m. Joan was asleep, but that didn't prevent Eddie from switching on the bedside lamp, covering the bedroom in a warm, soft glow. After giving Joan a couple of unsuccessful gentle shakes to try and wake her, Eddie decided a couple of not so gentle shakes were necessary.

"What is it?" Joan asked. Sounding still half asleep.

"Wake up, Joan. I want to speak to you about something."

"What time is it?"

"Don't worry about the time. This will only take a minute or two. Then you can go back to sleep." Eddie shook her again.

This time Joan sat up, a bit, and opened her eyes slightly to look at the clock, mumbling something incoherent when she saw what the time was.

Eddie wasn't too bothered. He had her awake, that was the important thing. "I want to ask you something, okay?" Eddie asked.

"Okay, Eddie. But you could have asked me it a bit later?" Joan said, and yawned.

"I have to ask you now. Have you ever had a dream about James?"

"About who?"

"About James. You know? Who visits you at work?"

"Oh-James! I can't remember." Joan yawned again.

"Come on, Joan. If you've had a dream about him, somehow, I think you would remember."

"Yes, I've dreamt about him, "she said as she closed her eyes.

"What was it about?"

Joan lay down turning her back to Eddie. "What?" she barely managed to answer.

"What was it about?" Eddie repeated.

"He told me something about going back to University to finish my degree." Joan gave another yawn.

Eddie had one more question to ask. "Joan, when you and James have spoken about Jenny-"

"What?" she asked.

"When you and James have spoken about Jenny," he repeated.

"I've never mentioned Jenny to James," she said, and within seconds appeared to be asleep.

Eddie shook Joan again, but she did not stir.

Eddie lay down in bed. *Of course she's spoken to him about Jenny. It's just that she's tired, that's all. What about the dream, about going to University? Did she also say that just because she's tired?* The name *Clint Eastwood* came into Eddie's head. "Clint Eastwood," Eddie spoke out loud. "When James first met Clive, he said Clive looked like Clint Eastwood. But he doesn't. He looks absolutely nothing like him. James obviously said it as he knew it would make his day?" Eddie then laughed as he pictured Clive walking up to James in the pub, sticking out his pigeon chest, and saying to him in his Clint Eastwood like drawl, 'Go ahead, James, make my day!' "How could James have known Clive thought he looked like Clint Eastwood, when he doesn't look anything remotely like him?" Eddie asked the almost silent bedroom; Joan was now snoring lightly.

As that question started swirling around Eddie's head, he said out loud another name, that of "Mary McDowell." It was a name that seemed to have come to him a lot recently, ever since he had met James. She'd had a dream, a vision, or whatever you want to call it about James. She's not the only one, by any means. Yet, she had a dream about him, but as far as Eddie knew, she had never actually met him. Brody only saw James a couple of times, in the passing, while in the bookies. As far as Eddie knew, Mary had been bedridden for over a year. There is no possible way she could have ever met James. But, somehow, he managed to appear in her dreams?

Eddie didn't have the answer to that particular question. Nor to any of the others, but he thought of a man who might. With his heart racing even faster, Eddie jumped out of bed and hurriedly put his clothes on. After a quick thirty second brush of his teeth, and an even quicker gargle of mouthwash, Eddie ran downstairs and phoned a taxi. He paced up and down his living room, constantly checking out the window until the taxi arrived, some fifteen minutes later. He got in, and then Eddie and driver made their early morning way to Abernethy Hospital.

245

The red Fiat Brava taxi drew up outside the gates of the hospital. Eddie paid the driver (exact fare wasn't necessary) and got out. Eddie immediately fastened up his jacket, and then walked through the front gates, with his head down. The grounds looked a lot more intimidating and daunting in the early morning grey, with only the odd street lamp giving off a faint orange glow of light.

When Eddie reached his destination, the door was locked, which you would expect at this time of the morning. Eddie knocked on the door, and then wondered exactly what he was going to say when someone answered. He didn't have long to think of something. Almost immediately, he heard someone on the other side of the door undo the locks. Eddie shivered as he waited for the door to open. When it finally did, he recognised straight away the person who opened it as Nurse Katie who'd been working yesterday.

She looked at Eddie and, to his surprise, let him in without saying a word. "You must be soaking?" she asked while closing the door.

"I'm a bit wet," Eddie said.

"Would you like a towel to dry yourself with?"

"I'm fine, thanks." Eddie shook his head to help dry what little hair he had left. "I'm sorry about the time," he said, "but I'm here to see-"

"You're here to see James," Nurse Katie said as she went behind the old-fashioned, dark mahogany, reception area. "I'm afraid he's gone."

"What do you mean gone?" Eddie asked, walking up to the other side of the reception.

"He wasn't here for his tea-time, or his supper-time medication."

"He can't be?"

"He is. And we've no idea where." The nurse opened a drawer and took a white envelope out.

"Maybe he's gone back home?" Eddie asked. "Do you know where that is?"

Nurse Katie's laugh echoed round the large, open spaced reception area. "We hardly know anything about him," she said. "He's an enigma, to say the least. We think he was originally from around here, but then moved away a long time ago. We have conflicting records about his previous addresses. At the last count there was over twenty of them. I mean, we don't even know his proper surname. As our records show at least a dozen different surnames he's given over the years. And, we're not even sure if James is his proper first name."

"What surname was the last one he was using?" Eddie asked, and wiped away some rain that was dripping in his eyes.

"The last surname was Allen."

"James-Allen." Eddie gave a wry smile.

"Anyway," Nurse Katie said, "you should feel honoured. He left a letter and a gift for you."

"For me?"

"Yes, here you are." She handed over a white envelope with *Eddie* written on it in black ink, and a smallish rectangular box wrapped in shiny red paper. Paper which resembled red silk.

He took the envelope and gift. "But how do you know I'm Eddie?" he asked. "I can't remember myself or James mentioning my name?"

"I know they're for you, because in all the time James has been here, he's only had two visitors."

"How do you know that this isn't for the other visitor he's had?"

"Quite easily. The only other visitor James ever had is a young girl who he walked around the grounds with."

"What did you say?"

"A young girl," Nurse Katie repeated.

"What... what did she look like?" There was something not right about this.

"She was maybe about ten or eleven years old and with long brown hair," Nurse Katie said. "I can't tell you much more. We only ever saw the two of them walking around the grounds. She never came up to the building."

Eddie's legs went weak. He staggered forward. For a second, he thought he might actually faint. "W-w-when was this?" Eddie barely managed to get the words out as he tried to stay upright.

"She didn't visit everyday. I can't say exactly when she first came to visit, but it was definitely over the summer. I remember it was before I went on holiday to America. That was six weeks ago." Nurse Katie obviously noticed the colour suddenly drain from Eddie. "Are you all right? Would you like a seat?" she asked, and pointed to a chair behind the reception.

"I'll be fine." *I think.* Eddie attempted an unconvincing smile to try and prove he was. "I better go," he said, then took a tentative step towards the door. It felt like he was walking through cement.

"Are you sure you're all right?" Nurse Katie asked again.

"Yes," Eddie replied, but didn't bother turning round. He had to focus all his attention in getting his legs to move normally.

When Eddie eventually struggled to the door, Nurse Katie shouted to him,"There's something else about the girl I noticed."

This time Eddie did turn round as he grabbed onto the front door for support. "What's that?" he asked.

"She always had this white dress on. Every time she visited. Mind you, I only saw her a handful of times. But she always wore the same white dress. It looked strange, James walking around the grounds, in his white suit, with the girl wearing a white dress."

Eddie nodded and headed for the door. He really had to get outside for some fresh air-storm or no storm. As he fumbled with the door, he heard Nurse Katie shout,"Goodbye."

"Goodbye, and thank you," Eddie said as he lurched outside and closed the door behind him at the third attempt.

The morning was getting brighter and the rain was now only a light drizzle as Eddie slowly walked towards the front gate, clutching the white envelope and box in his shaky right hand.

Was this also just a dream? Will I wake up shortly and find I am still lying in bed? Because if it wasn't a dream, then how can you explain what I've just been told?

The only explanation, unbelievable as it was, which Eddie could think of at the moment, was that Eddie's dead daughter has been visiting James. It's not only James who can see dead people, but, apparently, also the staff here. There had to be another explanation to all this, but, right now, Eddie couldn't think of one.

Eddie stopped and held up the envelope and box. He had a funny feeling what the box contained, so he put it in his coat pocket for now. He looked again at the envelope and wondered what was inside. Did he even want to know? Yes. Eddie wanted to know. He was desperate to find out, and decided he wasn't prepared to wait. There was a small wall, about two feet high, beside the path. Eddie went across and sat on it. It was damp. After recently standing in a cemetery in the pouring rain for over an hour, a damp wall was hardly an inconvenience. With his hands still trembling, he carefully opened the white envelope with *Eddie* written on it

248

Hello, Eddie, my good friend.

It has been a pleasure getting to know you over the last two months or so (has it really been two months? Doesn't time pass by so quickly?). If I have had to write you this letter, then it means the time is right for me to move on. Do not forget the things I've told you, for they will stand you in good stead, and will keep you away from the abyss that you were heading towards when we first met.

Remember there are so many things you do not have control over; the weather, your football team winning, other people's opinion of you, and, importantly, what has happened in the past. However, what you do have complete control over is perhaps most important of all. That is your thoughts and your actions. No one else controls them for you. It is you and you alone, who is responsible. What happened yesterday, last week, and last year, is no longer in your own hands. What happens tomorrow, next week, and next year, most certainly is, my friend. It can be as good or bad as you decide to make it. The Buddha taught that every one of us is free, we are the makers of our destiny through the choices we make, but in making those choices we must accept the consequences.

It is not what happens to you in life that matters-it is how you react that is important. You have the power to choose to do either the right or the wrong thing in whatever circumstance you are faced with. Socrates is believed to have said at his trial, "A good man cannot be harmed in life or death." I do believe you are a good man; it's just that you have to believe it too.

In the game of life each of us is dealt a hand. You cannot give this hand back for another, but must play it to the best of your ability, no matter how difficult it may sometimes be. Don't forget, in your darkest moment in life so far, the hand you were dealt was also dealt to Joan. Yet, she was able to play it differently from how you did.

There is a poem by G.K Chesterton entitled 'A ballade of suicide', which I think is about someone, who, like many, finds life dull and pointless. So much so, that they decide to commit suicide. But, at the moment they are about to take their own life, it suddenly occurs to them that maybe life isn't as bad as they thought it was? Unfortunately, like the poem from Caddyshack, I can't quite remember how it goes. So, again, I have made one up along the same lines.

When I awoke this morning, I wanted life to end
One problem after another, I am driven round the bend
I have finally had enough of so many things
The economy is down; the way Britney Spears sings
But then I noticed much to my glee
A documentary on the telly I wanted to see.
The sun was also shining; the sky a beautiful blue
And I finally remembered there is so much to do.

I've never been to Paris, London, or Rome
I still have to call my mother on the phone
There's also the garden; a letter to post
I haven't even tried caviar on toast
Some highlights of Seve playing golf in his prime
A cheeky little glass of Romanee Conti wine
So I came to a decision; I am happy to say
Perhaps I will give it just one more day?

*That's all any of us can really do. Just keep on giving it one more day,
because, eventually, we won't have any more. But I don't think you
opened this letter hoping for a few more words of wisdom. You have a
lot of questions, I'm sure, and I've no doubt you are hoping for some
answers. I'm afraid the answers you are looking for I'm unable to
give. You have to make your own mind up about the events that have
occurred since we first met, and the meaning behind them. Over time
you will come to your own conclusion, whatever that conclusion may
be. Only you can live your life, yet that doesn't mean there aren't
others looking out and watching over you, trying to gently help a
certain Edward Ernest Ryan make his way along the right path.*

*Saint Francis of Assisi: "Lord make me an instrument of thy peace.
Where there is hatred, let me sow love. Where there is injury, pardon.
Where there is doubt, faith. Where there is despair, hope. Where there
is darkness, light. Where there is sadness, joy. O Divine Master, grant
that I may not so much seek to be consoled as to console; to be
understood, as to understand; to be loved, as to love; for it is in giving
that we receive, it is in pardoning that we are pardoned, and it is in
dying that we are born to eternal life."*

The Koran: "Does it not occur to man that there was a time when he was nothing?"

I am sure you have heard the saying "water under the bridge". Never forget it, for it reminds us that everything in life; the good times and the bad, will someday all pass and be gone, just like "water under the bridge". Hopefully, it will be a long time yet before your time on earth passes under the bridge, but it will.

I have to go now. But before I do, there is one more thing to say. I know the name "The Midnight Special" means something to you, although you can't put your finger on what it is. I think there may be various reasons. One of those, is that it's the name of the song Joan keeps humming, practically everyday, which neither of you know the name of. This particular song just so happens to be one of your daughter Jenny's favourites. Whenever she hears it, it always makes her happy...

Take care, Eddie. And always remember: These are the days of our lives.

P.S. Do you believe in miracles?

Eddie sat, on the damp wall, as the sun rose in the early morning sky. He folded the letter carefully, put it in the envelope, then safely away in his coat pocket beside the box. Eddie patted his pocket for reassurance both items were still there as a white delivery van screeched into view. The driver gawped, open mouthed, at the unusual early morning sight when he drove past; Eddie smiled back, nodded, and patted his pocket again as tears trickled down his face.

CHAPTER TWENTY SIX

Some things in life, over the years, never seem to have changed; the *Queen's Head* pub was definitely one of them. For as long as Eddie had gone there, he could maybe remember it being redecorated once, perhaps twice, at a push, with the last time that occurred being well into the last century. Yet there was still something special about the place he always liked. If you wanted to go to a pub with bright lights, and loud music, filled with young drunken idiots, then there were plenty of other establishments in town where you wouldn't be disappointed. There's nothing fancy, or classy, about the place, but it's been Eddie's local since he first started drinking and it would remain so until he stopped.

Eddie, dressed in his yellow checked shirt Joan gave him for Christmas, and smelling of that manly fragrance *Hai Karate,* the item which Eddie knew would be in the box James left for him, sat at a table in the *Queen's Head* sipping a pint, while The Darkness's Christmas tune played in the background, despite today being New Year's Eve. As Justin Hawkins's, falsetto voice, told us not to let the bells end, Eddie reminisced about some of the good times he's had in there, with one time, in particular, being that day when James first introduced himself. Eddie was sitting in the same seat today as he was then, but James wasn't.

"Would you like another pint, Dad?" A younger version of Eddie, sat in the chair opposite, asked. The hair was much longer, without a hint of grey. There were also a lot less lines on the face, and, although Eddie would hate to admit it, he was also a few pounds lighter. Despite this, the resemblance was unmistakeable. Like his Dad, he too was wearing a shirt, but a blue and white striped Armani one, where Eddie's was a supermarket's own brand.

Eddie lifted his glass. It was still half full, but he said, "It's up to you, if you want to buy one? What time are we meeting your mum and Kathy again?"

"Not until seven. It's only five thirty five now. I'm sure we could manage another couple before then?" the younger version of Eddie said.

"If you insist, Steven. But you can do all the explaining to your Mum and Kathy if we turn up drunk."

Steven laughed; a laugh which was uncannily similar to Eddie's. "I'm sure one more pint won't push us over the edge," he said. "Then again, it might push one of us?"

"That's only because I don't drink so much, that's why," Eddie said in his defence. "I'm sure I could still outpace you at drinking if I got in more practice. I don't think your Mum would be too impressed if I did."

"Didn't you say the same thing about golf, that with a bit more practice you were going to teach me a lesson on the course?" Steven asked.

"I will, one day, don't you worry. They didn't call me Seve Ryan in my younger days for nothing." Eddie was unable to keep a straight face.

"I thought they called you Monty?" Steven asked.

Eddie was baffled, "No, I can't ever remember that?" he said.

Steven smiled. "Yes, they called you Monty. Not after Colin Montgomerie, the golfer. But the Field Marshal, because you spent so long battling in the sand!"

Eddie would have to give Steven that one as he couldn't think of a witty response. Instead, he pointed at his now empty glass and said, "Off you toddle to the bar, like a good boy, and get me another one, please."

Eddie watched Steven being served by Alison, the new, young, attractive barmaid who has replaced that other young, attractive barmaid called Stacy. Eddie hadn't seen her since that fateful morning, with the rumour being that her boyfriend, Colin, threw her out of the house because of her cheating on him. Every time he was away off shore, she was, apparently, with someone else. The final straw was when he actually caught her in the act. He came home early from off shore, but didn't tell her, as he wanted it to be a surprise. It certainly was a surprise for all concerned. Colin found her in bed with his then best mate. She was promptly kicked out, and had since moved back down South to live with her mother.

For some reason another Christmas tune came on the jukebox, The Pogue's 'Fairytale of New York'. When the song got to the part James talked about in the park, a shiver went down Eddie's spine.

When 'The Fairytale of New York' finished, Eddie had a look to see how Steven was getting on. He was still chatting away to the new barmaid, so Eddie sat back in his chair and awaited the next tune on the jukebox. *You can't beat the Festive season. Thank God it's Christmas! Well, it was a week ago.* But despite that, Eddie was sure he was about to be treated to another Christmas cracker. Maybe Mud's

Les Gray singing about being 'Lonely this Christmas', the song Eddie slow danced to with Joan that fateful Christmas Eve. Or, perhaps, the number 32 bus driver, more commonly known as Cliff Richard, singing about 'Mistletoe and Wine'? But Eddie hoped it wouldn't be about his 'Millennium Prayer'.

When the next song began, it didn't sound like a Christmas tune. At first, Eddie didn't recognise it. The song got to the chorus and started to sound strangely familiar. Eddie got up off his seat. His legs were wobbly, which he didn't think was because of one pint of Guinness, while he slowly walked across to the jukebox. When he reached it, the jukebox told him exactly what he had expected. The song was 'The Midnight Special'. But it wasn't sung by Abba, like Douglas had said; it was sung by Creedence Clearwater Revival, of 'Bad Moon Rising' fame.

"What are you laughing at?" Steven asked as he returned back to their table with two pints in his hands.

"Nothing," Eddie said, trying to stop, but was unable to.

"There's your pint." As Steven handed the pint over he had a look of bewilderment on his face.

"Cheers," Eddie took a sip; it tasted good. "I noticed you were having a friendly chat with the barmaid there," Eddie said as he wiped away a, white creamy, Guinness moustache.

"She seems nice," Steven replied, and sat down.

They usually do. "I wouldn't get too friendly," Eddie advised him.

A look of surprise appeared on Steven's face. "There's no chance of that. I'm happy with Kathy."

Eddie opened his mouth to speak, but took a gulp of his pint instead. *Maybe I should just take the Fifth Amendment on this subject? Or is it the second?* He shifted uneasily on his seat as he asked Steven, "Do you recognise that song?" Not expecting Steven to say 'yes', but hopefully moving the subject away from barmaids.

Steven listened, "Not really," he said. After taking another sip of his pint, Steven listened some more. His face lit up, "I think I do recognise it. But I haven't heard it for ages."

"You do?"

"It's called The...The...'The Midnight Special'. "

"That's right. But how do you-"

"It was in a film I used to watch with Jenny. I had it on video. I

254

didn't think that much of the film, but she used to want to watch it all the time. You remember the sort of films Jenny used to like? Not exactly your typical kids ones."

"I remember," Eddie said, nodding. "Was it a horror film?"

"No. I think the film was *Twilight Zone the Movie*. There's a car scene, at the start, where the driver and his passenger sing along to 'The Midnight Special' as it's being played on the car stereo. I lost count of the times Jenny made me rewind that part of the film. She used to love that song."

As the closing lines of the song faded out in the background, Eddie smiled and thought to himself, *I believe she still does*.

Beechwood Golf Club was noisy and full when Eddie, Joan, Steven, and Kathy walked in. Eddie wasn't sure if it was as noisy and full as last year because he could hardly remember a thing about being here, or what happened, or didn't happen, afterwards. The band was playing 'Proud Mary' when Eddie noticed Clive, sitting at their reserved table, waving across. The two men let the ladies go ahead of them. Kathy, with her dark wavy hair, and blue striped dress, which was similar to Steven's shirt, not only in style but probably price, went first. She was a good looking girl; about the same height and build as Joan. Good looking, but not stunning, as Joan, in Eddie's humble opinion, looked tonight. She was wearing a full length red dress, with a cut out upper back, which Eddie especially liked. Joan was also wearing the matching opal necklace and earrings Eddie gave her for Christmas. She had her hair up to show the earrings off.

Eddie sat down beside Joan at the table. He immediately felt under dressed in his shirt and slacks, when he realised Clive had on a black tuxedo, white shirt, and bow tie. Clive had an arm round Gloria, who was wearing a yellow and tan dress. Eddie noticed she'd had her blond hair permed since he last saw her. He also noticed she was as pleasing on the eye as always.

Eddie was pleased to see Douglas hadn't gone over the top, dress wise, like Clive. He was simply wearing a plain white shirt, while Brenda had on a grey dress with a pattern of yellow and green leaves. She was wearing very little make up.

Before anyone could say hello, Brenda leant across the table, tapped Joan on the arm, and asked, "Have you found out the date yet?"

"What date?" Joan replied as she put her, black leather, handbag under the table.

"You know. About your graduation?"

Joan nodded. "I phoned up the University the other day, and the graduation is definitely on the thirteenth of July."

Brenda clasped her hands on her chest, "Thank goodness!" she said. "I kept thinking it would clash with the wedding date."

"It's definitely the thirteenth," Joan confirmed again.

"When's the wedding again?" Eddie asked.

"It's the…" Douglas paused and scratched his shaved head.

"Twenty ninth of June," Brenda finished his sentence and glared at him.

"Can I see the ring?" Kathy asked with enthusiasm.

"You can." Brenda held out her left hand with obvious pride.

"That's right, Clive. How's the best man's speech coming along?" Eddie asked, while tapping the table to the closing verse of 'Proud Mary'.

"You should be asking me," Gloria answered, "as he reads it out every night. I haven't managed to hear my soaps for over a month now."

"How many jokes have you crammed in to it so far?" Steven asked, while fumbling about in Kathy's, brown Gucci, hand bag.

"About thirty."

"Thirty?" Douglas spluttered. "When I asked you to be best man, I didn't realise that instead of having a wedding day, it'll need to be a wedding week to fit in your entire speech?"

"I'm planning on editing it," Clive said.

"Down to how many jokes," Kathy asked, once she had managed to take her eyes off Brenda's diamond engagement ring.

"To about twenty five," Clive replied with a serious expression.

Eddie and Steven glanced at each other and shook their heads.

"But," Joan said, "I probably won't pass, so it won't matter when the graduation is."

"You'll pass with flying colours," Eddie said, and patted her hand.

"Too right you will," Douglas added. "I've seen some of your paintings, they're bloody brilliant!"

"Thank you," Joan said.

"Who wants a drink?" Eddie asked. It had been almost an hour since his last pint of Guinness.

"We've got a kitty," Douglas said. He pointed to a glass, in the middle of the table, stuffed with notes.

"How much?" Eddie got his wallet out.

"Ten pound each, so far," Clive said, and took his arm from Gloria's shoulder to pick up the glass.

Eddie saw Joan reach down for her handbag below the table. "It's all right," he said. "I'll put the money in for you."

Joan stared at Eddie in total disbelief, "Are you sure?" she asked.

"Yes."

Joan picked a beer mat off the table and wafted it in front of her face like a fan. "My God!" she said. "I think I feel faint." This brought laughter from everyone seated at the table, including Eddie.

"You can easily put your own money in," Eddie said.

"No, that's most kind of you," Joan said. She put the beer mat down.

"He's a real gentleman that hubby of yours," Gloria chipped in.

Joan turned to face Eddie. "He has his moments," she said, then whispered in his ear, "For that good deed. After the party, we can maybe try and bring the New Year in a bit more successfully than last year?"

Eddie smelt her perfume and gulped.

"Who knows?" she added. "I may even get my Shania Twain outfit looked out."

A wicked smile crossed Eddie's face. He took more money out of his wallet. "How about I put thirty pounds in the kitty for you instead," he said.

Joan moved away and playfully hit him on the arm. "I think we all need a drink," she said.

"We certainly do," Eddie agreed.

Eddie took a tray, some money, and a list of drinks to the bar. It was busy, so he turned to watch what was happening on the dance floor; there were a row of seven women line dancing to the Bellamy Brothers tune 'Reggae Cowboy'. Eddie was clicking his fingers in time to the music, whilst admiring some nifty line dance moves, when someone tapped him on the shoulder.

"If it isn't Mr Ryan," a female voice from behind him said.

Eddie turned round. The first thing that caught his eye was a neck line, in a purple velvet dress, that plunged further than Jack Cousteau would have dared. When his eyes moved upward, he saw the woman was attractive, in her late thirties, early forties, with straight brown hair. It was a woman Eddie didn't recognise.

"Will I call you Mr Ryan? Or, will Eddie do, now that we're not at the Job Centre?" she said. Obviously unaware that Eddie had no idea who she was.

"The Job Centre?" Eddie mumbled. *Bloody hell, it's Edith,* he finally realised. "Eddie's perfect," he said.

Edith put her hands on her hips and raised an eyebrow. "Is he now? Maybe I should've taken Eddie up on that offer of a fling?"

"What? No…I mean," Eddie stuttered. "I meant…"

Edith laughed and waved her hand at him. "Don't worry, I know what you meant. It's perfect to call you Eddie instead of Mr Ryan."

"Yes," Eddie let out a sigh. "I'm sorry. I have to admit, I didn't recognise you at first. Your hair's different and you don't have your glasses on."

Edith stroked her hair. "I straightened it for tonight. But if I straightened it before work, then I'd probably have to get up at about four in the morning as it takes so long." Edith pointed to her brown eyes. "I also have my contacts in. The reason I can't wear them at work is because I have trouble reading the computer screen with them."

"Edith, let me say, you look particularly bewitching tonight," Eddie said without a word of a lie. She did look bewitching. She also had a twinkle in her eyes that wasn't there before. *Or maybe it was? Eddie asked himself. Maybe the twinkle has always been there, it's just that I hadn't noticed it? Or didn't want to? I wanted to believe Edith lived a miserable existence of a life because it actually made me feel better thinking someone was unhappier than I was.*

"Are you harassing this gentleman, Edith?" A man handed her a drink. Maybe a man isn't the description most women would use? Adonis might be more appropriate; with his blond flowing locks and rippling torso, which his shirt was struggling to contain. This particular specimen of manhood, whom Eddie instantly felt inferior to, wouldn't look out of place modelling Armani underwear.

"This is Eddie," Edith said. "He used to come in to the Job Centre, but is Assistant Manager at a Charity shop now."

"Very good," the Adonis seemed impressed as he shook Eddie's hand with a grip that could crush walnuts.

"This is my partner Trevor, who I told you about," Edith said.

Eddie glanced up at six foot plus and at least 220 pounds of Trevor. "Pleased to meet you," he said, relieved that Trevor let go of his hand without breaking any bones

"And you, Eddie," the Adonis, called Trevor, replied.

"How are you getting on at the Charity Shop?" Edith asked.

"Pretty well," Eddie nodded. "I enjoy it there and think my position might become permanent."

"That's great!" Edith said.

Trevor also nodded his head in approval and asked, "Would you like a drink, Eddie?" He pointed at his glass.

"I'm in a kitty. But thank you."

Edith grabbed Eddie's hand. Slowly edging closer, she uttered seductively, "I hope I shall get a dance later?"

"I'm sure I can manage that."

"I'll look forward to it," she said and, in one quick graceful move, let go of Eddie's hand and gracefully pirouetted away from him.

"You don't know what you've let yourself in for," Trevor said, and then Edith led him away.

Back at the table, Eddie took an ice cube out of Joan's, almost empty, vodka glass. He dabbed it on his forehead, while letting out a sigh of relief. Edith got her dance, all right, and Eddie should've heeded the warning. As soon as she sets foot on the dance floor, Edith turns in to a whirling dervish, which Eddie tried his best to keep up with. He's danced with her three times, but, the last time, when the band played 'The Lambada', enough was enough. Eddie's heard of *Dirty Dancing*, but some of Edith's moves could only be described as *Filthy, X-rated, Dancing.*

Eddie made his excuses to Edith and came back for a much needed seat. He was alone at the table as the rest of the group were still up dancing. The time on his watch was 10:57 p.m. Not long to go till the end of the year. What a year it's been. Eddie watched everyone on the dance floor; Edith was still there, now dancing with Clive, who, from what Eddie could see, was giving as good as he got, despite his bad back. *Mind you,* Eddie thought, *if he attempts many more high kicks in those tight trousers, it'll be the stitching in them that gives way before his back does.*

Eddie had a sup of whisky, not his usual tipple, but he thought he'd have one tonight for the occasion. "What a year," he said to himself, and his thoughts drifted to Jenny, while surveying the people on the dance floor again; they all appeared to be having a ball. "I'll always think of you. But, I've still got a lot of livin' to do, Jenny, my dear. Here's to you!" he raised his glass and finished the whisky. Eddie put the empty glass down and decided to get back on the dance floor. When he tried to stand up, in front of him, looking resplendent, in navy blue blazer, white shirt, and red and yellow striped tie was Brody McDowell.

"All right, Eddie?" A tanned Brody, with neatly trimmed hair and beard, said. Eddie also smelt the faintest whiff of Joop aftershave coming from him.

"I'm fine, Brody. Would you like a seat?" Eddie said.

"I better not. It's my round at the bar, and at my age, once you sit down it's hard to get up again."

"I didn't know you were a member here?" Eddie sat down again.

"I used to be years ago. Mary and I played many a round together. I just renewed my membership a few months back, and go golfing at least three times a week in a foursome. And guess what?" Brody said with some excitement. "Last month on the short par three…I got a hole in one!"

"Well done."

"I took my trusty seven-iron and gave it a whack." Brody then swung an imaginary golf club, nearly hitting a woman with a tray of drinks as she walked past. Brody apologised before continuing. "The ball flew up in the air, but was going well right. It was also heading for the bunker. Then it happened."

"What?"

"A miracle, that's what." Brody's arms were flailing about. "It hit the lip of the bunker, and then it flew back towards the green, bouncing twice before going straight in the hole. Do you know who I have to thank for it?" Brody crossed his arms.

"I've no idea?"

"Mary, that's who. She's definitely up there keeping an eye on Brody the Oldie."

Eddie was not going to disagree. "How was the holiday to Benidorm?" he asked.

"I had a great time." The arms were flailing again. "There was plenty of sun and sangria as I sat at the pool side. Then, when I came back, I had another win at the bookies from that syndicate. That's how I paid my membership fees. Haven't seen you at the bookies for a while?" Brody scratched his chin and glanced in the direction of the bar.

Eddie shook his head. "I don't gamble as much anymore. Maybe the big events like the Open or Grand National, but that's about it."

"What about the Lottery?"

Eddie smiled. "Well…some habits do die hard!"

"I thought so," Brody said, and laughed. He appeared to check out the bar once more, "I better go and buy the rest of my foursome a drink. Would you care to join us?"

Eddie paused. The dance floor was beckoning. "I was about to…" He paused again, stood up, and put an arm around Brody's shoulder, "I would love to join you," he said. "Now, tell me the full story about your hole in one."

The band gathered everyone on the dance floor, to link hands and stand in a circle, when the time approached midnight. Eddie was linked between Joan and Steven. The band played the opening notes of "Auld Lang Syne". Then, as everyone sang, Eddie looked around him at the happy faces of people he knew. Clive and Gloria; *Should auld acquaintance be forgot, and never brought to mind.* Douglas and Brenda; *Should auld acquaintance be forgot, and auld lang syne.* Brody, Edith, and Trevor; *For auld lang syne, my dear.* Kathy and Steven; *for auld lang syne.*

Time seemed to freeze. Out of the corner of his eye, Eddie thought he glimpsed a figure wearing a white suit, raising a glass, while standing at the bar. James's unmistakeable voice then whispered to him, "The Stoic Epictetus told his pupil Arrian, 'God has placed at every man's side a guardian, the Daemon of each man, who is charged to watch over him; a Daemon that cannot sleep, nor be deceived. What greater and more watchful guardian could have been committed to us? So, when you have shut the doors, and made darkness in the house, remember, never say that you are alone; for you are not alone. But God is there, and your Daemon is there'."

We'll take a cup of kindness yet; James, Jenny, and Mary. *For auld lang syne.*

261

Summer, 2011.

Sam was enjoying sitting in the sun at Wyndon Park. It was good to get out for some fresh air. His joints never seemed to give him any peace nowadays, but the warm sun did seem to help a little. The sun and fresh air was good, but the best thing about being here was that his old friend, and neighbour, was here with him. Sam always enjoyed it when the two of them got together, and, even after all these years, his old friend still looked the same as he did when he first left, which Sam thinks might have been back in the seventies, but it could also have been some time in the eighties?

Sam's memory wasn't so good anymore. He even struggles with his kids', grandkids', and now great grandkids' names. But, he supposes, that's just a part of growing old. That's what the nurses at the home tell him anyway. So it must be true. But it's lucky Sam has these nurses to look after him, as he would forget to take his medication. He has no idea how much medication he's on now. A pill for this, and a pill for that. A pill to deal with the side effects of the first pill, plus another pill to deal with the side effects of the pill he has to take to deal with the side effects of the first pill. Sam doesn't think he really needs to take so much medication. A trip to the park seems to help him more than the tablets do, but he leaves it up to the doctors to tell him what medication he has to take. They're professionals so they obviously know what they're doing?

Although his memory might not be the same as it was, Sam can still remember, like it was yesterday, when he used to play here with his old friend before school, after school, and, on more than one occasion, during school. As well as the times when he and Marie, accompanied by his old friend and Georgina would come and dance to the Locarno band. It was only dancing, mind you, then a peck on the cheek at the end of the night. Sam and his old friend have always been perfect gentlemen.

Sam closed his eyes, and in his head, he could hear the band play 'Are you lonesome tonight?' That was his and Marie's tune. Sam wouldn't admit it to anyone, but he's lonely most nights, and days, now. His family visit when they can, but they live all over the world, so it's hard for them to visit too often. The only person who really comes to see Sam now is his old friend. He hasn't forgotten about him.

Sam grimaced as a bolt of pain flashed from his knee right up to his hip. The sun was good, but Sam was still in pain. He is always in pain, and tired. Sam admits he's had a good life, a very good life, but now, maybe, it could be time to move on. He's just too tired, sore, and lonely now.

"It's a wonderful day, isn't it, Sam?" His old friend, who was sitting beside him on the bench, said.

Sam opened his eyes. "Lovely," he agreed.

"Did you and Marie ever go on holiday to Holland?"

"No. Never been there. Marie always liked Spain. The Costa Del Sol, and Benalmadena in particular."

"Nice place Holland. A lot of culture, and home baking. There's also the ruins of a fifteenth century cathedral in Amsterdam, which has an inscription on it. The inscription is written in Flemish, but do you know what it says in English?"

"I don't."

"It says-'It is so. It cannot be otherwise'. No matter what has happened in our lives, Sam. Through the madness and the tears, there's nothing we can do about any of it now. For, it is so. It cannot be otherwise."

"You're right." Sam thinks his old friend is always right when he says things.

"Do you know what, Sam, it looks like the Locarno band are about to start playing at the bandstand," his old friend said.

"Are they?" Sam squinted his eyes. His eyesight wasn't very good now, either. "I think I can see them on the bandstand. And is that a crowd gathering round to listen to them?"

"It most certainly is," his old friend replied. "Georgina, Emily, and Henry are there, as well as a few other people I would like you to meet."

"Are they? It would be good to see them again. I haven't seen the three of them for a long time." Sam squinted his eyes again. It looked like someone beside the bandstand was waving at him. "Is that Georgina waving at me?" he asked.

"No," his old friend replied, and then stood up. "It's Marie. She's asked the band to play 'Are you lonesome tonight?' And she is waiting for her dance."

"My Marie?"

"Your Marie."

"I better go across then."

"I think you better."

Sam was helped up from the bench by his old friend. "By the way," Sam asked, as he got to his feet, "How's the back?"

His old friend smiled. "My back, like everything in time, has completely healed."

"That's good," Sam replied.

As Sam and his old friend made their way towards the music and laughter coming from the bandstand, a train could be heard in the distance.

Lightning Source UK Ltd.
Milton Keynes UK
UKOW05f0253221013

219515UK00001B/372/P